Essential
Electric
Circuits:

*Analysis and Design
with
Practical Considerations
and
Applications*

Duane Hanselman, Ph.D.
Electrical and Computer Engineering
University of Maine
Orono, ME 04429
USA

E-Man Press LLC

Library of Congress Control Number: 2017932188

ISBN 978-0-9826926-5-3

Printed in the United States of America

Second Printing

Table of Contents

Preface

This text is the result of the author's teaching of electric circuits courses for more than twenty years. Rather than simply try to replicate the material in established texts, this text takes a different approach, for several reasons.

First, this text recognizes that very few engineers need the breadth and depth found in traditional texts. In practice, circuit analysis and design has largely moved away from the focus on analysis and design of small circuits. Rather, real world circuit analysis and design focuses much more on the selection of integrated circuits and on the creation of circuits that interface integrated circuits to one another.

Second, this text recognizes that many analog circuits have been replaced by digital circuits in many applications. As a result, analog circuit design in a digital world focuses on analog signal conditioning and translation prior to conversion to digital, and also in the translation and conditioning of analog signals arising from digital signals.

Third, this text recognizes that modern computing tools have largely eliminated the need for being able to solve electric circuits by hand.

Fourth, this text recognizes that electric circuits can no longer be a central focus of the curriculum. There simply is not enough time available, given the need to adequately cover higher level concepts that are needed in the workplace.

Fifth, this text recognizes that textbooks have become outrageously priced.

Based on these observations, this text covers only the essential aspects of electric circuits. The fundamental aspects of DC, transient, and AC circuits are covered. Much of the excruciating detail found in traditional texts is absent. The philosophy for this is that students need to take the essential concepts with them in their careers, but they do not carry the excruciating detail with them, even if it is covered in circuits courses. And by excluding the excruciating detail, students will more likely retain the essential aspects they need.

To cite just one example among many, nodal analysis is covered, but mesh analysis is not. While neither of these analysis methods are commonly used for hand calculations, nodal analysis is the method underlying most circuit analysis software. Nodal analysis is covered because it solves for voltages, not currents. Voltages are the important variables in most electric circuits. In digital circuits, the presence or absence of a voltage dictates logic states. In analog circuits, voltages contain the information that is manipulated. Op amps and filters are almost always used to process voltages.

This text takes a different approach in the way material is presented as well. Here presentation more closely resembles the conversational tone and content one uses in lectures. For many students this improves comprehension. Because students often struggle with algebraic manipulations, this text explicitly shows the steps involved in derivations. Intermediate circuits are also shown.

Traditional texts do not make value judgments. As a result, students naturally believe that everything is equally valuable, when it clearly is not. Because making value judgments is vital and common in the workplace, this text addresses the relative importance of topics.

Most importantly, this text addresses practical workplace topics. For example, practical component values, the effect of tolerances, circuit loading, and real models for resistors, capacitors and inductors are included. Moreover, this text covers vital practical topics that cannot be found elsewhere. Topics include bypass capacitors, oscilloscope probes, power dissipation in logic circuits, single supply op amp operation, and crosstalk mitigation using twisted pairs, differential signaling, and common mode chokes.

1 Mathematical Background

The study of electric circuits requires familiarity with a number of mathematical topics. Some of these topics may be new to you, others may be fresh in your memory, and others may need to be refreshed. Therefore, the purpose of this chapter is to introduce or reintroduce mathematical topics that are required in the study of electric circuits. In addition to these topics, standard conventions and terminology adopted by engineers are presented. The material in this chapter relies on mathematics topics and concepts already familiar to you. There is no electric circuit analysis in this chapter. This material is meant for self study. It would be great if you studied this chapter before studying electric circuits, but you can always come back here when the material is needed later.

1.1 Notational Consistency

When describing how something works, we write equations and create mathematical variables to identify various properties and parameters. Whenever possible, it is customary to use consistent engineering notation, *i.e.*, to always use the same notation for a given property or parameter. We do this to minimize errors and improve productivity. For example, the Greek letter π is consistently used to denote the ratio of the circumference of a circle to its diameter. This ratio is never assigned to α or x. π is always the π we know. To cite another example, Einstein's famous mass-energy equivalence is always written $E = mc^2$ where E is energy, m is mass and is c the speed of light. If this equation were written as $T = xF^2$ in one place and as $C = em^2$ in another place, and in myriad other ways in yet other places, we would struggle tremendously. So, notational consistency is vitally important. Using notational consistency minimizes errors and maximizes productivity.

The following table documents the standard notation used in the study of electric circuits.

Quantity	Variables	Units
charge	q	coulombs, C
energy	w	joules, J
voltage	v, V	volts, V
current	i, I	amperes, A
power	p, P	watts, W
resistance	R	ohms, Ω
conductance	G	siemens, S, $1/\Omega$
time	t	seconds, s
frequency	f	hertz, Hz
frequency	ω	radians/second, rad/s
capacitance	C	farads, F
inductance	L, M	henries, H
angle	θ, ϕ	degrees, ° radians, rad
$\sqrt{-1}$	j	—
impedance	Z	ohms, Ω
reactance	X	ohms, Ω
admittance	Y	siemens, S, $1/\Omega$
susceptance	B	siemens, S, $1/\Omega$
complex power	S	volt-amperes, VA
reactive power	Q	volt-amperes reactive, VAR

It is important to use the standard variables and units cited in the table. Furthermore, when there are multiple variables for the same quantity type in a problem, the standard convention is to use subscripts to uniquely identify specific parameters. For example, several voltages might be identified by v_1, v_2, and v_3, or perhaps by V_x, V_y, and V_z. For voltages and currents, it is important to note that lowercase and uppercase variables are distinct variables. That is, v_a is not equal to V_a because lowercase v is not equivalent to uppercase V. This same policy applies to subscripts. For example, R_y is not equivalent to R_Y. Mixing notation increases the likelihood of confusion, which reduces productivity.

1.2 Significant Digits

Before the days of handheld calculators, numerical results were seldom presented with precision any greater than two or three significant digits. This was true because it required too much time and effort to produce greater precision. The commonly used slide rule simply did not accommodate greater precision. Now that handheld calculators are commonplace and the slide rule has been largely forgotten, it is easy to produce numerical results with ten or more significant digits. This precision is meaningless and misguided in most engineering work because the value being computed is often based on parameter values that do not have more than two or three digits of precision.

The number of significant digits in a number is the number of digits that convey the precision of the value. The significant digits in a number are the number of digits displayed, excluding all leading zeros and trailing zeros when they are merely placeholders to indicate where the decimal point resides.

Examples demonstrating how significant digits are counted include:

31 has two significant digits because two digits are given,

310 has two significant digits because the trailing zero identifies where the decimal point resides,

310.2 has four significant digits,

310.0 has four significant digits because the zero after the decimal point conveys the significance of the final digit similar to the last digit 2 in the preceding example,

310. has three significant digits because the decimal point conveys the significance of the final zero digit,

0.003 has only one significant digit because the leading zeros are not significant; they merely identify where the decimal point resides,

0.003 14 has three significant digits.

1.3 Rounding

Rounding is the process of eliminating excess digits in a computed value because the excess digits have no significance to the computation at hand. For example, consider the computation of 3.14/7.00. Both values in this ratio have 3 significant digits. Performing this division produces the result 3.14/7.00 = 0.448 571 428 57 to eleven significant digits. Most of these digits are meaningless since the result cannot have greater precision than the values used in its computation. In this case, the result should be rounded to at most three significant digits, i.e., 3.14/7.00 = 0.449.

There are numerous official and unofficial rules for rounding numerical values. When working with large data sets, different rules can lead to different interpretations of the results. However, when doing hand calculations, the following general rules provide sufficient accuracy.

(i) when the digit immediately to the right of the Nth digit is less than 5, do not change the Nth digit.

(ii) when the digit immediately to the right of the Nth digit is greater than or equal to 5, round the Nth digit up to the next number.

Examples demonstrating rounding include:

3.142 86 rounded to three significant digits yields 3.14 because the digit after the 4 is 2, which is less than 5.

0.003 14 286 rounded to four significant digits yields 0.003 143 because the digit after the 2 is 8, which is greater than 5. The leading zeros are not significant; they only serve to establish where the decimal point resides.

Rounding and Arithmetic

When performing a sequence of numerical computations where N significant digits are required in the final result, all preliminary computations leading to the final result should be computed with at least $N+1$ significant digits. This assures that the final result will be correct when rounded to one less significant digit, i.e., N significant digits.

For the most part in this text, final results are expressed with three significant digits, so all computations leading to the final result need to maintain four or more significant digits.

Results that are exact integers should not be expressed with a decimal point and trailing zeros to demonstrate three or four significant digits. For example, if a result is the integer value twelve, it is simply written as 12, rather than as 12.0 or 12.00. Integer values written without a decimal point have infinite precision. The presence of trailing zeros, *e.g.*, 12.0, implies that the actual result is not an exact integer, but simply rounds to an integer value.

The number of significant digits in noninteger values that appear in a computation determines the number of significant digits in final results. For example, 1.256·(31/7) yields 5.56 accurate to three significant digits because 1.256 was specified using four significant digits even though 31 has only two significant digits and 7 has only one. This holds because the values 31 and 7 are exact integers and they are assumed to have infinite precision.

Significant Digits and Rounding
To have 3 significant digits accuracy for final results, use 4 or more significant digits for preliminary results.
Exact integer values have infinite precision.
When rounding to N digits, if the digit immediately to the right of the Nth digit is less than 5, do not change the Nth digit. If not, round the Nth digit up to the next number.

1.4 Humans and Numbers

Typical engineering computations yield values that span very large number ranges, such as from 10^{-12} to 10^{12}. For example, a computation might lead to the result 0.000 000 314 2 or 3 142 000 000. When values such as these appear, it becomes difficult to express them verbally without error. Moreover, it is relatively easy to miscount the zero digits when transcribing results from one place to another, especially if there is no visible separation after every third digit. Both of these things increase the likelihood of making mistakes and therefore reduce productivity.

To make wide ranging values easier to speak and easier to transcribe, one can use scientific notation or International System of Units (SI) metric prefixes. Scientific notation expresses values as a quantity between one and ten followed by a power of ten multiplier.

For example, 0.000 000 314 2 expressed in scientific notation yields $3.142 \cdot 10^{-7}$. On a handheld calculator this is commonly entered and displayed less formally as 3.142E–7. Similarly, 3 142 000 000 expressed in scientific notation yields $3.142 \cdot 10^{9}$ or less formally as 3.142E9 on a calculator.

SI Prefixes

SI metric prefixes are even more convenient and are used whenever possible in engineering because SI notation is concise and easily spoken. Of the metric prefixes in existence, those associated with factors of 1,000 are most commonly used. This limits the number of prefixes that must be memorized and also makes most values expressible by a number between 1 and 1,000 followed by a metric prefix. The metric prefix is then followed by the units of the quantity computed. The following table identifies the common metric prefixes used in engineering.

Common Metric Prefixes		
Power of 10	Symbol	Prefix
10^{-12}	p	pico
10^{-9}	n	nano
10^{-6}	μ	micro
10^{-3}	m	milli
10^{0}	—	—
10^{3}	k	kilo
10^{6}	M	mega
10^{9}	G	giga
10^{12}	T	tera

For example, using the table, 3 142 meters becomes 3.142 kilometers or 3.142 km. This is much easier to speak than saying "3.142 times ten to the third meters." The consistent use of metric prefixes maximizes productivity.

It is vitally important to be able to jump from one way of expressing numbers to another among the three possible ways: (i) use of SI prefixes, (ii) scientific notation, and (iii) calculator notation. The following table contains examples that demonstrate the three ways of expressing numerical values.

Value	Use of SI Prefix	Scientific Notation	Calculator Notation
0.000 000 007 2	7.2 n	$7.2 \cdot 10^{-9}$	7.2E–9
0.000 000 314 2	314.2 n	$3.142 \cdot 10^{-7}$	314.2E–9
0.000 417	417 µ	$4.17 \cdot 10^{-4}$	417E–6
0.000 061 5	61.5 µ	$6.15 \cdot 10^{-5}$	61.5E–6
0.012 5	12.5 m	$1.25 \cdot 10^{-2}$	12.5E–3
0.001 023	1.023 m	$1.023 \cdot 10^{-3}$	1.023E–3
630	630	630	630
9 754	9.754 k	$9.754 \cdot 10^{3}$	9.754E3
12 290	12.29 k	$1.229 \cdot 10^{4}$	12.29E3
8 110 000	8.11 M	$8.11 \cdot 10^{6}$	8.11E6
11 355 000	11.355 M	$1.1355 \cdot 10^{7}$	11.355E6

It should be clear that using SI prefixes makes values visually simple, and both easier to write down and easier to speak. When using SI prefixes, scientific notation, or calculator notation, values are expressed by a numerical values greater than or equal to one followed by the scale factor. For example, 0.000 19 is not expressed as 0.19 m, rather, it is expressed as 190 µ.

Because humans find it easier to visualize and manipulate numbers between 1 and 1000, other disciplines outside engineering also use scale factors. Perhaps the most common scale factor is percent, %. In this case, values are scaled by a factor of 100 (0.01 = 1%). For example, 0.05 becomes 5% and it is much easier to say "5 percent" than it is to say "zero point zero five." In financial transactions it is common to deal with fractions of one percent. In this case, basis point units (bp) are commonly used where 100 basis points equals one percent (100 bp = 1%). So, 0.25% is 25 basis points. Concentrations of very small quantities are commonly measured in parts per million (10,000 ppm = 1%) or even smaller measures such as parts per billion. Whenever a quantity typically appears having values outside of the range 1 to 1,000, units are established that facilitate easy visualization and manipulation. This is done to minimize errors and maximize productivity.

Fractions

Modern calculators can produce results in the form of fractions, such as 27/11 or 710/113. While such results are succinct, visually simple, and often easily

spoken, they are often difficult for humans to judge. To understand this, quickly answer the following question: "Between what two integer values does 710/153 reside?" When 710/153 is rounded to three significant digits, 4.64, it is immediately obvious that it resides between 4 and 5. Because of this difficulty, one should not express final results in fractional form since doing so reduces productivity.

Tolerances and Precision

When a value is given by a simple count, e.g., there are 12 eggs in a dozen, the count 12 is exact. However, when a value is given by a measurement, such as the mass of one large egg, the value cannot be exact. There will always be some uncertainty in values. For this reason, values have a tolerance often expressed as a percentage. For example, large eggs in the USA have an average mass of 60.5 grams with a 5.78% tolerance. The maximum mass large egg has a mass 5.78% larger than the average, i.e., $(1 + 0.05780) \cdot 60.5 = 64$ grams, and the minimum mass large egg has a mass 5.78% lower than the average, i.e., $(1 - 0.0578) \cdot 60.5 = 57$ grams.

When values used in a computation have tolerances, the nominal final result also has a tolerance. For example, one dozen large eggs have a total mass of $12 \cdot 60.5 = 726$ grams with a 5.78% tolerance. In other words, one dozen large eggs have a mass between 684 and 768 grams. The inherent lack of precision in the final result makes expressing final results with more than three significant digits generally meaningless.

In practice, as long as tolerances are greater than or equal to 1%, three significant digits for the nominal result are sufficient. This is especially true since it is often difficult to measure experimental results with greater resolution or precision. If you can't measure results in the laboratory with greater than three digits precision, there is usually no need to compute results with any greater precision.

1.5 Adding Fractions

Adding fractions occurs frequently in circuit analysis. As a result, it is beneficial to become reacquainted with the algebra of adding fractions. For example, consider the expression

$$y = \frac{1}{a} + \frac{1}{b}$$

This expression simplifies by creating a common denominator so that the addition operation can be performed,

$$y = \frac{1}{a} + \frac{1}{b}$$

$$y = \frac{1}{a}\left(\frac{b}{b}\right) + \frac{1}{b}\left(\frac{a}{a}\right)$$

$$y = \frac{b}{ab} + \frac{a}{ab}$$

$$y = \frac{a + b}{ab}$$

This correct result is **not equal** to the mistake of simply adding the denominators,

$$y = \frac{1}{a} + \frac{1}{b} = \frac{a + b}{ab} \neq \frac{1}{a+b}$$

Given that adding fractions is thoroughly covered well before college, this mistake most often appears when one is distracted or when one is stressed as might occur during a test. Being mindful of this may help you avoid making this mistake.

1.6 Logarithms

Because the scale of the values in many engineering problems extends over very large ranges, it is common to express values in terms of their common logarithms. The common logarithm or log of a value x is the value y that satisfies $x = 10^y$, which is defined as the function $y = \log(x)$. Thus, $x = 10^y$ and $y = \log(x)$ are inverse functions of each other.

Simply put, the log of a value is equal to the power of ten associated with the value. For example, $\log(1) = \log(10^0) = 0$ and $\log(10) = \log(10^1) = 1$. Values greater than one have logarithms that are positive and values between 0 and 1 have logarithms that are negative. For example, $\log(1/10) = \log(10^{-1}) = -1$, $\log(1/100) = \log(10^{-2}) = -2$, and $\log(0) = \log(10^{-\infty}) = -\infty$. Negative numbers do not have logarithms because 10^y is a positive quantity.

Use of the notation $y = \log(x)$ to denote the inverse of $x = 10^y$ is not universally accepted. The common logarithm is sometimes denoted by $y = \log_{10}(x)$, in which case the preceding notation $y = \log(x)$ is called the natural logarithm, which is the solution to $x = e^y$ where e is Euler's number (~2.718). When $y = \log(x)$ is used to denote the common logarithm, the notation $y = \ln(x)$ is used to denote the natural logarithm.

Handheld calculators commonly use $y = \log(x)$ and $y = \ln(x)$ for the common and natural logarithms respectively. On the other hand, computer programming languages commonly use $y = \log10(x)$ and $y = \log(x)$ to express the common and natural logarithms respectively. Engineers keep track of these notational inconsistencies. In this text, the following notations are used.

Logarithm	Notation	Inverse
Common	$y = \log(x)$	$x = 10^y$
Natural	$y = \ln(x)$	$x = e^y$

Properties of Logarithms

Logarithms have some useful properties, including:

Multiplication becomes Addition
$\log(x \cdot y) = \log(x) + \log(y)$
$\log(100) = \log(10 \cdot 10) = \log(10) + \log(10) = 1 + 1 = 2$

Division becomes Subtraction
$\log(x/y) = \log(x) - \log(y)$
$\log(100) = \log(1000/10) = \log(1000) - \log(10) = 3 - 1 = 2$

Exponentiation becomes Multiplication
$\log(x^k) = k \cdot \log(x)$
$\log(1000) = \log(10^3) = 3 \cdot \log(10) = 3 \cdot 1 = 3$

Inversion becomes Negation
$\log(1/x) = \log(x^{-1}) = -\log(x)$
$\log(1/100) = \log(100^{-1}) = -\log(100) = -2$

1.7 bels and decibels

Power calculations are commonplace in engineering. In addition to computing power, it is common to compare one power to another. Taking the ratio of one power to another allows one to express power in a relative manner. For example, given $P_1 = 10$ W and $P_2 = 20$ W, the ratio $P_1/P_2 = 10/20 = 1/2 = 50\%$ expresses the power P_1 as being equal to 50% of the power P_2. Because power is often expressed in this way, and because the range of power ratios is so large, it is common to compute the common logarithm of this ratio. That is, compute $\log(P_1/P_2)$. The argument P_1/P_2 has no units since watts cancels between the numerator and denominator, leaving the result dimensionless. To give the results distinction, they are given the unit bel, abbreviated B. For example,

$$\log(10/20) = -0.301 \text{ bels} = -0.301 \text{ B}$$
$$\log(20/10) = 0.301 \text{ bels} = 0.301 \text{ B}$$

These power ratios of 1/2 and 2 appear quite often, but the results, as shown above, are fractions of one bel. Since fractional values are more difficult to keep track of mentally, the universal convention is to multiply the result by 10 and use the 10^{-1} metric prefix deci, abbreviated d, to express the result. Doing so, the above examples become

$$10 \cdot \log(10/20) = -3.01 \text{ decibels} = -3.01 \text{ dB} \approx -3 \text{ dB}$$
$$10 \cdot \log(20/10) = 3.01 \text{ decibels} = 3.01 \text{ dB} \approx 3 \text{ dB}$$

Now power ratios of 1/2 and 2 lead to easily recalled results. Power ratios that are powers of ten also lead to easily recalled results. For example,

$$10 \cdot \log(100/1) = 10 \cdot 2 = 20 \text{ dB}$$
$$10 \cdot \log(1/100) = 10 \cdot (-2) = -20 \text{ dB}$$

The unit bel is seldom if ever used in engineering, whereas the scaled unit decibel is commonplace.

Later it will be shown that power is directly proportional to the square of two fundamental electrical quantities, voltage and current. That is, if V_1 and V_2 are voltages associated with the powers P_1 and P_2 respectively, then P_1 is proportional to V_1^2, P_2 is proportional to V_2^2, and the power ratio P_1/P_2 can be expressed as

$$10\log\left(\frac{P_2}{P_1}\right) = 10\log\left(\frac{V_2^2}{V_1^2}\right) = 10\log\left(\left(\frac{V_2}{V_1}\right)^2\right) = 20\log\left(\left|\frac{V_2}{V_1}\right|\right)$$

Similarly, if I_1 and I_2 are currents associated with the powers P_1 and P_2, then P_1 is proportional to I_1^2, P_2 is proportional to I_2^2, and the power ratio P_1/P_2 can be expressed as

$$10\log\left(\frac{P_2}{P_1}\right) = 10\log\left(\frac{I_2^2}{I_1^2}\right) = 10\log\left(\left(\frac{I_2}{I_1}\right)^2\right) = 20\log\left(\left|\frac{I_2}{I_1}\right|\right)$$

Therefore, power ratios expressed in dB are given by $10 \log(P_2/P_1)$, whereas power ratios expressed in dB for voltages and currents are given by $20 \log(|V_2/V_1|)$ and $20 \log(|I_2/I_1|)$ respectively. In all three cases, deci-

bels express a power ratio, even if the ratios used are ratios of voltages or currents.

Power Ratios in dB	
Power	$10\log(P_2/P_1)$
Voltage	$20\log(|V_2/V_1|)$
Current	$20\log(|I_2/I_1|)$

When expressing a power ratio in decibels it is common to simply speak the two letter abbreviation 'd'-'B' ('dee bee') rather than say "decibels." So, 3 decibels is commonly spoken as 'three dee bee.' It is a mistake to make the abbreviation plural as in dBs or say 'dee beeze.' Abbreviations for all common units are not plural. For example, 3 meters is 3 m, not 3 ms; it is just simply 3 m. dB already means decibels, so usage of dBs must then denote the double plural of decibel, *i.e.*, decibelss? Or perhaps the square of decibels? Engineers recognize the silliness in this and refrain from making this mistake.

1.8 Exponentials

The natural exponential function

$$y = f(x) = e^x = \exp(x), \quad x \geq 0$$

describes fundamental properties found in nature. Its inverse is the natural logarithm, which is most often written as $x = \ln(y)$. The exponential function has the unique property that its derivative is equal to itself,

$$\frac{d}{dx}\left(e^x\right) = e^x$$

The value of the function at any point is equal to its slope at that point. Amazing.

In engineering, the exponential function most commonly appears with a negative argument,

$$y = f(x) = e^{-x} = \exp(-x), \quad x \geq 0$$

The following plot illustrates this function.

The negative exponential starts at one at $x = 0$, then decays to zero as its argument goes to infinity,

$$y(0) = e^{-0} = e^0 = 1$$
$$y(\infty) = \lim_{x \to \infty} e^{-x} = e^{-\infty} = 0$$

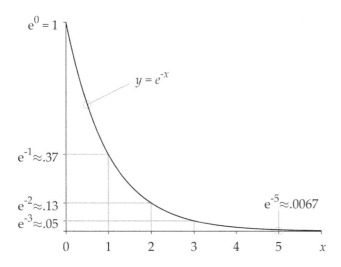

While mathematically the argument x must reach infinity before the negative exponential reaches zero, engineers note that $e^{-5} \approx 0.006\ 7$ which is less than 1% of its initial value $e^0 = 1$, so it is appropriate to let $e^{-x} = 0$ for $x \geq 5$. For $x \geq 5$, the negative exponential is so close to zero that setting it equal to zero has sufficient accuracy for practical problems.

The variables in an electric circuit are functions of time t, not position x. Therefore, the negative exponential is commonly written in either of the two forms

$$y = f(t) = K e^{-\alpha t}, \quad t \geq 0$$

or

$$y = f(t) = K e^{-t/\tau}, \quad t \geq 0$$

where $f(0) = K \cdot e^{-0} = K \cdot 1 = K$ is the initial value and α and τ are constants that are inverses of each other,

$$\tau = \frac{1}{\alpha} \qquad \alpha = \frac{1}{\tau}$$

Because time has units of seconds and the argument to the exponential function must be dimensionless, the units for α must be inverse seconds so that the units work out,

$$\alpha \cdot t \;\Rightarrow\; s^{-1} \cdot s \;\Rightarrow\; \text{dimensionless}$$

Though it is seldom noted, the units assigned to α are nepers or Np.

Given the above relationship, the units for τ must be seconds so the units work out,

$$t/\tau \;\Rightarrow\; s/s \;\Rightarrow\; \text{dimensionless}$$

The scale factor τ is a constant and it has units of seconds so it is called the **time constant**.

To assist in making hand drawn sketches of the decaying exponential,

$$y = f(t) = K e^{-t/\tau}, \quad t \geq 0$$

it is useful to evaluate it at one time constant, $t = \tau$,

$$y = f(\tau) = K e^{-\tau/\tau} = K e^{-1} \approx 0.37\, K$$

which says that the function decays to about 37% of its initial value at $t = \tau$. Visually this is slightly greater than 1/3. Evaluating it at five time constants, $t = 5\tau$, gives

$$y = f(5\tau) = K e^{-5\tau/\tau} = K e^{-5} \approx 0.0067\, K \approx 0$$

which is where the function effectively reaches zero. Since the value of the exponential at a point equals its slope at that point, the slope at five constants is effectively zero as well.

In addition to these two points, further sketching assistance can be found by finding the derivative or slope of the negative exponential and evaluating it at the initial point $t = 0$. Doing so gives

$$y = f(t) = K e^{-t/\tau}$$
$$\dot{y} = \frac{df}{dt} = -(K/\tau) e^{-t/\tau}$$
$$\dot{y}(0) = -(K/\tau) e^{-0/\tau}$$
$$\dot{y}(0) = -(K/\tau) \cdot 1$$

which leads to the final result

$$\dot{y}(0) = -K/\tau$$

This slope describes the initial direction the decaying exponential moves in as time increases from zero. This direction can be described as a line in the common form ($y = m \cdot x + b$) as

$$y = g(t) = -(K/\tau) \cdot t + K$$

Evaluating this line at $t = 0$ gives

$$y = g(0) = -(K/\tau) \cdot 0 + K = K$$

and $t = \tau$ gives

$$y = g(\tau) = -(K/\tau) \cdot \tau + K = -K + K = 0$$

Therefore, this line starts at K at $t = 0$, and reaches zero at one time constant, $t = \tau$. This line of initial slope and its associated decaying exponential are illustrated in the following figure.

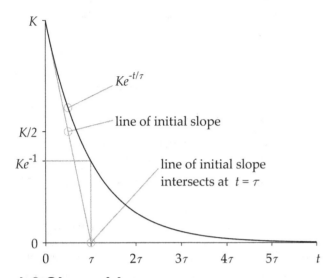

1.9 Sinusoids

The sinusoidal functions

$$y = \sin(\theta)$$

$$y = \cos(\theta)$$

are yet other fundamental shapes found in nature. These functions are periodic with period 2π radians because they satisfy the constraint

$$\sin(\theta) = \sin(\theta + 2\pi n)$$
$$\cos(\theta) = \cos(\theta + 2\pi n)$$

for any integer n. In simple words, sinusoidal functions repeat every 2π radians.

Note that radians are really a dimensionless unit because π is defined as $\pi = c/d$, where c is the circumference of a circle and d is its diameter. Both c and d have units of length, so the ratio c/d has no units. Radians are used because angles do have significance that is important to identify.

While radians are the natural units for angles, they are cumbersome to deal with mentally because π is an irrational number and 2π radians is the angular circumference of a circle. While the origin of the angular unit degrees, denoted °, is unknown, dividing the circumference of a circle into 360 degrees, 360 °, is very useful. 360 is divisible by twenty four factors including 1, 2, 3, 4, 5, 6, 8, 9, 10, 12, and 15. This makes identifying angles and fractions of a circle easy to remember and recall. For example, you probably have an immediate mental image when someone says 45 °, but you would not if someone said 0.7854 radians. Similarly, it is easy to recognize that one third of a circle encompasses 120 ° but not at all easy to know that

it is also 2.094 radians. Degrees are extremely convenient mentally, so they are used extensively. As with radians, degrees are dimensionless. One degree is simply $2\pi/360 = \pi/180 \approx 0.017\ 45$ radians.

The general shape or form of $\sin(\theta)$ and $\cos(\theta)$ is the same. As illustrated in the following figure, $\cos(\theta)$ is simply $\sin(\theta)$ shifted left or advanced by 90 °. And if $\cos(\theta)$ is shifted right or delayed by 90 ° it becomes $\sin(\theta)$.

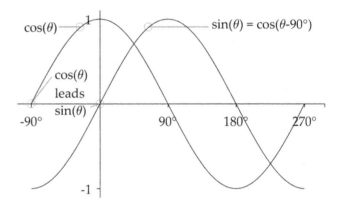

Rather than use advance or delay, in engineering, the terms **leading** and **lagging** are often used to describe these phase shift relationships. Thus, $\cos(\theta)$ leads $\sin(\theta)$ by 90 ° because $\cos(\theta)$ passes through zero increasing in value 90 ° ahead of $\sin(\theta)$ as θ increases. Alternatively, $\sin(\theta)$ lags $\cos(\theta)$.

Leading and Lagging	
$\cos(\theta)$ leads $\sin(\theta)$	$\cos(\theta) = \sin(\theta + 90\ °)$
$\sin(\theta)$ lags $\cos(\theta)$	$\sin(\theta) = \cos(\theta - 90\ °)$

The derivative of a sinusoid is also a sinusoid. For example,

$$\frac{d}{d\theta}\sin(\theta) = \cos(\theta)$$

and

$$\frac{d}{d\theta}\cos(\theta) = -\sin(\theta) = \cos(\theta + 90°)$$

This latter derivative is illustrated in the following figure. This illustration shows that differentiation produces a result that leads the sinusoid being differentiated.

The derivative of a sinusoid produces another sinusoid that **leads** the original sinusoid by 90 °.

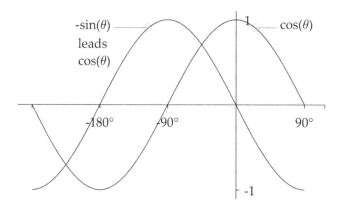

Since the variables in an electric circuit are functions of time t, not angle θ, sinusoids are expressed as functions of time t by letting $\theta = 2\pi t/T$,

$$\sin(\theta) \Rightarrow \sin(2\pi t/T)$$
$$\cos(\theta) \Rightarrow \cos(2\pi t/T)$$

The period of sinusoidal functions remains 2π radians. Therefore, as a function of time t, the period is now T seconds since the expressions have the same value at $t = 0$ and $t = T$,

$$\sin(2\pi(0)/T) = \sin(0) = \sin(2\pi) = \sin(2\pi(T)/T)$$
$$\cos(2\pi(0)/T) = \cos(0) = \cos(2\pi) = \cos(2\pi(T)/T)$$

Given the **period** T, the associated frequency f in hertz, Hz, is defined as

$$f = 1/T$$

Using the **frequency** f, the sinusoids can be written as

$$y = \sin(2\pi f t)$$
$$y = \cos(2\pi f t)$$

Because $2\pi f$ appears so frequently and because it becomes tedious to repeatedly write $2\pi f$, frequency in radians/s, rad/s, is the **radian frequency** defined as

$$\omega = 2\pi f = 2\pi/T$$

which allows the sinusoids to also be written as

$$y = \sin(\omega t)$$
$$y = \cos(\omega t)$$

Sinusoidal Time Functions	
Period in seconds	T
Frequency in hertz, Hz	$f = 1/T$
Frequency in radians/s, rad/s	$\omega = 2\pi f = 2\pi/T$

To minimize the probability of introducing errors, it is very useful to use just the cosine form. In this case $\sin(\omega t)$ can be written in terms of a cosine as

$$\sin(\omega t) = \cos(\omega t - 90°)$$

Written in this way, the units in the cosine argument are inconsistent. ωt has units of radians and the phase angle 90 has units of degrees. In this special case, mixed units are both preferred and acceptable because degrees are so informative. This use of mixed units need only be considered if $\cos(\omega t - 90°)$ is numerically evaluated.

Because sinusoidal variables in electric circuits can have any amplitude and phase, meaning that they are not just $\sin(\omega t)$ or $\cos(\omega t)$, a general sinusoidal function can be written as

$$y = f(t) = F_m \cos(\omega t + \theta)$$

where F_m is the amplitude or magnitude of the sinusoid, and θ is the **phase** or **phase angle** of the sinusoid. If θ is zero, $f(t)$ is a cosine. If $\theta = -90°$, $f(t)$ is a sine. For other phase angles, $f(t)$ is simply a phase shifted sinusoid.

This general sinusoidal function commonly occurs in the study of electric circuits. For this reason, it is beneficial to consider its derivative. Performing the steps gives

$$\dot{f}(t) = \frac{dy}{dt} = \frac{d}{dt} F_m \cos(\omega t + \theta)$$
$$\dot{f}(t) = -\omega F_m \sin(\omega t + \theta)$$
$$\dot{f}(t) = -\omega F_m \cos(\omega t + \theta - 90°)$$
$$\dot{f}(t) = \omega F_m \cos(\omega t + \theta - 90° + 180°)$$

which leads to the final result

$$\dot{f}(t) = \omega F_m \cos(\omega t + \theta + 90°)$$

where the fact that a sinusoidal function changes sign every $180°$, $-\cos(\theta) = \cos(\theta \pm 180°)$, has been used to eliminate the leading negative sign. Positive $180°$ was used in the above derivation, because if $-180°$ were used, the final result would have been

$$\dot{f}(t) = \omega F_m \cos(\omega t + \theta - 270°)$$

While this expression is technically correct, standard convention dictates that angles should be expressed in the range $-180°$ to $180°$. The reason for this standard is simple. Angles in this range are easier to visualize. For example, $315°$ and $-45°$ are the same angle, but −45° creates an immediate mental image, whereas 315° likely does not. Once again, engineers adopt standards that minimize errors.

Sinusoid Differentiation
$y = f(t) = F_m \cos(\omega t + \theta)$
$\dot{f}(t) = dy/dt = \omega F_m \cos(\omega t + \theta + 90°)$

Because angles are expressed in the limited range −180° to 180°, the use of three significant digits for angles in degrees is not appropriate. Rather, the resolution of an angle should be the same anywhere an angle resides around a circle. For this reason, it is common to express angles to the nearest 0.1°. So angles near zero, e.g., 2.1°, and angles near 180°, e.g., 176.3° have the same precision. By adopting this standard, a circle is divided into 3,600 equal angular segments, each 0.1° wide. In doing so, all angles have the same absolute accuracy.

Express angles in the range −180° to 180° and express them to the nearest 0.1°.

Two integrals of the general cosine form will be useful in later chapters. Both of these integrals involve finding the average. Finding the average of a list of numbers, such as test scores, means adding up the values and dividing by the number of values N summed,

$$Average = \frac{1}{N} \sum_{k=1}^{N} values$$

Finding the average of a function follows accordingly. The summation becomes an integral, and N becomes the duration over which the integral is computed. That is, the average of a function $f(t)$ is

$$F = \frac{1}{T} \int_{t_o}^{t_o+T} f(t)\,dt$$

where t_o is the beginning of the interval T and $t_o + T$ is the end of the interval over which the average is computed.

For periodic functions, the average can be computed over any one period. Letting $t_o = 0$ and $T = 2\pi$, and applying this to the cosine gives

$$F = \frac{1}{2\pi} \int_0^{2\pi} \cos(\theta)\,d\theta = \frac{1}{2\pi}\left[\sin(2\pi) - \sin(0)\right] = 0$$

Therefore, the area under one period of a sinusoid is zero. The positive area over the first half period from 0 to π is equal in magnitude to the negative area over the second half period from π to 2π. Therefore the sum of two half period areas is zero.

It should also be clear that it does not matter where the integral starts. As long as the integral is over one complete period, the net resulting area is zero. Not only that, it does not matter how many complete periods the average is computed over. If the average over one period is zero, then the average over two periods is also zero as well because the net area under the cosine remains zero.

The other useful integral is the average of a cosine squared over one period,

$$F = \frac{1}{2\pi} \int_0^{2\pi} \cos^2(\theta)\,d\theta$$

This integral is easily computed by making use of the trigonometric identity

$$\cos^2(\theta) = \frac{1}{2}\left[1 + \cos(2\theta)\right]$$

Substituting this identity into the integral and simplifying gives

$$F = \frac{1}{2\pi} \int_0^{2\pi} \cos^2(\theta)\,d\theta$$

$$F = \frac{1}{2\pi} \int_0^{2\pi} \frac{1}{2}\left[1 + \cos(2\theta)\right]d\theta$$

$$F = \frac{1}{4\pi}\left[\int_0^{2\pi} 1\,d\theta + \int_0^{2\pi} \cos(2\theta)\,d\theta\right]$$

$$F = \frac{1}{4\pi}\left[(2\pi - 0) + (\sin(4\pi) - \sin(0))\right] = \frac{2\pi}{4\pi} = \frac{1}{2}$$

Therefore, the average of the square of a sinusoid is equal to one half. Rewriting these two averages for the general sinusoidal function $f(t) = \cos(\omega t + \theta)$ leads to the results shown in the table below.

Integrals of Sinusoids
$F = \frac{1}{T} \int_{t_o}^{t_o+T} \cos(\omega t + \theta)\,dt = 0$
$F = \frac{1}{T} \int_{t_o}^{t_o+T} \cos^2(\omega t + \theta)\,dt = \frac{1}{2}$

1.10 Complex Numbers

Complex numbers play a significant role in the solution of engineering problems. Complex numbers cannot be measured in the laboratory. There is no such thing as a complex valued voltage or current. The square root of –1, $\sqrt{-1}$, is not measurable. However, it is extremely convenient to use complex numbers to represent measurable values mathematically. Doing so converts common and very difficult analytical problems into problems involving straightforward algebra with complex numbers. **So, from this point of view, complex numbers are simply a mathematical tool that makes it much easier to solve many engineering problems.**

Complex numbers arise naturally in very simple problems. For example, consider the polynomial or quadratic equation

$$ax^2 + bx + c = 0$$

There are two values of x for which this equation holds. These two values, called roots, are given by the solutions of the quadratic equation

$$x_{1,2} = \frac{-b \pm \sqrt{b^2 - 4ac}}{2a}$$

For the example

$$x^2 + 6x + 25 = 0$$

the roots are given by

$$x_{1,2} = \frac{-6 \pm \sqrt{6^2 - 4 \cdot 1 \cdot 25}}{2 \cdot 1}$$

$$x_{1,2} = \frac{-6 \pm \sqrt{36 - 100}}{2}$$

$$x_{1,2} = -3 \pm \frac{1}{2}\sqrt{-64}$$

$$x_{1,2} = -3 \pm \frac{1}{2}\sqrt{64} \cdot \sqrt{-1}$$

$$x_{1,2} = -3 \pm 4\sqrt{-1}$$

That is, the two roots are

$$x_1 = -3 + 4\sqrt{-1} \qquad x_2 = -3 - 4\sqrt{-1}$$

All complex numbers have this form, a **real part** and an imaginary part. The **imaginary part** is that part of the number that is multiplied by $\sqrt{-1}$. Rather than write $\sqrt{-1}$ all the time, the letter i is commonly used in most disciplines, *i.e.*,

$$i = \sqrt{-1}$$

With this notation, the above example solution can be rewritten as

$$x_{1,2} = -3 \pm 4i$$

While this is standard notation and it is how calculators display complex numbers, it is **NOT** the standard in electrical and computer engineering. In electrical and computer engineering, the variable i is reserved for electric current. As a result, a different letter is needed. That letter is j,

$$\boxed{j = \sqrt{-1}}$$

Using j, the above example is written

$$x_{1,2} = -3 \pm j4$$

Note that $j4$ is equal to $4j$ since the product of two values can be expressed in either order.

The above example demonstrates the electrical and computer engineering standard for writing complex numbers. If the real part of a complex number is a and the imaginary part is b, the complex number is written as

$$x = a + jb$$

Clearly complex numbers can be written in many equivalent forms such as

$$a + jb = a + bj = jb + a = bj + a$$

Despite the equivalence of the above forms, $a + jb$ is the standard form used by engineers. Once again, by choosing a standard form, mistakes are minimized.

Complex Numbers in Rectangular Form

$$a + jb$$

The real part a is written first. The imaginary part jb appears second, and the j appears before the imaginary value b.

Complex plane

Because complex numbers have two distinct parts, real and imaginary, they can be visualized on a two-dimensional set of axes where the horizontal axis identifies the real part and the vertical axis identifies the imaginary part, as illustrated in the following figure.

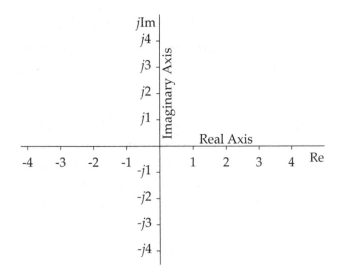

This set of axes is simply two number lines set at right angles to each other. This set of axes is called the **complex plane** to distinguish it from other sets of axes such as plots of functions versus time.

The horizontal real number line by itself is commonly used in early elementary education. In that setting it is used to visualize the addition and subtraction of numbers and to illustrate the concept of negative numbers.

Placing complex numbers on the complex plane is straightforward as shown by the following examples.

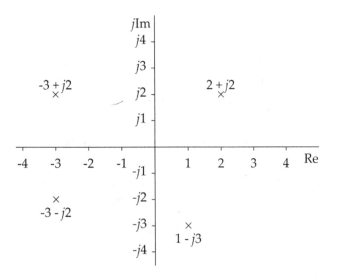

Once a complex number is placed on the complex plane, one can create a right triangle with the origin {0, 0}, the real part a, and the complex number $a + jb$ being the vertices of the triangle as shown in the following illustration.

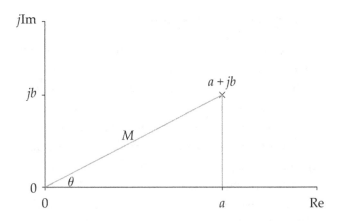

Given this geometric interpretation, it should be apparent that the complex number can also be uniquely identified by the triangle hypotenuse M and the associated angle θ between the positive real axis and the hypotenuse. This describes the complex number in polar coordinates. When described in this way, a complex number is expressed in **polar form** and written using the notation $M\angle\theta$. That is, the rectangular form is equal or equivalent to the polar form

$$a + jb = M\angle\theta$$

Simple geometry provides the relationships between the rectangular and polar forms of a complex number. For a general complex number $a + jb$, the radial distance from the origin to the complex number is called the **magnitude, M**. It is given by the hypotenuse of the right triangle, which is given by the Pythagorean theorem relationship

$$M = \sqrt{a^2 + b^2}$$

It is important to note that the length along the imaginary axis is b, not jb. If it were jb, the magnitude would be $M = \sqrt{a^2 + (jb)^2} = \sqrt{a^2 - b^2}$, which is a silly result. This expression says that the hypotenuse is shorter than the two sides or is complex if $b > a$. Geometry says this cannot happen. The length of the hypotenuse is a real quantity that is longer than each of the triangle sides. Do not make this mistake; the length along the imaginary axis is the length as you would measure it with a ruler. This length is b, not jb.

The angle of a complex number follows from simple geometry. Given a right triangle shown in the following illustration, the trigonometric relationships for the **angle θ** are

$$\cos(\theta) = \frac{\text{adjacent}}{\text{hypotenuse}}$$

$$\sin(\theta) = \frac{\text{opposite}}{\text{hypotenuse}}$$

$$\tan(\theta) = \frac{\text{opposite}}{\text{adjacent}}$$

Four Quadrant arctangent		
Quadrant	$a + jb$	$\theta = \text{atan2}(y,\ x)$
1	$a > 0, b > 0$	$\theta = \tan^{-1}(b/a)$
2	$a < 0, b > 0$	$\theta = 180\,° + \tan^{-1}(b/a)$
3	$a < 0, b < 0$	$\theta = -180\,° + \tan^{-1}(b/a)$
4	$a > 0, b < 0$	$\theta = \tan^{-1}(b/a)$

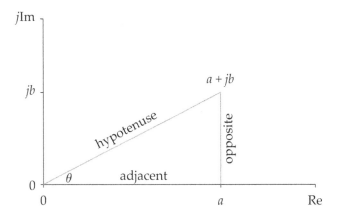

The inverse of the tangent expression gives the angle θ as

$$\theta = \tan^{-1}\!\left(\frac{\text{opposite}}{\text{adjacent}}\right) = \text{atan}\!\left(\frac{\text{opposite}}{\text{adjacent}}\right)$$

Depending on the quadrant in the complex plane a complex number resides, this relationship gives the corresponding angle of the complex number. In the following quadrant illustration, the angle θ with respect to the positive real axis can be described by the **four quadrant arctangent, $\theta = \text{atan2}(y, x)$**, for the complex number $a + jb$.

The four quadrant arctangent function is common in scientific calculators, programming languages, and spreadsheet applications. Calculators and computer programming languages commonly implement this function as atan2(y, x) where y is the length along the vertical axis and x is the length along the horizontal axis. Spreadsheet programs often swap the order of these arguments, atan2(x, y). Since there is no standard, it is important to check each application.

Starting with a complex number in polar form, $M \angle \theta$, the equivalent rectangular form can be found using the sine and cosine relationships for a right triangle as shown earlier. Rearranging the cosine expression gives

$$\cos(\theta) = \frac{\text{adjacent}}{\text{hypotenuse}}$$

$$\text{adjacent} = \text{hypotenuse} \cdot \cos(\theta)$$

Applying this expression to the complex number $a + jb = M \angle \theta$ gives

$$a = M\cos(\theta)$$

Rearranging the sine expression and applying it to the complex number $a + jb = M \angle \theta$ gives

$$\sin(\theta) = \frac{\text{opposite}}{\text{hypotenuse}}$$

$$\text{opposite} = \text{hypotenuse} \cdot \sin(\theta)$$

$$b = M\sin(\theta)$$

The conversions between the rectangular and polar forms of a complex number are summarized in the following table.

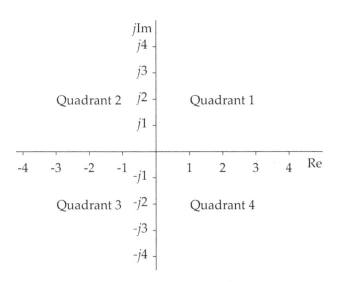

Complex Number Conversion	
Rectangular Form	**Polar Form**
$a + jb$	$M = \sqrt{a^2 + b^2}$ $\theta = \text{atan2}(b,\ a)$
$a = M\cos(\theta)$ $b = M\sin(\theta)$	$M \angle \theta$

The following table provides some examples of complex numbers expressed in equivalent rectangular and polar forms.

Complex Number Examples	
Rectangular Form	**Polar Form**
$2+j2$	$2.83\angle 45°$
$2-j2$	$2.83\angle -45°$
$3-j4$	$5\angle -53.1°$
$3+j4$	$5\angle 53.1°$
$-4-j3$	$5\angle -143.1°$
$-4+j3$	$5\angle 143.1°$
$j=0+j1$	$1\angle 90°$
$-j=0-j1$	$1\angle -90°$
$2=2+j0$	$2\angle 0°$
$-2=-2+j0$	$2\angle -180°$

The notation $M\angle\theta$ is simply that: notation. In reality, it describes a formal mathematical expression that starts with the Euler identity

$$e^{j\theta} = \cos(\theta) + j\sin(\theta)$$

Multiplying the Euler identity through by a constant M gives

$$Me^{j\theta} = M\cos(\theta) + jM\sin(\theta)$$

The right hand side of this expression is the rectangular form of the complex number written in terms of the polar form,

$$Me^{j\theta} = M\cos(\theta)+jM\sin(\theta)$$
$$Me^{j\theta} = \quad a \quad + \quad jb$$

Because $M\angle\theta=a+jb$, the above form, called the complex exponential form, is a formal mathematical equivalent to the polar form. Therefore, complex numbers can be written in any one of the three forms shown in the following table.

Complex Number Forms	
Rectangular	$a+jb$
Polar	$M\angle\theta$
Complex Exponential	$Me^{j\theta}$

Addition

Basic arithmetic operations with complex numbers are straightforward. Addition is easily done in rectangular form. For example, let $x=a+jb$ and $y=c+jd$, then

$$x + y = a + jb + c + jd = (a+c) + j(b+d)$$

The real parts add to form the real part of the sum, and the imaginary parts add to form the imaginary part of the sum. Addition using complex numbers in polar or complex exponential form requires conversion to rectangular form, addition, and then conversion back to polar or complex exponential form.

Multiplication

Multiplying complex numbers can be done in all three forms. In rectangular form, the product $x\cdot y$ is

$$\begin{aligned} c &+ jd \\ a &+ jb \\ \hline ac &+ jad \\ jcb &+ j^2bd \\ \hline (ac-bd) &+ j(ad+cb) \end{aligned}$$

In complex exponential form, if two complex numbers are described by

$$x = M_x e^{j\theta_x} \quad \text{and} \quad y = M_y e^{j\theta_y}$$

then

$$x\cdot y = M_x e^{j\theta_x} \cdot M_y e^{j\theta_y}$$
$$x\cdot y = M_x \cdot M_y \cdot e^{j\theta_x} \cdot e^{j\theta_y}$$
$$x\cdot y = (M_x \cdot M_y)\, e^{j(\theta_x+\theta_y)}$$

The magnitudes multiply to form the magnitude of the product and the phases add to form the phase of the product. Because of the equivalence between the polar and complex exponential forms, the product of two complex numbers in polar form gives the same result. That is, given

$$x = M_x \angle\theta_x \quad \text{and} \quad y = M_y \angle\theta_y$$

the product $x \cdot y$ is

$$x\cdot y = (M_x \angle\theta_x) \cdot (M_y \angle\theta_y)$$
$$x\cdot y = (M_x \cdot M_y)\angle(\theta_x+\theta_y)$$

Division

Division of the complex numbers x and y in complex exponential form follows as

$$\frac{x}{y} = \frac{M_x e^{j\theta_x}}{M_y e^{j\theta_y}} = \frac{M_x}{M_y}\left(e^{j\theta_x} \cdot e^{-j\theta_y}\right) = \frac{M_x}{M_y} e^{j(\theta_x - \theta_y)}$$

or equivalently in polar form

$$\frac{x}{y} = \frac{M_x \angle \theta_x}{M_y \angle \theta_y} = \frac{M_x}{M_y} \angle (\theta_x - \theta_y)$$

For division, the magnitudes divide and the phases subtract.

Division of complex numbers in rectangular form is easily done by first converting the values to polar or complex exponential form, performing the division, and then converting the result back to rectangular form.

Complex Arithmetic Summary	$x = a + jb = M_x \angle \theta_x = M_x e^{j\theta_x}$ $y = c + jd = M_y \angle \theta_y = M_y e^{j\theta_y}$
Addition	$x + y = (a+c) + j(b+d)$
Multiplication	$x \cdot y = (M_x \cdot M_y) \angle (\theta_x + \theta_y)$ $x \cdot y = (M_x \cdot M_y) e^{j(\theta_x + \theta_y)}$
Division	$x/y = (M_x/M_y) \angle (\theta_x - \theta_y)$ $x/y = (M_x/M_y) e^{j(\theta_x - \theta_y)}$

Functions

The **complex conjugate** of a complex number is the complex number with the sign of the imaginary part changed. A superscript * is used to denote the complex conjugate. In rectangular form, the complex conjugate is

$$(a+jb)^* = a - jb \quad \text{and} \quad (a-jb)^* = a + jb$$

In polar and complex exponential forms, the complex conjugate simply changes the sign on the angle,

$$(M \angle \theta)^* = M \angle -\theta$$

and

$$(M e^{j\theta})^* = M e^{-j\theta}$$

The complex conjugate provides one way to express the magnitude squared of a complex number,

$$(a+jb)\cdot(a-jb) = a^2 - jab + jab + b^2 = a^2 + b^2 = M^2$$

or equivalently in complex exponential form,

$$M e^{j\theta} \cdot (M e^{j\theta})^* = M e^{j\theta} \cdot M e^{-j\theta} = M^2 e^{j(\theta - \theta)} = M^2$$

and in polar form,

$$M \angle \theta \cdot (M \angle \theta)^* = M \angle \theta \cdot M \angle (-\theta) = M^2$$

The product of a complex number and its complex conjugate is equal to its magnitude squared in all three forms: rectangular,

$$M^2 = (a + jb) \cdot (a + jb)^*$$

polar,

$$M^2 = M \angle \theta \cdot (M \angle \theta)^*$$

and complex exponential,

$$M^2 = M e^{j\theta} \cdot (M e^{j\theta})^*$$

The complex conjugate also allows one to express the inverse of a complex number in rectangular form. Multiplying and dividing by the complex conjugate of the complex number leads to

$$\frac{1}{a+jb} = \frac{1}{a+jb}\left(\frac{a-jb}{a-jb}\right) = \frac{a-jb}{M^2} = \frac{a}{M^2} - j\frac{b}{M^2}$$

or

$$\frac{1}{a+jb} = \frac{a}{M^2} - j\frac{b}{M^2}$$

Note that the above is not equal to the common mistake $1/(a+jb) \neq 1/a + 1/(jb)$. This is not true.

The **magnitude** of a complex number is denoted using absolute value notation,

$$M = |a + jb| = \sqrt{a^2 + b^2} = |M e^{j\theta}| = |M \angle \theta|$$

The **phase, argument, or angle** of a complex number is simply θ or $\angle \theta$. Sometimes this is written in mathematics as the function arg($\cdot$), meaning the argument of the exponential function, as

$$\theta = \arg(a + jb) = \arg(M \angle \theta) = \arg\left(M e^{j\theta}\right)$$

Given the complex number $x = a + jb$, the **real part** is extracted and written using the function Re($\cdot$) as

$$a = \text{Re}(x) = \text{Re}(a + jb) = \text{Re}(M \angle \theta) = \text{Re}(M e^{j\theta})$$

In most textbooks, this function often appears as the fancy script letter $\Re$ as $a = \Re(x) = \Re(a + jb)$.

The **imaginary part** is extracted and written using the function Im($\cdot$) as

$$b = \text{Im}(x) = \text{Im}(a + jb) = \text{Im}(M \angle \theta) = \text{Im}(M e^{j\theta})$$

In most textbooks, this function often appears as the fancy script letter $\Im$ as $b = \Im(x) = \Im(a + jb)$.

Functions	$x = a + jb = M\angle\theta = Me^{j\theta}$
Conjugate	$x^* = a - jb = M\angle{-\theta} = Me^{-j\theta}$
Magnitude	$\|x\| = \|a + jb\| = \sqrt{a^2 + b^2} = M$
Phase	$\theta = \text{atan2}(b, a) = \theta$
Real Part	$a = \text{Re}(x) = \text{Re}(a+jb) = \text{Re}(M\angle\theta)$
Imaginary Part	$b = \text{Im}(x) = \text{Im}(a+jb) = \text{Im}(M\angle\theta)$

Calculators and Complex Numbers

Scientific calculators seamlessly perform complex arithmetic. Complex numbers can be entered in any form in any part of a mathematical computation. For example, one can enter $(3 + j4) \cdot (5\angle 53.1\,°)$. Behind the scenes, the calculator converts forms as needed, and then produces results in the chosen display format. This fact is both a benefit and a detriment. It is a benefit because it speeds complex number computations greatly since there is no need to manually convert between forms ahead of time. It is a detriment because some calculations can be done quickly by hand when the correspondence between polar and rectangular forms is well known. This correspondence is lost when the calculator performs calculations so readily.

The most common mistake made in performing complex number arithmetic on a calculator is failing to transcribe the letter i as j. This occurs because calculators uniformly display the letter i for $\sqrt{-1}$. In electrical and computer engineering, the letter i is reserved for current, so using it for the imaginary part of a complex number is an error to be avoided! For example, a calculator may display a complex number as $4 + 3i$, which is transcribed to the standard form $4 + j3$ in engineering work.

1.11 Euler Identity

The Euler identity appears in many areas in engineering. In addition to applying to complex number algebra as shown earlier, it also finds application when manipulating sinusoidal functions.

Sine and cosine functions can be written in terms of complex exponentials by using the Euler identity

$$e^{j\theta} = \cos(\theta) + j\sin(\theta)$$

If $-j$ is substituted for j, the Euler identity becomes

$$e^{-j\theta} = \cos(\theta) - j\sin(\theta)$$

Adding these two Euler identity forms and simplifying gives a fundamental identity for cosine,

$$e^{j\theta} + e^{-j\theta} = (\cos(\theta) + j\sin(\theta)) + (\cos(\theta) - j\sin(\theta))$$
$$e^{j\theta} + e^{-j\theta} = \cos(\theta) + \cos(\theta) + j\sin(\theta) - j\sin(\theta)$$
$$e^{j\theta} + e^{-j\theta} = 2\cos(\theta)$$

Dividing through by 2 and rewriting the final result gives

$$\cos(\theta) = \frac{e^{j\theta} + e^{-j\theta}}{2}$$

Similarly, subtracting the second identity from the first and simplifying gives an identity for sine,

$$e^{j\theta} - e^{-j\theta} = (\cos(\theta) + j\sin(\theta)) - (\cos(\theta) + j\sin(\theta))$$
$$e^{j\theta} - e^{-j\theta} = \cos(\theta) - \cos(\theta) + j\sin(\theta) + j\sin(\theta)$$
$$e^{j\theta} - e^{-j\theta} = j2\sin(\theta)$$

Dividing through by $j2$ and rewriting the final result gives

$$\sin(\theta) = \frac{e^{j\theta} - e^{-j\theta}}{j2}$$

These two fundamental identities are useful in many areas in engineering. For example, they can be used to find or prove trigonometric identities.

First Trigonometric Identity: One identity that will prove useful later is the following

$$B_1\cos(\theta) + B_2\sin(\theta) = A_1 e^{j\theta} + A_2 e^{-j\theta}$$

where

$$B_1 = (A_1 + A_2) \quad \text{and} \quad B_2 = j(A_1 - A_2)$$

The relationships among the coefficients can be shown by substituting the Euler identify for $e^{j\theta}$ and $e^{-j\theta}$ into the right hand side of the identity, then simplifying, as illustrated below.

$$A_1 e^{j\theta} + A_2 e^{-j\theta}$$
$$A_1[\cos(\theta) + j\sin(\theta)] + A_2[\cos(\theta) - j\sin(\theta)]$$

Gathering the cosine and sine terms gives

$$(A_1 + A_2)\cos(\theta) + j(A_1 - A_2)\sin(\theta)$$
$$(B_1)\cos(\theta) + \quad\quad (B_2)\sin(\theta)$$

Comparing the coefficients in the last two equations gives the desired variable relationships for the above identity.

Second Trigonometric Identity: Another trigonometric identity that is very useful in the analysis of electric circuits is the following

$$D\cos(\theta-\phi) = B_1\cos(\theta) + B_2\sin(\theta)$$

where D and ϕ are the polar form of the complex number $B_1 + jB_2$, i.e., $D\angle\phi = B_1 + jB_2$, which are explicitly given by

$$D = \sqrt{B_1^2 + B_2^2} \quad \text{and} \quad \phi = \angle(B_1 + jB_2) = \text{atan}\,2(B_2, B_1)$$

How B_1 and B_2 are related to D and ϕ is easily shown using the Euler identities for sine and cosine. Working with just the right hand side and simplifying gives

$$B_1\cos(\theta) + B_2\sin(\theta)$$

$$B_1\left(\frac{e^{j\theta} + e^{-j\theta}}{2}\right) + B_2\left(\frac{e^{j\theta} - e^{-j\theta}}{j2}\right)$$

$$\frac{B_1}{2}\left(e^{j\theta} + e^{-j\theta}\right) + \frac{B_2}{j2}\left(e^{j\theta} - e^{-j\theta}\right)$$

Getting rid of j in the denominator of the second term by multiplying by j/j leads to

$$\frac{B_1}{2}\left(e^{j\theta} + e^{-j\theta}\right) + \left(\frac{j}{j}\right)\cdot\frac{B_2}{j2}\left(e^{j\theta} - e^{-j\theta}\right)$$

$$\frac{B_1}{2}\left(e^{j\theta} + e^{-j\theta}\right) + \frac{jB_2}{(-1)2}\left(e^{j\theta} - e^{-j\theta}\right)$$

$$\frac{B_1}{2}\left(e^{j\theta} + e^{-j\theta}\right) - \frac{jB_2}{2}\left(e^{j\theta} - e^{-j\theta}\right)$$

and finally regrouping the terms results in

$$\left(\frac{B_1 - jB_2}{2}\right)e^{j\theta} + \left(\frac{B_1 + jB_2}{2}\right)e^{-j\theta}$$

The complex conjugate terms $B_1 - jB_2$ and $B_1 + jB_2$ can be written in polar and complex exponential form as

$$B_1 + jB_2 = D\angle\phi = De^{j\phi}$$
$$B_1 - jB_2 = D\angle-\phi = De^{-j\phi}$$

where

$$D = \left|B_1 - jB_2\right| = \left|B_1 + jB_2\right| = \sqrt{B_1^2 + B_2^2}$$

and

$$\phi = \text{atan}\,2(B_2, B_1) = \angle(B_1 + jB_2) = -\angle(B_1 - jB_2)$$

Substituting these into the last equation in the above derivation and simplifying further leads to

$$\frac{1}{2}\left(De^{-j\phi}\right)e^{j\theta} + \frac{1}{2}\left(De^{j\phi}\right)e^{-j\theta}$$

$$\frac{D}{2}e^{j(\theta-\phi)} + \frac{D}{2}e^{j(\phi-\theta)}$$

$$\frac{D}{2}\left(e^{j(\theta-\phi)} + e^{-j(\theta-\phi)}\right)$$

$$D\left(\frac{e^{j(\theta-\phi)} + e^{-j(\theta-\phi)}}{2}\right)$$

$$D\cos(\theta-\phi)$$

This final statement is what we sought. So, the desired variable relationships are given by those relating the complex conjugate terms $A - jB$ and $A + jB$ to their equivalent complex exponential form as shown.

This identity shows that sine and cosine terms having different amplitudes A and B combine to form a single cosine term having an amplitude and phase associated with the amplitudes A and B. Or stated more simply, a sine and cosine combine to form a cosine shifted in phase. This important identity will be used later to simplify expressions.

Third Trigonometric Identity, The Phasor Transform: The final useful trigonometric identity is,

$$F\cos(\theta+\phi) = A\cos(\theta+\phi_a) + B\cos(\theta+\phi_b)$$

where F and ϕ are given by the complex sum in polar form as

$$F\angle\phi = A\angle\phi_a + B\angle\phi_b$$

or in complex exponential form as

$$Fe^{j\phi} = Ae^{j\phi_a} + Be^{j\phi_b}$$

This is an amazing identity. Create complex numbers in polar form from the amplitude and relative phase of each sinusoid. Then add these complex numbers. The resulting complex number identifies the amplitude and relative phase of the sinusoidal result.

This relationship can be shown by noting that multiplying the Euler identity by a constant K and substituting $\theta + \phi$ for θ gives

$$Ke^{j(\theta+\phi)} = K\cos(\theta + \phi) + jK\sin(\theta + \phi)$$

The real part of this expression can be written as

$$\mathrm{Re}\left[Ke^{(j\theta + \phi)}\right] = K\cos(\theta + \phi)$$

Using this relationship, the right hand side of the identity can be written as

$$A\cos(\theta + \phi_a) + B\cos(\theta + \phi_b)$$
$$\mathrm{Re}\left[Ae^{(j\theta + \phi_a)}\right] + \mathrm{Re}\left[Be^{(j\theta + \phi_b)}\right]$$

Noting that the real parts of complex numbers add, e.g., $\mathrm{Re}(2 + j4) + \mathrm{Re}(1 + j2)) = 1 + 2 = \mathrm{Re}(3 + j6) = 3$, the above can be rewritten as the real part of the sum of the two terms

$$\mathrm{Re}\left[Ae^{(j\theta + \phi_a)} + Be^{(j\theta + \phi_b)}\right]$$

and simplified as follows by pulling out the $e^{j\theta}$ term,

$$\mathrm{Re}\left[e^{j\theta}\cdot\left(Ae^{j\phi_a} + Be^{j\phi_b}\right)\right]$$

Substituting the result

$$Fe^{j\phi} = Ae^{j\phi_a} + Be^{j\phi_b}$$

into this expression and continue simplifying gives

$$\mathrm{Re}\left[e^{j\theta}\left(Fe^{j\phi}\right)\right]$$
$$\mathrm{Re}\left[Fe^{(j\theta + \phi)}\right]$$
$$\mathrm{Re}\left[F\angle(\theta + \phi)\right]$$
$$F\cos(\theta + \phi)$$

which demonstrates the desired final result.

> This identity plays a key role in the solution of circuits energized by sinusoidal voltages and currents. This identity is known as the **phasor transform**. Without this identity, the solution of such circuits would be very difficult.

1.12 Lines and Plots

The adage "A picture is worth a thousand words" fits engineering work. While engineers use mathematics to describe and analyze the world, creating visual diagrams and plots of mathematical expressions facilitates visualization, comprehension, and discovery that would otherwise be hard to come by. In addition to plots of exponentials and sinusoids as illustrated earlier, straight lines are also important.

Several example lines are illustrated in the figure shown in the next column.

Euler Identity Summary
$e^{j\theta} = \cos(\theta) + j\sin(\theta)$
$e^{-j\theta} = \cos(\theta) - j\sin(\theta)$
$\cos(\theta) = \dfrac{e^{j\theta} + e^{-j\theta}}{2}$ $\quad$ $\sin(\theta) = \dfrac{e^{j\theta} - e^{-j\theta}}{j2}$
$B_1\cos(\theta) + B_2\sin(\theta) = A_1 e^{j\theta} + A_2 e^{-j\theta}$
$B_1 = (A_1 + A_2)$ and $B_2 = j(A_1 - A_2)$
$D\cos(\theta - \phi) = B_1\cos(\theta) + B_2\sin(\theta)$
$D = \left\|B_1 + jB_2\right\| = \sqrt{B_1^2 + B_2^2}$
$\phi = \angle(B_1 + jB_2) = \mathrm{atan2}(B_2, B_1)$
$F\cos(\theta + \phi) = A\cos(\theta + \phi_a) + B\cos(\theta + \phi_b)$
$F\angle\phi = A\angle\phi_a + B\angle\phi_b$

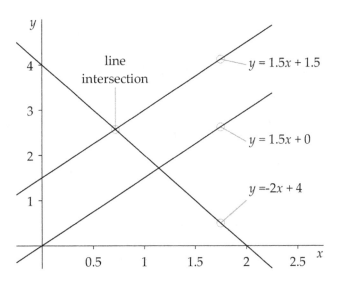

Mathematically straight lines can be described in a number of ways, each with its own advantages and disadvantages. Perhaps the most common description is the slope-intercept form

$$y = m\cdot x + b$$

where x is the independent variable placed on the horizontal axis of a plot, and y is the dependent variable placed on the vertical axis of a plot. The constant m is the slope of the line, and it is equal to

$$m = \frac{dy}{dx} = \frac{\Delta y}{\Delta x} = \frac{y_2 - y_1}{x_2 - x_1}$$

where $\{x_1, y_1\}$ and $\{x_2, y_1\}$ are two arbitrary points on the line. When the line points upward with increasing x, the slope is positive. When the line points downward with increasing x, the slope is negative.

The variable b is called the y-intercept because it is the value of y where the line crosses the vertical axis, which is where $x = 0$,

$$y = y(x) = m \cdot x + b$$
$$y = y(0) = m \cdot 0 + b$$
$$y(0) = b$$

When $b = 0$, the line passes through the origin $\{0, 0\}$.

When two lines intersect on a plot, the point of intersection $\{x^*, y^*\}$ is the graphical solution of the two equations in two unknowns formed from the two line equations. For example, the intersection of the two illustrated lines $y = 1.5x + 1.5$ and $y = -2x + 4$ occurs at $x^* = 0.7143$ and $y^* = 2.571$. The validity of these values can be checked by substituting x^* into both equations to get $y = y^*$.

When two lines are parallel to each other, as the illustrated lines $y = 1.5x + 1.5$ and $y = 1.5x + 0$ are, they have the same slope and they do not intersect.

1.13 Simultaneous Equations

The need to solve simultaneous linear equations appears in many areas of engineering. They inherently appear in the solution of linear electric circuits. Simultaneous linear equations are easily solved on scientific calculators, using online websites, or using standalone computer apps or applications. Even though one or more ways to solve these equations were likely covered in earlier school years, there is no need to know how to solve them by hand. Technology makes solving them much quicker and less prone to errors.

The fundamental concept behind the solution of simultaneous linear equations is that N distinct equations are required if there are N unknown variables. Each equation must provide a unique constraint on or unique information about the N variables to be found. One cannot simply repeat a previous equation to generate more equations. Doing so does not provide any additional unique information. Similarly, one cannot create an additional equation by forming a linear combination of the preceding equations. An example of a linear combination would be to multi-

ply one equation by a constant and then add or subtract it from another. This new equation does not provide any unique information that does not already exist in the other equations.

When there are fewer equations than there are unknowns, an infinite number of solutions exist. When there are more equations than there are unknowns, no solution exists. Neither of these cases appears when solving electric circuits using simultaneous linear equations. Since electric circuits exist in the real world, the variables in their solution must exist as well. Therefore, a valid set of N equations in N unknowns describing a circuit will always lead to a unique solution. If it does not, the set of equations is incorrect and said to be inconsistent.

Computing the solution of a set of simultaneous equations usually starts by putting the equations into matrix form. To illustrate this process, consider the example set of simultaneous equations

$$1x_1 + 2x_2 + 3x_3 = 3$$
$$4x_1 + 5x_2 + 6x_3 = 2$$
$$7x_1 + 8x_2 + 0x_3 = 1$$

where x_1, x_2, and x_3 are the unknown variables being sought. These three equations in three unknowns are written in matrix form as

$$\begin{bmatrix} 1 & 2 & 3 \\ 4 & 5 & 6 \\ 7 & 8 & 0 \end{bmatrix} \cdot \begin{bmatrix} x_1 \\ x_2 \\ x_3 \end{bmatrix} = \begin{bmatrix} 3 \\ 2 \\ 1 \end{bmatrix}$$

which is symbolically written as

$$A \cdot \underline{x} = \underline{y}$$

where A is the matrix of coefficients, $\underline{x}$ is the vector of unknowns, and $\underline{y}$ is the right hand side vector.

The solution of this set of equations is described symbolically by

$$\underline{x} = A^{-1} \cdot \underline{y}$$

where A^{-1} is the inverse of the matrix A. In practice, this set of equations is most often solved using Gaussian elimination, which is faster and more accurate than using A^{-1}. You can easily find information about Gaussian elimination algorithm online.

The answers to the above example problem are $x_1 = -11/3 = -3.67$, $x_2 = 10/3 = 3.33$, and $x_3 = 0$.

1.14 Differential Equations

Many natural phenomena or processes are described by ordinary differential equations. These equations describe how a process responds as a function of time. This response is called the dynamic response. This differs from the static response, which is constant as a function of time.

For example, a ball resting in place at the top of a hill is static; the ball's position is constant, unmoving. However, if the ball is pushed so that it rolls down the hill, its motion becomes dynamic. The ball accelerates and proceeds down the hill toward the bottom. At some point the ball reaches the bottom of the hill where it decelerates and comes to a stop where its position becomes static again. The entirety of this response is called the transient response. The transient response begins with a static state, then some action initiates a dynamic response, which eventually decays and the response returns to a static state. The ball is at rest, it speeds down the hill, and then it comes to a rest once again.

The differential equations describing the transient response can vary in complexity depending on the phenomena being described. In electric circuits, there are two fundamental phenomena that form the basis for many electric circuit designs. Luckily, these two phenomena lead to simple differential equations as will be analyzed in Chapter 5.

First Order Differential Equations

The simplest differential equation that appears in electric circuits has the form

$$\tau \frac{dx}{dt} + x = 0, \quad t \geq 0$$

where $x = x(t)$ is a function of time describing the transient response. This is called a first order differential equation because the derivative dx/dt is the first derivative of x. If you have taken a course in differential equations, you may have called this the homogeneous equation. The solution to this differential equation is called the **natural response**.

Before finding the solution, it is beneficial to study units. If x has units of meters, then dx/dt has units of m/s. Since dx/dt has units of m/s, τ must also have units of seconds so that the two terms on the left hand side can be added as shown. That is, using just the units, the differential equation is

$$\tau \frac{dx}{dt} + x = 0$$
$$(s) \cdot (m/s) + m = m$$

To find the solution to this differential equation, it is beneficial to rewrite it by dividing through by τ so that the highest order derivative term appears without a factor multiplying it, *i.e.*,

$$\frac{dx}{dt} + \frac{1}{\tau} x = 0$$

Clearly, $x = x(t) = 0$ is a solution to this equation,

$$\frac{d(0)}{dt} + \frac{1}{\tau}(0) = 0 + 0 = 0$$

This is the static or trivial solution. x is at rest, like the ball resting at the top of the hill. The dynamic solution appears when some action initiates it. Let the time when that initiating action occurs be $t = 0$.

So, we seek a function of time $x(t)$ that makes the differential equation correct for all positive time, $t \geq 0$. There are numerous ways to find this dynamic solution. If you have studied differential equations before, you probably learned a number of techniques to solve them. Perhaps the simplest way follows a technique often taught in elementary school, namely "guess and check." That is, guess the solution, then check to see if it is correct. If it is not correct, use the intuition gained from the incorrect solution to choose a new solution to try.

Using guess and check, the solution

$$x(t) = Ke^{st}, \quad t \geq 0$$

is proposed where K and s are constants. To check if this is correct, it must be substituted into the differential equation. The derivative of $x(t)$ is

$$\frac{dx}{dt} = sKe^{st}$$

Substituting $x(t)$ and dx/dt into the differential equation and simplifying gives

$$\frac{dx}{dt} + \frac{1}{\tau} x = 0$$
$$sKe^{st} + \frac{1}{\tau} Ke^{st} = 0$$
$$K\left(s + \frac{1}{\tau}\right)e^{st} = 0$$

For this potential solution to be correct or true, the product of terms in this last form must equal zero for all $t \geq 0$. $K = 0$ is one possible solution, but it is the trivial solution, $x(t) = Ke^{st} = (0)e^{st} = 0$. Alternatively, if $e^{st} = 0$ for all $t \geq 0$, then $s = -\infty$ is required, which again leads to the trivial solution because $e^{-\infty t} = 0$. Therefore, the only possibility is that the remaining term must be zero,

$$s + \frac{1}{\tau} = 0$$

This is called the **characteristic equation** because it characterizes the differential equation. Clearly it is possible for this term to be true for all $t \geq 0$ by simply solving for the value of s that makes it true,

$$s = -\frac{1}{\tau}$$

Substituting this into the proposed solution gives

$$x(t) = Ke^{st} = Ke^{-t/\tau}, \quad t \geq 0$$

This expression was considered earlier in this chapter. Evaluating this expression at $t = 0$, shows that K is simply the initial value of the function,

$$x(t) = Ke^{-t/\tau}$$
$$x(0) = Ke^{-0/\tau}$$
$$x(0) = K \cdot 1$$

Therefore,

$$x(0) = K$$

and the natural response solution to the first order differential equation can be written as

$$x(t) = x(0)e^{t/\tau}, \quad t \geq 0$$

Illustrative plots of this function can be found earlier in this chapter.

The other common first order differential equation has the form

$$\tau \frac{dx}{dt} + x = F, \quad t \geq 0$$

where F is a constant having the same units as x. In mathematics, this is called an nonhomogeneous equation. Rewriting it so that the highest order derivative has no factor multiplying it gives

$$\frac{dx}{dt} + \frac{1}{\tau}x = \frac{F}{\tau}, \quad t \geq 0$$

A good first guess would be that the previous solution for the homogeneous equation may work here. The fact that the right hand side is a nonzero constant rather than zero suggests that a constant should be added to the previous solution, i.e.,

$$x(t) = Ke^{st} + X, \quad t \geq 0$$

The derivative of $x(t)$ is the same as it was earlier since X is a constant,

$$\frac{dx}{dt} = sKe^{st}$$

Substituting $x(t)$ and dx/dt into the differential equation gives

$$\frac{dx}{dt} + \frac{1}{\tau}x = \frac{F}{\tau}$$
$$sKe^{st} + \frac{1}{\tau}\left(Ke^{st} + X\right) = \frac{F}{\tau}$$
$$sKe^{st} + \frac{1}{\tau}Ke^{st} + \frac{X}{\tau} = \frac{F}{\tau}$$
$$K\left(s + \frac{1}{\tau}\right)e^{st} = \frac{F - X}{\tau}$$

The only practical solution to this last expression for all positive time, $t \geq 0$, is when $s = -1/\tau$ as before and when $F = X$. Therefore, the solution can be written as

$$x(t) = Ke^{-t/\tau} + X, \quad t \geq 0$$

The value for X can be found by evaluating $x(t)$ at $t = \infty$,

$$x(t) = Ke^{-t/\tau} + X$$
$$x(\infty) - Ke^{-\infty/\tau} + X$$
$$x(\infty) = K \cdot 0 + X$$

so

$$x(\infty) = X$$

and value for K can be found by evaluating $x(t)$ at $t = 0$

$$x(t) = Ke^{-t/\tau} + X$$
$$x(0) = Ke^{-0/\tau} + X$$
$$x(0) = K \cdot 1 + X$$
$$x(0) = K + X$$
$$x(0) = K + x(\infty)$$

Therefore,

$$K = x(0) - x(\infty)$$

and the solution can be rewritten as

$$x(t) = Ke^{-t/\tau} + X, \quad t \geq 0$$

$$x(t) = \left[x(0) - x(\infty)\right]e^{-t/\tau} + x(\infty), \quad t \geq 0$$

which is more commonly rearranged as

$$x(t) = x(\infty) + \left[x(0) - x(\infty)\right]e^{-t/\tau}, \quad t \geq 0$$

This solution is called the **complete response** and is illustrated in the following plot.

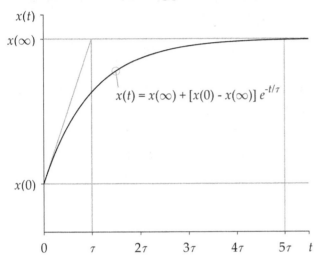

The complete describes the sum of two responses. When $F = x(\infty) = 0$ and $x(0) \neq 0$, it describes the **natural response**,

$$x(t) = x(\infty) + \left[x(0) - x(\infty)\right]e^{-t/\tau}, \quad t \geq 0$$

$$x(t) = 0 + \left[x(0) - 0\right]e^{-t/\tau}, \quad t \geq 0$$

$$x(t) = x(0)e^{-t/\tau}, \quad t \geq 0$$

When $x(0) = 0$ and $x(\infty) \neq 0$, it describes the **forced response** or **step response**,

$$x(t) = x(\infty) + \left[x(0) - x(\infty)\right]e^{-t/\tau}, \quad t \geq 0$$

$$x(t) = x(\infty) + \left[0 - x(\infty)\right]e^{-t/\tau}, \quad t \geq 0$$

$$x(t) = x(\infty) - x(\infty)e^{-t/\tau}, \quad t \geq 0$$

$$x(t) = x(\infty)\left[1 - e^{-t/\tau}\right], \quad t \geq 0$$

The following table summarizes the three first order differential equation solutions.

First Order Differential Equations	
Response	**Solution**
Natural	$x(t) = x(0)e^{-t/\tau}, \quad t \geq 0$
Step	$x(t) = x(\infty)\left[1 - e^{-t/\tau}\right], \quad t \geq 0$
Complete	$x(t) = x(\infty) + \left[x(0) - x(\infty)\right]e^{-t/\tau}, \quad t \geq 0$

All three of these responses have the same graphical characteristics that were illustrated earlier in this

chapter. The response starts at any given $x(0)$, then moves to any given $x(\infty)$ along an exponential curve. The line of initial slope starting at $x(0)$ and ending when the final value $x(\infty)$ is reached identifies the time where $t = \tau$. And the final value $x(\infty)$ of the solution is reached when $t = 5\tau$.

Second Order Differential Equations

Another differential equation that appears in circuit analysis is

$$\frac{1}{\omega_o^2}\frac{d^2x}{dt^2} + \frac{2\alpha}{\omega_o^2}\frac{dx}{dt} + x = 0$$

which is more commonly written as

$$\frac{d^2x}{dt^2} + 2\alpha\frac{dx}{dt} + \omega_o^2 x = 0$$

where α and ω_o are constants. This is a second order differential equation because the highest order derivative is second order. In mathematics, this is also called the homogeneous equation since the right hand side is zero. The solution to this equation is called the natural response just as the solution to the homogeneous first order differential equation was called the natural response.

Before finding the solution, it is beneficial to study units. If x has units of meters, then d^2x/dt^2 has units of m/s^2. So the other terms must also have units of m/s^2 as well. Therefore, α and ω_o must have units of $1/s$. The squaring of ω_o will give it the correct units of $1/s^2$.

The variable α is called the **damping factor** and the variable ω_o is called the **undamped natural frequency** or **resonant frequency**.

Since $x(t) = Ke^{st}$, $t \geq 0$ was a solution for the homogeneous first order differential equation, it is a good guess here as well. The first and second derivatives of $x(t)$ are

$$\frac{dx}{dt} = sKe^{st}$$

and

$$\frac{d^2x}{dt^2} = s^2Ke^{st}$$

Substituting these into the differential equation and simplifying gives

$$\frac{d^2 x}{dt^2} + 2\alpha \frac{dx}{dt} + \omega_o^2 x = 0$$

$$s^2 K e^{st} + 2\alpha s K e^{st} + K e^{st} = 0$$

$$K\left(s^2 + 2\alpha s + \omega_o^2\right)e^{st} = 0$$

As before, this last expression is true if the characteristic equation is equal to zero,

$$s^2 + 2\alpha s + \omega_o^2 = 0$$

This polynomial equation has two roots that are found by applying the quadratic formula,

$$a s^2 + b s + c = 0$$
$$a(s - s_1)(s - s_2) = 0$$
$$s_1, s_2 = \frac{-b \pm \sqrt{b^2 - 4ac}}{2a}$$

Applying this formula to the characteristic equation and simplifying yields

$$s_1, s_2 = \frac{-b \pm \sqrt{b^2 - 4ac}}{2a}$$

$$s_1, s_2 = \frac{-2\alpha \pm \sqrt{(2\alpha)^2 - 4 \cdot 1 \cdot \omega_o^2}}{2 \cdot 1}$$

$$s_1, s_2 = \frac{-2\alpha \pm \sqrt{4\alpha^2 - 4\omega_o^2}}{2}$$

$$s_1, s_2 = \frac{-2\alpha \pm \sqrt{4(\alpha^2 - \omega_o^2)}}{2}$$

$$s_1, s_2 = \frac{-2\alpha \pm 2\sqrt{\alpha^2 - \omega_o^2}}{2}$$

which leads to the desired final result

$$s_1, s_2 = -\alpha \pm \sqrt{\alpha^2 - \omega_o^2}$$

It is now clear why 2α and ω_o^2 were chosen as the coefficients in the differential equation. They simplify the expressions for the two roots s_1 and s_2.

Since there are two values of s that are valid as solutions to the differential equation, using each one gives a possible solution,

$$x_1(t) = K_1 e^{s_1 t}, \quad t \geq 0$$

$$x_2(t) = K_2 e^{s_2 t}, \quad t \geq 0$$

Which one of these is the solution? Is it $x_1(t)$, or $x_2(t)$, or somehow both? The answer is that it is a linear combination of both. That is, the actual solution is

$$x(t) = x_1(t) + x_2(t) = K_1 e^{s_1 t} + K_2 e^{s_2 t}, \quad t \geq 0$$

Given the possible values for s_1 and s_2, there are four different cases to consider, depending on the argument inside the square root.

When the argument inside the square root is positive, e.g., $\alpha > \omega_o$, the values for s_1 and s_2 are two negative, real, and distinct values. This solution is said to be **overdamped**.

When the argument inside the square root is negative, the values for s_1 and s_2 are two complex conjugate values, e.g., $-3 + j4$ and $-3 - j4$, having a negative real part. This solution is said to be **underdamped**.

When $\alpha = 0$, the values for s_1 and s_2 are equal to $\pm j\omega_o$ and the solution is said to be **undamped**.

When the argument inside the square root is zero, the values for s_1 and s_2 are both equal to $-\alpha$. This solution is said to be **critically damped**.

These four cases are summarized in the following table and figure showing the root locations on the complex plane.

Second Order Differential Equation Types	
Damping	**Roots**
Overdamped	negative real roots, s_1 and s_2
Underdamped	complex conjugate roots, $-\alpha \pm j\omega_d$
Undamped	imaginary roots, $\pm j\omega_o$
Critically damped	equal negative real roots, $-\alpha$ and $-\alpha$

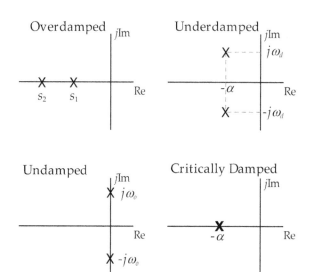

The solution for each of these four cases have unique characteristics, so they are considered individually in what follows.

Overdamped $\alpha > \omega_o$: The overdamped case closely resembles the solution to the first order differential equation, except that there are two terms in the solution. The solution in this case is unchanged from the general solution

$$x(t) = K_1 e^{s_1 t} + K_2 e^{s_2 t}, \quad t \geq 0$$

where the values for s_1 and s_2 are

$$s_1, s_2 = -\alpha \pm \sqrt{\alpha^2 - \omega_o^2}$$

Since ω_o is less than α, both of these root values are negative as illustrated in the earlier figure. Therefore each solution term has the same shape as the solution to the first order differential equation. In that sense, this solution is not something new. It is simply two decaying exponentials having different time constants.

The unknown coefficients are found by fitting the solution to the given problem. The first fitting point is at $t = 0$,

$$x(t) = K_1 e^{s_1 t} + K_2 e^{s_2 t}$$
$$x(0) = K_1 e^{s_1 \cdot 0} + K_2 e^{s_2 \cdot 0}$$
$$x(0) = K_1 \cdot 1 + K_2 \cdot 1$$

so

$$x(0) = K_1 + K_2$$

is the first equation in the two unknowns.

Another fitting point is needed. Since s_1 and s_2 are negative quantities, the final value of $x(t)$ is zero,

$$x(t) = K_1 e^{s_1 t} + K_2 e^{s_2 t}$$
$$x(\infty) = K_1 e^{s_1 \cdot \infty} + K_2 e^{s_2 \cdot \infty}$$
$$x(\infty) = K_1 \cdot 0 + K_2 \cdot 0 = 0$$

so $x(\infty)$ does not provide another fitting point. The derivative of $x(t)$ at $t = 0$ provides the other point,

$$\frac{dx(t)}{dt} = \dot{x}(t) = K_1 s_1 e^{s_1 t} + K_2 s_2 e^{s_2 t}$$
$$\dot{x}(0) = K_1 s_1 e^{s_1 \cdot 0} + K_2 s_2 e^{s_2 \cdot 0}$$
$$\dot{x}(0) = K_1 s_1 \cdot 1 + K_2 s_2 \cdot 1$$

so

$$\dot{x}(0) = K_1 s_1 + K_2 s_2$$

is the second equation in the two unknowns.

These two equations can be combined to form two equations in two unknowns as

$$K_1 + K_2 = x(0)$$
$$K_1 s_1 + K_2 s_2 = \dot{x}(0)$$

or in matrix form as

$$\begin{bmatrix} 1 & 1 \\ s_1 & s_2 \end{bmatrix} \cdot \begin{bmatrix} K_1 \\ K_2 \end{bmatrix} = \begin{bmatrix} x(0) \\ \dot{x}(0) \end{bmatrix}$$

In a given problem, $x(0)$ and $\dot{x}(0)$ will be known initial conditions, so the above equations can be solved for K_1 and K_2.

Overdamped $\alpha > \omega_o$ Solution	
Differential Equation	$\dfrac{d^2 x}{dt^2} + 2\alpha \dfrac{dx}{dt} + \omega_o^2 x = 0$
Roots	$s_1, s_2 = -\alpha \pm \sqrt{\alpha^2 - \omega_o^2}$
Solution	$x(t) = K_1 e^{s_1 t} + K_2 e^{s_2 t}, \quad t \geq 0$
Coefficients	$\begin{bmatrix} 1 & 1 \\ s_1 & s_2 \end{bmatrix} \cdot \begin{bmatrix} K_1 \\ K_2 \end{bmatrix} = \begin{bmatrix} x(0) \\ \dot{x}(0) \end{bmatrix}$

Example: The following example demonstrates the solution of an overdamped case. Let the differential equation be

$$\frac{d^2 x}{dt^2} + 2\alpha \frac{dx}{dt} + \omega_o^2 x = 0$$

$$\frac{d^2 x}{dt^2} + 6 \frac{dx}{dt} + 8x = 0$$

Then, comparing the coefficients here with the general form,

$$2\alpha = 6 \quad \text{and} \quad \omega_o^2 = 8$$

so $\alpha = 6/2 = 3$, and the roots of the characteristic equation are

$$s_1, s_2 = -\alpha \pm \sqrt{\alpha^2 - \omega_o^2} = -3 \pm \sqrt{3^2 - 8} = -3 \pm \sqrt{1} = -3 \pm 1$$

so the two roots are

$$s_1 = -3 + 1 = -2 \quad \text{and} \quad s_2 = -3 - 1 = -4$$

The form of the solution is

$$x(t) = K_1 e^{s_1 t} + K_2 e^{s_2 t}, \quad t \geq 0$$

$$x(t) = K_1 e^{-2t} + K_2 e^{-4t}, \quad t \geq 0$$

Let the initial conditions be $x(0) = -8$ and $\dot{x}(0) = 36$, then the set of equations to be solved is

$$\begin{bmatrix} 1 & 1 \\ s_1 & s_2 \end{bmatrix} \cdot \begin{bmatrix} K_1 \\ K_2 \end{bmatrix} = \begin{bmatrix} x(0) \\ \dot{x}(0) \end{bmatrix}$$

$$\begin{bmatrix} 1 & 1 \\ -2 & -4 \end{bmatrix} \cdot \begin{bmatrix} K_1 \\ K_2 \end{bmatrix} = \begin{bmatrix} -8 \\ 36 \end{bmatrix}$$

The solution to this set of equations gives $K_1 = 2$ and $K_2 = -10$. Therefore, the solution can be written as

$$x(t) = 2e^{-2t} - 10e^{-4t}, \quad t \geq 0$$

This can be rewritten in terms of time constants by recognizing that

$$\tau_1 = -1/s_1 = -1/(-2) = 0.5 = 500 \, \text{ms}$$

$$\tau_2 = -1/s_2 = -1/(-4) = 0.25 = 250 \, \text{ms}$$

Then

$$x(t) = 2e^{-t/\tau_1} - 10 e^{-t/\tau_2}, \quad t \geq 0$$

$$x(t) = 2e^{-t/500 \, \text{m}} - 10e^{-t/250 \text{m}}, \quad t \geq 0$$

By writing the solution in this way, the two time constants are visually apparent. The first term in the solution

$$x_1(t) = 2e^{-t/500 \text{m}}, \quad t \geq 0$$

decays to zero in 5 time constants, or 5·(500 m) = 2.5 seconds. Likewise, the second term in the solution

$$x_2(t) = -10e^{-t/250 \text{m}}, \quad t \geq 0$$

decays to zero in 5 time constants, or 5·(250 m) = 1.25 seconds. Since the first term takes longer to decay, it determines how long it takes the solution given by $x(t) = x_1(t) + x_2(t)$ to decay to zero.

This solution is illustrated in the following figure.

Underdamped $\alpha < \omega_o$: The underdamped case is the most interesting case by far. It also appears very frequently in electric circuits. The solution to this case can be described by the general solution

$$x(t) = K_1 e^{s_1 t} + K_2 e^{s_2 t}, \quad t \geq 0$$

where the values for s_1 and s_2 are

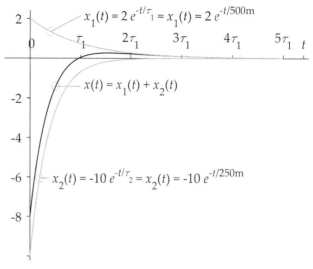

$$s_1, s_2 = -\alpha \pm \sqrt{\alpha^2 - \omega_o^2}$$

However, since $\alpha < \omega_o$, the argument inside the square root is negative. So the square root term leads to an imaginary value,

$$s_1, s_2 = -\alpha \pm \sqrt{\alpha^2 - \omega_o^2}$$

$$s_1, s_2 = -\alpha \pm \sqrt{-1 \cdot (\omega_o^2 - \alpha^2)}$$

$$s_1, s_2 = -\alpha \pm \sqrt{-1} \cdot \sqrt{\omega_o^2 - \alpha^2}$$

$$s_1, s_2 = -\alpha \pm j \sqrt{\omega_o^2 - \alpha^2}$$

which gives

$$s_1, s_2 = -\alpha \pm j\omega_d$$

where

$$\omega_d = \sqrt{\omega_o^2 - \alpha^2}$$

The two roots are described by α, called the **damping factor**, by ω_o, called the **resonant frequency**, and by ω_d, called the **damped resonant frequency**.

Using the above description for the roots the solution can be rewritten as

$$x(t) = K_1 e^{s_1 t} + K_2 e^{s_2 t}, \quad t \geq 0$$

$$x(t) = K_1 e^{(-\alpha + j\omega_d)t} + K_2 e^{(-\alpha - j\omega_d)t}, \quad t \geq 0$$

$$x(t) = K_1 e^{-\alpha t} e^{j\omega_d t} + K_2 e^{-\alpha t} e^{-j\omega_d t}, \quad t \geq 0$$

or more simply as

$$x(t) = e^{-\alpha t}\left(K_1 e^{j\omega_d t} + K_2 e^{-j\omega_d t} \right), \quad t \geq 0$$

Interestingly, the right hand side of this solution contains complex values $e^{\pm j\omega_d t} = \cos(\omega_d t) \pm j\sin(\omega_d t)$, but the left hand side cannot. It cannot, because the solution $x(t)$ is a quantity measurable in the laboratory and $\sqrt{-1}$ cannot be measured. It only exists mathematically. When evaluating the right hand side, the imaginary parts must cancel each other out so that only the real and measurable part remains. This requires K_1 and K_2 to be complex values.

It is possible to eliminate the complex values on the right hand side by using the identity established in the Euler Identity section of this chapter,

$$B_1 \cos(\theta) + B_2 \sin(\theta) = A_1 e^{j\theta} + A_2 e^{-j\theta}$$

where

$$B_1 = (A_1 + A_2) \quad \text{and} \quad B_2 = j(A_1 - A_2)$$

Applying this identity to the underdamped solution leads to

$$x(t) = e^{-\alpha t}\left[B_1 \cos(\omega_d t) + B_2 \sin(\omega_d t)\right], \quad t \geq 0$$

The above form is the standard form for solving underdamped second order differential equations. The constants, B_1 and B_2 are real values, rather than complex values, because sine and cosine are real and the left hand side must be real. The values of B_1 and B_2 are found directly, rather than working with the original underdamped solution to find K_1 and K_2. So, at this point, the original form is discarded.

The unknown coefficients B_1 and B_2 are found by fitting the equation to $x(0)$ and $\dot{x}(0)$ as was done in the overdamped case. Finding $x(0)$ provides the relationship

$$x(t) = e^{-\alpha t}\left[B_1 \cos(\omega_d t) + B_2 \sin(\omega_d t)\right]$$
$$x(0) = e^{-\alpha \cdot 0}\left[B_1 \cos(\omega_d \cdot 0) + B_2 \sin(\omega_d \cdot 0)\right]$$
$$x(0) = e^{0}\left[B_1 \cos(0) + B_2 \sin(0)\right]$$
$$x(0) = 1 \cdot \left[B_1 \cdot 1 + B_2 \cdot 0\right]$$

Therefore

$$B_1 = x(0)$$

determines the value for B_1.

Finding $\dot{x}(0)$ provides the other needed relationship. Taking the derivative of $x(t)$ in this case requires the multiplication rule for differentiation,

$$\frac{d(u \cdot v)}{dt} = u\frac{dv}{dt} + v\frac{du}{dt}$$

Applying this rule to $x(t)$,

$$\dot{x}(t) = e^{-\alpha t}\left[-B_1 \omega_d \sin(\omega_d t) + B_2 \omega_d \cos(\omega_d t)\right]$$
$$- \alpha e^{-\alpha t}\left[B_1 \cos(\omega_d t) + B_2 \sin(\omega_d t)\right]$$

Evaluating at $t = 0$ gives

$$\dot{x}(0) = e^{-\alpha \cdot 0}\left[-B_1 \omega_d \sin(\omega_d \cdot 0) + B_2 \omega_d \cos(\omega_d \cdot 0)\right]$$
$$- \alpha e^{-\alpha \cdot 0}\left[B_1 \cos(\omega_d \cdot 0) + B_2 \sin(\omega_d \cdot 0)\right]$$
$$\dot{x}(0) = 1 \cdot \left[-B_1 \omega_d \cdot 0 + B_2 \omega_d \cdot 1\right] - \alpha \cdot 1 \cdot \left[B_1 \cdot 1 + B_2 \cdot 0\right]$$
$$\dot{x}(0) = \left[B_2 \omega_d\right] - \alpha\left[B_1\right]$$
$$\dot{x}(0) = B_2 \omega_d - \alpha B_1$$

Solving this last expression for B_2 gives

$$B_2 = \frac{\dot{x}(0) + \alpha B_1}{\omega_d}$$

The solution form

$$x(t) = e^{-\alpha t}\left[B_1 \cos(\omega_d t) + B_2 \sin(\omega_d t)\right], \quad t \geq 0$$

is very convenient for finding the unknown coefficients. However, it is not readily apparent what this function looks like because it is formed by the sum of cosine and sine terms each having a different amplitude. These two terms can be combined to form a single sinusoid using the identity established in the Euler Identity section of this chapter,

$$D\cos(\theta - \phi) = B_1 \cos(\theta) + B_2 \sin(\theta)$$

where

$$D = \left|B_1 + jB_2\right| = \sqrt{B_1^2 + B_2^2}$$
$$\phi = \angle(B_1 + jB_2) = \text{atan2}(B_2, B_1)$$

Applying this identity to the above solution gives

$$D\cos(\omega_d t - \phi) = B_1 \cos(\omega_d t) + B_2 \sin(\omega_d t)$$

So a third way to write the underdamped solution is

$$x(t) = D e^{-\alpha t}\cos(\omega_d t - \phi), \quad t \geq 0$$

where D and ϕ are computed from B_1 and B_2 as shown above. This solution can be modified one final time by recognizing that the time constant is $\tau = 1/\alpha$, which leads to

$$x(t) = D e^{-t/\tau}\cos(\omega_d t - \phi), \quad t \geq 0$$

The underdamped case leads to a solution that is a decaying sinusoid. The amplitude of the sinusoid is $De^{-t/\tau}$, which decays to zero in five time constants. As the time constant τ increases (or as the damping factor α decreases) the longer it takes the solution to decay to zero. The frequency of the sinusoid is the damped resonant frequency ω_d.

A plot of $x(t)$ has interesting properties. First note that sinusoidal functions produce values that are always within the range from –1 to 1. That is,

$$-1 \le \cos(\omega_d t - \phi) \le 1$$

So, if $\cos(\omega_d t - \phi)$ in $x(t)$ is replaced by its lower extreme, –1, the resulting function is called the lower envelope,

$$x_l(t) = D e^{-t/\tau}(-1) = -D e^{-t/\tau}, \quad t \ge 0$$

and if $\cos(\omega_d t - \phi)$ in $x(t)$ is replaced by its upper extreme, +1, the resulting function is called the upper envelope,

$$x_u(t) = D e^{-t/\tau}(+1) = D e^{-t/\tau}, \quad t \ge 0$$

For all values of $\cos(\omega_d t - \phi)$, $x(t)$ resides between these two limits or envelopes,

$$x_l(t) \le x(t) \le x_u(t), \quad t \ge 0$$
$$-D e^{-t/\tau} \le D e^{-t/\tau} \cos(\omega_d t - \phi) \le D e^{-t/\tau}, \quad t \ge 0$$

The decaying sinusoid solution fits between its lower and upper envelopes as illustrated in the following figure.

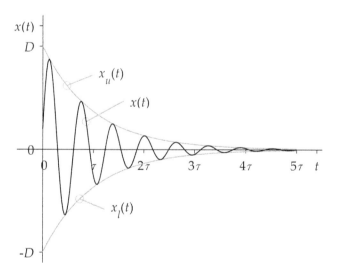

If the underdamped solution $x(t)$ was an audible sound, it would resemble the sound of a ringing bell, namely a tonal frequency that decays in amplitude over time. For this reason, the underdamped solution is often called **ringing**. The degree of ringing is related to the damping coefficient $\alpha = 1/\tau$.

When a phenomenon or process is lightly damped, it rings for a relatively long time. The larger the time constant τ is, the longer the response rings since it takes to reach five time constants (5τ) for the transient response to effectively reach zero. In addition, as the time constant τ gets larger, the damping factor $\alpha = 1/\tau$ gets smaller, and the sinusoidal frequency ω_d increases toward the resonant frequency ω_o.

A lightly damped solution is illustrated below. Many periods of the sinusoid appear before the five time constants pass and the solution decays to zero. This solution would sound like a bell. This illustration exhibits less damping and therefore more ringing than the previous moderately damped illustration.

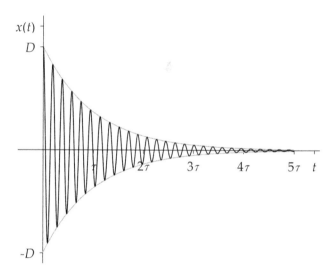

Alternatively, as the damping coefficient α increases, the time constant τ gets shorter, and the ringing becomes less pronounced because it decays faster while the sinusoidal frequency decreases.

A heavily damped solution is shown in the next illustration at the top of the next page. Only about one period of the sinusoid appears before the five time constants pass by and the solution to decays to zero. This solution would not sound like a bell at all.

Example: Consider the differential equation

$$\frac{d^2 x}{dt^2} + 2\alpha \frac{dx}{dt} + \omega_o^2 x = 0$$

$$\frac{d^2 x}{dt^2} + 10 \frac{dx}{dt} + 169 x = 0$$

Then, comparing the coefficients here with the general form gives

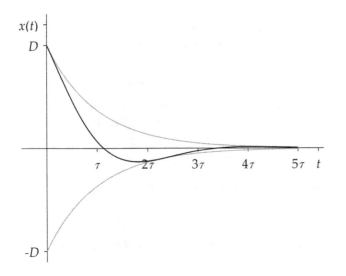

$$2\alpha = 10 \quad \text{and} \quad \omega_0^2 = 169$$

so the damping factor is

$$\alpha = 10/2 = 5$$

the resonant frequency is

$$\omega_0 = \sqrt{169} = 13 \ \text{rad/s}$$

and the damped resonant frequency is

$$\omega_d = \sqrt{\omega_0^2 - \alpha^2} = \sqrt{169 - (5)^2} = \sqrt{169 - 25} = \sqrt{144} = 12 \ \text{rad/s}$$

The form of the solution is

$$x(t) = e^{-\alpha t}\left[B_1 \cos(\omega_d t) + B_2 \sin(\omega_d t)\right], \quad t \geq 0$$

If $x(0) = 5$ and $\dot{x}(0) = -61$, then the coefficients B_1 and B_2 are

$$B_1 = x(0) = 5$$

$$B_2 = \frac{\dot{x}(0) + \alpha B_1}{\omega_d} = \frac{-61 + 5 \cdot 5}{12} = \frac{-61 + 25}{12} = \frac{-36}{12} = -3$$

Therefore the solution can be written as

$$x(t) = e^{-\alpha t}\left[B_1 \cos(\omega_d t) + B_2 \sin(\omega_d t)\right], \quad t \geq 0$$

$$x(t) = e^{-5t}\left[5\cos(12t) - 3\sin(12t)\right], \quad t \geq 0$$

Expressing the solution in the alternative form gives

$$D = \sqrt{B_1^2 + B_2^2} = \sqrt{5^2 + (-3)^2} = \sqrt{25 + 9} = \sqrt{34} = 5.83$$

$$\phi = \text{atan}\,2(B_2, B_1) = \text{atan}\,2(-3, 5) = -31.0°$$

$$\tau = \frac{1}{\alpha} = \frac{1}{5} = 0.2\,\text{s} = 200 \ \text{ms}$$

and the solution becomes

$$x(t) = D e^{-t/\tau} \cos(\omega_d t - \phi), \quad t \geq 0$$

$$x(t) = 5.83 \ e^{-t/200\text{m}} \cos(12t + 31.0°), \quad t \geq 0$$

So it takes $5\tau = 5 \cdot 0.2 = 1$ second for the natural response to decay to zero. The following figure illustrates this solution.

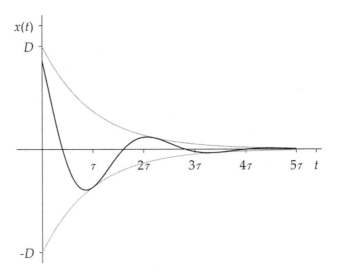

Note that this plot appears to agree with the given initial conditions. Visually the initial value $x(0) = 5$ is slightly less than $D = 5.83$, and the initial steep negative slope appears to agree with the initial condition $\dot{x}(0) = -61$.

Underdamped $\alpha < \omega_0$ Solution	
Differential Equation	$\dfrac{d^2 x}{dt^2} + 2\alpha \dfrac{dx}{dt} + \omega_0^2 x = 0$
Roots	$s_1, s_2 = -\alpha \pm j\omega_d \quad \omega_d = \sqrt{\omega_0^2 - \alpha^2}$
Variables	$\alpha = $ damping factor $\omega_0 = $ resonant frequency $\omega_d = $ damped resonant frequency
Solution	$x(t) = e^{-\alpha t}\left[B_1 \cos(\omega_d t) + B_2 \sin(\omega_d t)\right]$
Coefficients	$B_1 = x(0) \quad B_2 = (\dot{x}(0) + \alpha B_1)/\omega_d$
Solution	$x(t) = D e^{-t/\tau} \cos(\omega_d t - \phi), \quad t \geq 0$
Coefficients	$D = \lvert B_1 + jB_2 \rvert = \sqrt{B_1^2 + B_2^2}$ $\phi = \angle(B_1 + jB_2) = \text{atan}\,2(B_2, B_1)$ $\tau = 1/\alpha$

Undamped $\alpha = 0$: The undamped case occurs when there is no damping, *i.e.*, $\alpha = 0$. This special case has the same general properties as the underdamped case, except that the response does not decay to zero over time. By setting $\alpha = 0$, the roots of the characteristic equation become

$$s_1, s_2 = -\alpha \pm j\sqrt{\omega_o^2 - \alpha^2} = -0 \pm j\sqrt{\omega_o^2 - 0^2} = \pm j\sqrt{\omega_o^2} = \pm j\omega_o$$

That is, the frequency of the sinusoidal term is equal to the resonant frequency and $\omega_d = \omega_o$. The solution then has the form

$$x(t) = e^{-\alpha t}\left[B_1\cos(\omega_d t) + B_2\sin(\omega_d t)\right], \quad t \geq 0$$
$$x(t) = e^{-0 \cdot t}\left[B_1\cos(\omega_o t) + B_2\sin(\omega_o t)\right], \quad t \geq 0$$
$$x(t) = B_1\cos(\omega_o t) + B_2\sin(\omega_o t), \quad t \geq 0$$

or the equivalent form

$$x(t) = De^{-\alpha t}\cos(\omega_d t - \phi), \quad t \geq 0$$
$$x(t) = De^{-0 \cdot t}\cos(\omega_o t - \phi), \quad t \geq 0$$
$$x(t) = D\cos(\omega_o t - \phi), \quad t \geq 0$$

The solution is a constant amplitude sinusoid. An electric circuit that produces this response is called an **oscillator**. The frequency of oscillation is the natural undamped frequency or resonant frequency. Since this solution never decays to zero, it requires a continuous source of energy to keep it from decaying to zero. This requires electronic circuitry that is beyond the scope of this text. The unknown coefficients in this form are found in the same manner that they are for the underdamped case.

Critically damped $\alpha = \omega_o$: The final special case is called critically damped. This case occurs when $\alpha = \omega_o$, which makes the two roots of the characteristic equation equal to each other,

$$s_1, s_2 = -\alpha \pm \sqrt{\alpha^2 - \omega_o^2} = -\alpha \pm \sqrt{\omega_o^2 - \omega_o^2} = -\alpha \pm \sqrt{0} = -\alpha$$

It is important to note that this case does not appear in practice. It does not appear simply because it is impossible to choose parameter values, *e.g.*, electric circuit component values, so that α is exactly equal to ω_o. Nominal component values can be chosen so that these are equal, but all component values have tolerances that prevent these from being exactly equal in practice. A phenomenon or process will either be overdamped or underdamped, but never exactly critically damped. The critically damped case exists as

the boundary or dividing line between the overdamped and underdamped cases. The appeal of this case is purely mathematical. It exhibits unique characteristics that are worth noting.

When $\alpha = \omega_o$, and $s_1 = s_2 = -\alpha$, it is natural to assume that the solution becomes

$$x(t) = K_1 e^{s_1 t} + K_2 e^{s_2 t} \quad t \geq 0$$
$$x(t) = K_1 e^{-\alpha t} + K_2 e^{-\alpha t} \quad t \geq 0$$
$$x(t) = (K_1 + K_2) e^{-\alpha t} \quad t \geq 0$$
$$x(t) = K e^{-\alpha t} \quad t \geq 0$$

It turns out that this is not true. In this case, our guess and check approach to solving the problem failed to identify the other possible solution! The other valid solution form is

$$x(t) = K t e^{-\alpha t} \quad t \geq 0$$

So, for the critically damped case, the general form of the solution is

$$x(t) = D_1 e^{-\alpha t} + D_2 t e^{-\alpha t}, \quad t \geq 0$$

or

$$x(t) = D_1 e^{-t/\tau} + D_2 t e^{-t/\tau}, \quad t \geq 0$$

As with the other cases, the unknown coefficients are found by finding $x(0)$ and $\dot{x}(0)$. Doing so gives

$$x(t) = D_1 e^{-\alpha t} + D_2 t e^{-\alpha t}$$
$$x(0) = D_1 e^{-\alpha \cdot 0} + D_2 \cdot 0 \cdot e^{-\alpha \cdot 0}$$
$$x(0) = D_1$$

and

$$\dot{x}(t) = -\alpha D_1 e^{-\alpha t} - \alpha D_2 t e^{-\alpha t} + D_2 e^{-\alpha t}$$
$$\dot{x}(t) = (D_2 - \alpha D_1 - \alpha D_2 t)e^{-\alpha t}$$
$$\dot{x}(0) = (D_2 - \alpha D_1 - \alpha D_2 \cdot 0)e^{-\alpha \cdot 0}$$
$$\dot{x}(0) = (D_2 - \alpha D_1)\cdot 1$$
$$\dot{x}(0) = D_2 - \alpha D_1$$

Complete Response: Except for the undamped case, all natural response solutions to the homogeneous second order differential equation decay to zero as time goes to infinity. Though not as common, the nonhomogeneous differential equation

$$\frac{1}{\omega_o^2}\frac{d^2 x}{dt^2} + \frac{2\alpha}{\omega_o^2}\frac{dx}{dt} + x = F$$

sometimes appears in applications.

In the first order differential equation problem, the nonhomogeneous solution was simply the homogeneous solution with a final value $x(\infty)$ added. So, rather than derive this fact again, let's just state it.

The general solution to the nonhomgeneous differential equation is

$$x(t) = K_1 e^{s_1 t} + K_2 e^{s_2 t} + x(\infty), \quad t \geq 0$$

This makes perfect sense if you recognize that the first two terms decay to zero as time goes to infinity, so the only term left is exactly what it must be,

$$x(\infty) = K_1 e^{s_1(\infty)} + K_2 e^{s_2(\infty)} + x(\infty)$$
$$x(\infty) = K_1 \cdot 0 + K_2 \cdot 0 + x(\infty)$$
$$x(\infty) = x(\infty)$$

The appearance of $x(\infty)$ in the solution changes the expressions for $x(0)$, but not for $\dot{x}(0)$ because the derivative of the constant $x(\infty)$ is zero. So it disappears when computing the derivative.

The process of finding the solution to the nonhomogeneous problem directly follows that of the homogeneous case. A summary for the overdamped and underdamped cases follows.

Overdamped $\alpha > \omega_o$: The overdamped solution is

$$x(t) = K_1 e^{s_1 t} + K_2 e^{s_2 t} + x(\infty), \quad t \geq 0$$

and the coefficients are found from

$$x(t) = K_1 e^{s_1 t} + K_2 e^{s_2 t} + x(\infty)$$
$$x(0) = K_1 e^{s_1 \cdot 0} + K_2 e^{s_2 \cdot 0} + x(\infty)$$
$$x(0) = K_1 \cdot 1 + K_2 \cdot 1 + x(\infty)$$
$$x(0) - x(\infty) = K_1 + K_2$$

and from earlier,

$$\dot{x}(0) = K_1 s_1 + K_2 s_2$$

which combine to form the set of equations

$$\begin{bmatrix} 1 & 1 \\ s_1 & s_2 \end{bmatrix} \cdot \begin{bmatrix} K_1 \\ K_2 \end{bmatrix} = \begin{bmatrix} x(0) - x(\infty) \\ \dot{x}(0) \end{bmatrix}$$

Underdamped $\alpha < \omega_o$: The underdamped solution has the forms

$$x(t) = e^{-\alpha t}\left[B_1 \cos(\omega_d t) + B_2 \sin(\omega_d t)\right] + x(\infty), \quad t \geq 0$$

and

$$x(t) = D e^{-t/\tau} \cos(\omega_d t - \phi) + x(\infty), \quad t \geq 0$$

The coefficients are found from

$$x(t) = e^{-\alpha t}\left[B_1 \cos(\omega_d t) + B_2 \sin(\omega_d t)\right] + x(\infty)$$
$$x(0) = e^{-\alpha \cdot 0}\left[B_1 \cos(\omega_d \cdot 0) + B_2 \sin(\omega_d \cdot 0)\right] + x(\infty)$$
$$x(0) = 1 \cdot \left[B_1 \cdot 1 + B_2 \cdot 0\right] + x(\infty)$$
$$x(0) = B_1 + x(\infty)$$

or

$$B_1 = x(0) - x(\infty)$$

and

$$B_2 = \frac{\dot{x}(0) + \alpha B_1}{\omega_d}$$

Alternative Notation: The form of the characteristic equation used in the second order differential equation was

$$s^2 + 2\alpha s + \omega_o^2 = 0$$

This form is not uniformly adopted. Sometimes other notation is used. Other forms include

$$s^2 + 2\zeta\omega_o s + \omega_o^2 = 0$$

and

$$s^2 + 2\zeta\omega_n s + \omega_n^2 = 0$$

where $\omega_n = \omega_o$ is called the undamped natural frequency, and ζ, i.e., zeta or informally "wiggle," is a normalized damping coefficient because it expresses the damping factor α as a fractional amount ζ of the resonant frequency ω_o,

$$\alpha = \zeta\omega_o$$

For these alternative forms, the roots of the characteristic equation are given by

$$s_{1,} s_2 = -\zeta\omega_o \pm \omega_o\sqrt{\zeta^2 - 1}$$

Using this notation, the solution is underdamped when $0 < \zeta < 1$, overdamped when $\zeta > 1$, undamped when $\zeta = 0$, and critically damped when $\zeta = 1$.

1.15 Summary

Logarithm	Notation	Inverse
Common	$y = \log(x)$	$x = 10^y$
Natural	$y = \ln(x)$	$x = e^y$

Significant Digits and Rounding

To have 3 significant digits accuracy for final results, use 4 or more significant digits for preliminary results.

Exact integer values have infinite precision.

When rounding to N digits, if the digit immediately to the right of the Nth digit is less than 5, do not change the Nth digit.
If not, round the Nth digit up to the next number.

Power Ratios in decibels (dB)

Power	$10 \log(P_2/P_1)$
Voltage	$20 \log(|V_2/V_1|)$
Current	$20 \log(|I_2/I_1|)$

Common Metric Prefixes

Power of 10	Symbol	Prefix
10^{-12}	p	pico
10^{-9}	n	nano
10^{-6}	μ	micro
10^{-3}	m	milli
10^{0}	—	—
10^{3}	k	kilo
10^{6}	M	mega
10^{9}	G	giga
10^{12}	T	tera

Leading and Lagging

$\cos(\theta)$ leads $\sin(\theta)$	$\cos(\theta) = \sin(\theta + 90°)$
$\sin(\theta)$ lags $\cos(\theta)$	$\sin(\theta) = \cos(\theta - 90°)$

Sinusoidal Time Functions

Period in seconds	T
Frequency in Hz	$f = 1/T$
Frequency in rad/s	$\omega = 2\pi f = 2\pi/T$

Properties of Logarithms

Multiplication becomes Addition

$$\log(x \cdot y) = \log(x) + \log(y)$$

$$\log(100) = \log(10 \cdot 10) = \log(10) + \log(10) = 1 + 1 = 2$$

Division becomes Subtraction

$$\log(x/y) = \log(x) - \log(y)$$

$$\log(100) = \log(1000/10) = \log(1000) - \log(10) = 3 - 1 = 2$$

Exponentiation becomes Multiplication

$$\log(x^k) = k \cdot \log(x)$$

$$\log(1000) = \log(10^3) = 3 \cdot \log(10) = 3 \cdot 1 = 3$$

Inversion becomes Negation

$$\log(1/x) = \log(x^{-1}) = -\log(x)$$

$$\log(1/100) = \log(100^{-1}) = -\log(100) = -2$$

Sinusoid Differentiation

$$y = f(t) = F_m \cos(\omega t + \theta)$$

$$\dot{f}(t) = dy/dt = \omega F_m \cos(\omega t + \theta + 90°)$$

Integrals of Sinusoids

$$F = \frac{1}{T} \int_{t_o}^{t_o + T} \cos(\omega t + \theta)\, dt = 0$$

$$F = \frac{1}{T} \int_{t_o}^{t_o + T} \cos^2(\omega t + \theta)\, dt = \frac{1}{2}$$

Complex Number Conversion

Rectangular Form $a+jb$	Polar Form $M\angle\theta$
$a+jb$	$M = \sqrt{a^2+b^2}$ $\theta = \text{atan2}(b, a)$
$a = M\cos(\theta)$ $b = M\sin(\theta)$	$M\angle\theta$

Complex Arithmetic Summary	$x = a+jb = M_x\angle\theta_x = M_x e^{j\theta_x}$ $y = c+jd = M_y\angle\theta_y = M_y e^{j\theta_y}$
Addition	$x+y = (a+c) + j(b+d)$
Multiplication	$x\cdot y = (M_x\cdot M_y)\angle(\theta_x+\theta_y)$ $x\cdot y = (M_x\cdot M_y) e^{j(\theta_x+\theta_y)}$
Division	$x/y = (M_x/M_y)\angle(\theta_x-\theta_y)$ $x/y = (M_x/M_y) e^{j(\theta_x-\theta_y)}$

Complex Functions	$x = a+jb = M\angle\theta = Me^{j\theta}$
Complex Conjugate	$x^* = a-jb = M\angle-\theta = Me^{-j\theta}$
Magnitude	$\lvert x\rvert = \lvert a + jb\rvert = \sqrt{a^2 + b^2} = M$
Phase	$\theta = \text{atan2}(b, a)$
Real Part	$a = \text{Re}(x) = \text{Re}(a+jb) = \text{Re}(M\angle\theta)$
Imaginary Part	$b = \text{Im}(x) = \text{Im}(a+jb) = \text{Im}(M\angle\theta)$

First Order Differential Equations

Equation	$\dfrac{dx}{dt} + \dfrac{1}{\tau}x = \dfrac{x(\infty)}{\tau}, \quad t\geq 0$
Response	**Solution Form**
Natural	$x(t) = x(0) e^{-t/\tau}, \quad t\geq 0$
Step	$x(t) = x(\infty)\left[1 - e^{-t/\tau}\right], \quad t\geq 0$
Complete	$x(t) = x(\infty) + \left[x(0)-x(\infty)\right]e^{-t/\tau}, \quad t\geq 0$

Second Order Differential Equation Types

Equation	$\dfrac{d^2x}{dt^2} + 2\alpha\dfrac{dx}{dt} + \omega_o^2 x = 0$
Damping	**Roots**
Overdamped	negative real roots, s_1 and s_2 $s_1, s_2 = -\alpha \pm \sqrt{\alpha^2 - \omega_o^2}$
Underdamped	complex conjugate roots, $-\alpha \pm j\omega_d$ $s_1, s_2 = -\alpha \pm j\omega_d$ $\omega_d = \sqrt{\omega_o^2 - \alpha^2}$
Undamped	imaginary roots, $s_1, s_2 = \pm j\omega_o$
Critically Damped	equal negative real roots, $s_1, s_2 = -\alpha$

Overdamped $\alpha > \omega_o$ Solution

Differential Equation	$\dfrac{d^2x}{dt^2} + 2\alpha\dfrac{dx}{dt} + \omega_o^2 x = 0$
Roots	$s_1, s_2 = -\alpha \pm \sqrt{\alpha^2 - \omega_o^2}$
Solution	$x(t) = K_1 e^{s_1 t} + K_2 e^{s_2 t}, \quad t\geq 0$
Coefficients	$\begin{bmatrix} 1 & 1 \\ s_1 & s_2 \end{bmatrix}\cdot\begin{bmatrix} K_1 \\ K_2 \end{bmatrix} = \begin{bmatrix} x(0) \\ \dot{x}(0) \end{bmatrix}$

Underdamped $\alpha < \omega_o$ Solution

Differential Equation	$\dfrac{d^2x}{dt^2} + 2\alpha\dfrac{dx}{dt} + \omega_o^2 x = 0$
Roots	$s_1, s_2 = -\alpha \pm j\omega_d \qquad \omega_d = \sqrt{\omega_o^2 - \alpha^2}$
Solution	$x(t) = e^{-\alpha t}\left[B_1\cos(\omega_d t) + B_2\sin(\omega_d t)\right]$
Coefficients	$B_1 = x(0) \qquad B_2 = (\dot{x}(0) + \alpha B_1)/\omega_d$
Solution	$x(t) = D e^{-t/\tau}\cos(\omega_d t - \phi), \quad t\geq 0$
Coefficients	$D = \lvert B_1+jB_2\rvert = \sqrt{B_1^2 + B_2^2}$ $\phi = \angle(B_1+jB_2) = \text{atan2}(B_2, B_1)$ $\tau = 1/\alpha$

2 The Basics

2.1 Plumbing

The study of electric circuits is similar to the study of plumbing. All plumbing systems have similar characteristics. They all control the movement of a fluid. You are most likely familiar with indoor plumbing. The water inside plumbing pipes is under pressure so that when you open a faucet, water is forced out. In this case, water is the fluid, and pressure created by a pump or gravity makes the fluid flow when a conductive path for water to flow exists. When a faucet is closed the water remains under pressure, but there is no flow because the faucet completely resists the flow of water.

Plumbing systems are governed by two fundamental quantities, **pressure and flow**. Pressure describes the force that makes fluid flow. In a water system, pressure might be specified in pounds per square inch (psi) with the typical pressure in a residential water system being between 30 and 60 psi. Water flow is measured by its flow rate that can be specified in numerous ways. One measure is gallons per minute (gpm). If you fill a 2 gallon bucket from a garden hose and it takes one minute to fill the bucket, the flow rate is 2 g/1 m = 2 gpm.

The intuitive understanding of plumbing and a water system is very helpful because electric circuits are another plumbing system. In electric circuits, the fluid is electric charge. **Voltage** provides the force or pressure that pushes it. When charge moves, its flow rate is called **current**. So it is helpful to visualize the idea that **"voltage is pressure and current is flow rate."** Keeping this in mind will help spot errors in the analysis and design of electric circuits.

2.2 Fundamental Uses

There are two fundamental uses of electricity. The first is the generation, transmission, and consumption of energy. When you turn on a lamp, wash a load of clothes, or cook with a microwave oven, you are consuming electrical energy that was most likely generated many kilometers away. That energy is transmitted through transformers and power lines to your residence. You then consume it. Because the amount of energy generated, transmitted, and consumed is huge, maximizing efficiency is of utmost priority. If the transmission efficiency of electrical energy was only 50%, meaning that one half of the energy is lost or wasted as heat, when you turn on your microwave oven that consumes 1000 watts, 2000 watts of power must be generated. That is extremely wasteful when you think about the many billions of watts of power generated daily. Efficiency is of utmost priority when dealing with the generation, transmission, and consumption of electrical energy.

The second fundamental use of electricity is the generation, transmission, and consumption of information, *i.e.*, processing information. The telegraph, land line telephone, radio, and broadcast television are early examples of this fundamental use. These have been superseded by cable and satellite TV, satellite radio, GPS, cell phones, all sorts of wireless devices, and the internet. Energy efficiency plays no role. Information and electrical energy are not related to each other. A cell phone that consumes twice as much electric energy does not inherently provide twice as much information, but it does require charging more often. For this reason, the goal is simply to process the required information while minimizing energy consumption. Minimizing energy consumption means making currents as small as possible.

Fundamental Uses of Electricity
Generation, transmission, and consumption of **energy**. (Maximizing efficiency is most important.)
Generation, transmission, and consumption of **information**. (Minimizing power consumption is important.)

2.3 Voltage and Current

As described earlier, the study of electric circuits is like the study of plumbing. In this case, the fluid flowing through the plumbing is charge. It is useful to visualize that the pressure that pushes charge through the plumbing is voltage, and the rate at which charge moves through the plumbing is current. Just as one is generally not interested in what happens to individual water molecules in a water system, one is generally not interested in what happens to individual particles of charge in an electric circuit. One is more interested in the overall pressure and flow rate. That is, one is more interested in the voltage and current associated with the charge and its movement.

Fluid Analogy
"Voltage is Pressure"
"Current is Flow Rate"

Voltage

Voltage is defined by how much energy there is per unit charge. From this point of view, the more energy applied to a given charge, the greater the voltage the charge experiences. Stated mathematically, voltage is

$$v = \frac{dw}{dq}$$

where v is the standard variable for voltage in volts (V), q is the standard variable for charge in coulombs (C), and where w is a standard variable for energy in joules (J).

Voltage is sometimes called "potential difference" or "electromotive force (EMF)." Potential difference identifies the fact that voltage is the potential difference between two points, whereas EMF most often describes the voltage produced by a battery, generator, or other source of voltage. If you think about a common AA battery, its voltage is the potential difference between its two terminals; it is the increased pressure charge experiences as it flows through the battery from the terminal marked (–) to the one marked (+).

Voltage is a relative measure. It only has meaning when comparing one point to another. To understand this, consider the air pressure in an automobile tire. When you measure tire pressure, the value you read with a tire gauge is the pressure in the tire relative to the atmosphere. A tire gauge is marked with positive numbers indicating how much higher the pressure is in the tire relative to that outside the tire.

In this case, the **reference point** is the atmosphere outside the tire.

Equivalently, the tire gauge could be marked with negative numbers, in which case the value read would be how much lower the pressure is in the atmosphere relative to that inside the tire. In this case, the reference point is the inside of the tire. The atmosphere is at a lower pressure relative to the inside of the tire, so the pressure is negative.

> Pressure and voltage are relative to the two points where the pressure or potential difference are compared. **Voltage does not exist at a point.** It exists between one point and some other point.

When measured, voltage is relative to the negative (–) terminal on the meter being used. As illustrated in the following figure, if you measure an AA battery with the negative terminal of the meter placed on the negative terminal of the battery, the meter reads a positive voltage, 1.5 V as shown on the left in the figure. This occurs because there is a voltage increase between the negative and positive terminals of the battery. However, if you place the negative terminal of the meter on the positive terminal of the battery, the meter will read a negative voltage –1.5 V as shown on the right in the figure. This occurs because the meter uses the placement of its negative terminal as its reference. In this case, the positive terminal of the meter is at a voltage 1.5 V lower than its negative terminal.

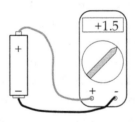 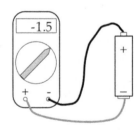

Because voltage is relative to where it is measured, the two measurement points must be identified and the polarity of the voltage must be identified. These are not noted when measuring tire pressure because tire pressure is always specified as the pressure inside the tire with respect to the atmosphere. So, tire gauges always give a positive reading. The downside of this is that it is easy to believe that pressure in this case is measured at a point, when it is not.

Voltage

Voltage is measured between two points. The two measurement points must be identified with plus (+) and minus (−) labels so that the voltage polarity is uniquely identified. If the voltage value between these two labels is positive, the voltage increases or rises from the negative terminal to the positive terminal, otherwise it decreases or drops.

Current

Current is defined as the rate or speed that charge moves through a path. It is the flow rate of charge,

$$i = \frac{dq}{dt}$$

where i is the standard variable for the current in amperes or amps (A), q is charge in coulombs (C) and t is time in seconds (s). **Current is measured at a point.** In a residence supplied by a municipal water supply, a water meter measures the amount of water consumed. All the water in the residence flows through the water meter. As with water, current is always measured through an element as illustrated in the figure below.

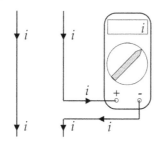

Because current is always measured through an element, current is often more difficult to measure than voltage. In a circuit, measuring current means breaking the circuit so that a meter can be inserted into the current flow path as shown above. On a printed circuit board (PCB) this means cutting conductor paths that exist on the board, or it means adding features to the board design that permit insertion of a meter for measuring current. For this reason, voltage measurements are much more common. **All that is required for measuring voltage are access to the two desired measurement points. There is no need to cut paths or add features such as jumpers.**

Going back to the example of filling a bucket with water, if it takes one minute to fill a 2 gallon bucket, the water flow rate is 2 gpm. With suitable measure-

ment equipment, this rate can be measured anywhere in the plumbing system supplying the water to the bucket. For example, the water is moving at the same rate at any and all points in the hose supplying water to the bucket. Current is measured at a point.

While it is not clear from this bucket example, fluid moves in a closed path because fluid is conserved. Once the water in the bucket is used, it eventually finds its way back into the earth, where it becomes available for use again. Because of this, fluid flow rate is constant around a closed path as well. If water is entering the hose at a 2 gpm rate, it must also fill the bucket at a 2 gpm rate because the path within the hose is closed, *i.e.*, it does not leak.

For example, as illustrated in the following figure, in a battery operated device such as a flashlight, the direction of current flow is out of the positive terminal of the battery as denoted by the arrow pointing in the direction of current flow.

The current flows through the LED and back into

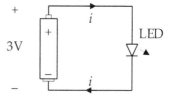

the negative terminal of the battery. The battery acts as a pump pushing charge through the device circuitry. The current is the same everywhere around the closed path. If it were not the same, charge would have to pile up or be depleted at points along the path so that the flow rate could vary. This simply cannot happen in a closed path.

Current

Current is measured at a point. Measuring current requires that a circuit be **broken** so that the desired current flows through the meter being used. This generally makes measuring current more difficult than measuring voltage, which just requires access to two measurement points.

The direction of current flow must be identified by an arrow, (→). If the current value is positive, the current flows in the direction of the arrow, otherwise it flows in the opposite direction.

2.4 Electric Circuits

An electric circuit is formed whenever circuit elements are connected in a useful way. For example, consider a simple flashlight as shown in various ways in the following circuit diagrams. The two batteries are pumps that produce voltage that pushes charge through conductors, through the LED, and back through the batteries. The speed at which the charge moves is current and the current everywhere in the closed circuit is the same.

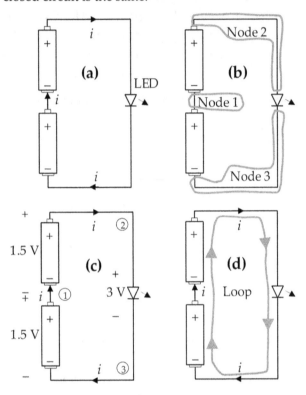

There are three circuit elements in circuit (a), two batteries and one LED. These circuit elements are in series because they all share the same current i. **The connections between each of the elements are called nodes.** So there are three nodes in this circuit as noted by the encircled areas illustrated in circuit (b) and simply noted by the numbered labels in circuit (c). While labeling nodes by encircling areas as shown in circuit (b) may be helpful at first, doing so gets very cumbersome and confusing for more complicated circuits. For this reason, nodes are customarily labeled with circled identifiers as shown in circuit (c).

The circuit itself forms a loop as shown in circuit (d), which is any closed path that starts at one node, takes a path through the circuit back to the initial node and does not cross any node more than once.

The wires or conductors connecting the three elements are considered perfect conductors. That is, they do not hinder the flow of current in any way. While technically this is not possible, common conductors hinder the flow of current so very little, that this is a very good approximation. If this approximation is not used, then the analysis of even simple circuits becomes complicated and tedious, while not producing results of any greater usefulness. Engineers recognize this and routinely make simplifications when doing so increases productivity and has negligible impact on results.

Electric Circuit Fundamental Features	
Node	The conducting paths or connections between circuit elements. Nodes are separated by circuit elements.
Loop	Any closed path that starts at one node and takes a path through a sequence of circuit elements back to the initial node and does not cross any node more than once.

Kirchhoff's Voltage Law (KVL)

As shown in circuit (c), each battery creates a voltage or pressure of 1.5 V. Current entering the lower battery experiences a voltage increase of 1.5 V as it passes through the lower battery. It then experiences another voltage increase of 1.5 V as it passes through the upper battery. The total voltage increase is the sum of these two, 1.5 + 1.5 = 3 V. Therefore, the LED has a voltage across it of 3 V as shown in circuit (c). This fact, that pressure must add up, is a fundamental axiom. It is embodied in the first of two fundamental circuit laws, called **Kirchhoff's Voltage Law (KVL)**. If you start at node ③ at the bottom of the circuit, and sum increases in voltage or voltage **rises** going clockwise around the loop, you get 1.5 + 1.5 – 3 = 0 V. The – 3 appears because the voltage decreases or **drops** across the LED and a decrease is a negative rise. **Kirchhoff's Voltage Law states that the sum of voltage rises around a loop is zero.**

Note that this is one of several ways that Kirchhoff's Voltage Law can be stated. It could also be stated in terms of the sum of voltage decreases or drops around a loop, or in terms of the sum of voltage rises being equal to the sum of voltage drops. For example, we could say that the sum of the voltage rises across the batteries, 1.5 + 1.5, is equal to the voltage drop across the LED, or 1.5 + 1.5 = 3 V.

To minimize errors, engineers generally use KVL as the sum of voltage rises around a loop is equal to zero. In some cases, using the underlying premise behind KVL that voltage must add up, such as 1.5 + 1.5 = 3 V for the flashlight, is the simplest and clearest statement of KVL.

Kirchhoff's Voltage Law (KVL)

The sum of all voltage **rises**, *i.e.*, voltage increases, around a loop is zero.

A voltage drop or voltage decrease is equal to a negative voltage rise.

KVL holds at all times and around every loop.

Kirchhoff's Current Law (KCL)

Next consider the following circuit where the circuit elements are identified only as generic rectangles and are labeled using lowercase letters.

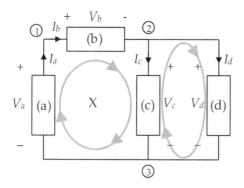

This circuit has three nodes that are identified by the circled number labels. Nodes identify points where voltages can be measured. For example, V_a is labeled as the voltage across element (a), and so on. The (−) and (+) labels identify the polarity assigned to the voltages. Note that the voltage across element (c) is equal to the voltage across element (d), $V_c = V_d$, because both of these elements are connected between the same nodes ② and ③. These two elements share the same voltage and when this happens, these elements are said to be in **parallel**. Elements (a) and (b) share the same current, $I_a = I_b$, therefore they are in **series**, as noted earlier where the flashlight batteries were in series.

The second of two fundamental circuit laws, called **Kirchhoff's Current Law (KCL)**, states the funda-

mental fact that flow must add up. It should be clear at node ② in the circuit that the sum $I_c + I_d$ must equal I_b. The current leaving element (b) simply has no other place to go other than to split between elements (c) and (d). When seen in this way, KCL states that the sum of currents entering a node is equal to the sum of currents leaving a node. Sometimes this is the simplest and clearest statement of KCL. However, **KCL is more formally stated as the sum of all currents leaving a node is zero.** Applying this to node ② gives $-I_b + I_c + I_d = 0$, where I_b is negative because I_b entering a node is equal to $-I_b$ leaving the node. The sign on a current is negative when its arrow points toward the node where KCL is being applied.

Kirchhoff's Current Law (KCL)

The sum of all currents **leaving** a node is zero.

Current entering a node is equal to a negative current leaving the node.

KCL holds at all times and at every node.

Essential versus Nonessential

KVL must hold around every loop, but applying it around some loops is not productive. For example, writing KVL clockwise around the loop formed by elements (c) and (d), gives $V_c - V_d = 0$, or $V_c = V_d$. The fact that these voltages are equal to each other does not need to be demonstrated by applying KVL. Elements (c) and (d) are in parallel. **Any loop formed by two elements in parallel is called a nonessential loop**, because it is just that; it is not essential. By inspection the voltages across elements in parallel are equal.

KVL need only be applied to essential loops, which are not formed of elements in parallel. KVL applied to an essential loop will result in an equation containing more than two terms. The loop identified as X in the preceding figure is an essential loop. Applying KVL to it, starting in the lower left corner, gives $V_a - V_b - V_c = 0$. The terms in this equation are positive when the voltage is labeled positive (+) on the outgoing side of an element as the loop is traversed in the chosen direction. It is sometimes helpful to visualize yourself walking the loop and observing the sign on the element voltages as you pass by them. That observed sign is the sign used for that element when writing the loop's KVL equation.

KCL must hold at every node, but applying it at some nodes is not productive. For example, consider node ① in the previous circuit. Applying KCL at node ① gives $-I_a + I_b = 0$, or $I_a = I_b$. That fact that these currents are equal to each other does not need to be demonstrated by applying KCL. Elements (a) and (b) are in series. **Any node formed between two elements in series is called a nonessential node,** because it is just that; it is not essential. By inspection, the current through elements in series are equal. **KCL need only be applied to essential nodes, which are nodes having more than two elements connected to them.** Nodes ② and ③ in the circuit are essential nodes because three elements are connected to these nodes. KCL applied to an essential node will result in an equation containing more than two terms.

Nonessential Loops and Nodes	
Loop	A nonessential loop is one composed of only two circuit elements.
Node	A nonessential node is one formed where only two circuit elements are connected to each other.

Series and Parallel	
Series	Two circuit elements are in **series** if they share the same current. Two elements are in **series** if they share a nonessential node.
Parallel	Two circuit elements are in **parallel** if they share the same voltage. Two circuit elements are in **parallel** if they form a nonessential loop. (Do not confuse this definition with the geometric definition of parallel lines.)

Example: To illustrate the concepts just presented consider the following circuit.

This circuit has seven nodes labeled accordingly. Nodes ① and ③ are nonessential nodes because they connect just two elements. Applying KCL to these nonessential nodes simply confirms that what flows out of one element flows into the next. These nonessential nodes identify that elements (a) and (b) are in series because they share the same current. The same is true for elements (d) and (h). They share the same current, so they are in series.

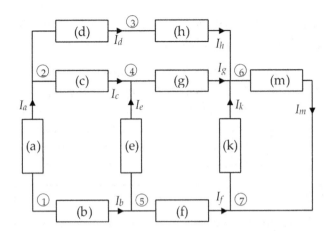

The elements (k) and (m) are in parallel even though they are geometrically perpendicular to each other. **The circuit concept of parallel means that elements share the same voltage; geometry plays no role in this definition.** These elements are in parallel because they share the same two nodes, ⑥ and ⑦. Elements (a), (e), and (k) may appear to be in parallel, but they are not, because they do not share common nodes. Confusing the geometric and circuit concept of parallel invariably leads to errors.

Applying KCL to all the nodes in the circuit gives the following results.

Node	Kirchhoff's Current Law (KCL)
1	$I_a + I_b = 0$
2	$-I_a + I_c + I_d = 0$
3	$-I_d + I_h = 0$
4	$-I_c - I_e + I_g = 0$
5	$-I_b + I_e + I_f = 0$
6	$-I_g - I_h - I_k + I_m = 0$
7	$-I_f + I_k - I_m = 0$

Next consider the same circuit with some of the many possible loops identified as shown on the top of the next page.

The four loops A, B, C, and D in the circuit are called **meshes** because they are loops that have no other loops contained within them. Loop C is the only nonessential loop because it is the only loop containing just two elements. Applying KVL to the four loops gives the results in the table below.

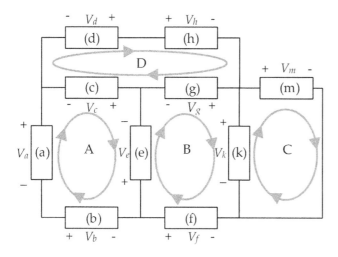

Loop	Kirchhoff's Voltage Law KVL
A	$V_a + V_c + V_e + V_b = 0$
B	$-V_e + V_g - V_k + V_f = 0$
C	$V_k - V_m = 0$
D	$V_d - V_h - V_g - V_c = 0$

There are many possible loops in a circuit. And there are closed paths that are not loops as shown in the redrawn circuit below.

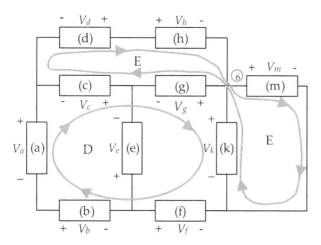

For example, the closed path labeled D is a loop, but not a mesh because it encloses the loops labeled A and B in the preceding drawing of the same circuit. Applying KVL to loop D gives $V_a + V_c + V_g - V_k + V_f + V_b = 0$.

The closed path labeled E is not a loop because it crosses node ⑥ twice, which violates the rule that loops do not cross any node more than once.

Power

Electric circuits consume power because it takes power to push fluid around. Power is very simply related to voltage and current by noting that the product of voltage and current has units of joules/second (J/s), which is watts (W); 1 J/s = 1 W.

$$vi = \frac{dw}{dq}\frac{dq}{dt} = \frac{dw}{dt} = p$$

Power is the product of pressure and flow rate. A fluid at very high pressure (voltage) having low flow rate (current) can have the same power as a fluid at low pressure (voltage) having a high flow rate (current). This is a very important relationship. Higher currents, inherently require larger diameter pipes, *i.e.*, conductors, which take up more space and are more costly. Therefore, when dealing with high power, it is generally better to make the voltage as large as possible so that the current and associated conductor size can be as small as possible.

The power relationship $p = vi$ captures the magnitude of power, but it does not convey whether the power is being generated or being absorbed. Consider the flashlight example again as shown below.

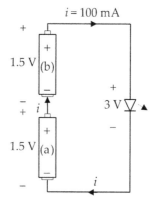

If the current flowing around the loop is 100 mA as shown, then the power in each circuit element is

Element	v	i	$p = vi$
Battery (a)	1.5	0.1	$(1.5)\cdot(0.1) = 0.15 = 150$ mW
Battery (b)	1.5	0.1	$(1.5)\cdot(0.1) = 0.15 = 150$ mW
LED	3	0.1	$(3)\cdot(0.1) = 0.3 = 300$ mW

There is no way to tell from the results which elements are generating power and which are absorbing power. In this case, it is obvious that the batteries are generating power and the LED is absorbing power.

However, for general circuits, there must be a way to determine which elements are generating power and which are absorbing power.

To solve this problem, the established standard is to make power a positive quantity if an element absorbs power and make it a negative quantity if an element generates power. For example, in the flashlight example, the power in each battery becomes –150 mW since they generate power. The LED absorbs power so its power is +300 mW.

Interestingly, the sum of the power in all the elements is zero. For the flashlight, the sum is –150 – 150 + 300 = 0 mW. This is a statement of energy conservation. All the energy generated by the circuit is absorbed by the circuit. This must hold for all electric circuits.

Energy conservation must hold for all circuits. All power generated in a circuit must also be absorbed by the circuit. So the total power in a circuit is zero.

For general circuits, the sign associated with power in a circuit element is determined by the **Passive Sign Convention (PSC)**. Power is given by $p = +vi$ if the labeled current is entering the element terminal labeled positive (+) for the voltage. When this is true, an element is said to obey the passive sign convention. Otherwise, $p = -vi$ and the element does not obey the passive sign convention.

Passive Sign Convention (PSC)	
PSC = True $p = +vi$	PSC = False $p = -vi$
current enters the side labeled +	current enters the side labeled −

Alternatively, the passive sign convention can be applied by writing the power expression as $p = svi$ where the variable s is simply a sign term where $s = +1$ if the passive sign convention is true, and $s = -1$ if it is not. Stated in this way, s is determined by the

logical selection where $s = +1$ when PSC = True, and where $s = -1$ when PSC = False.

Applying the passive sign convention to the flashlight circuit illustrated earlier gives

Element	v	i	PSC	$p = svi$
Battery (a)	1.5	0.1	$s = -1$	$-(1.5) \cdot (0.1) = -150$ mW
Battery (b)	1.5	0.1	$s = -1$	$-(1.5) \cdot (0.1) = -150$ mW
LED	3	0.1	$s = +1$	$+(3) \cdot (0.1) = +300$ mW
				Sum = 0 mW

The total or net power in the circuit is zero watts, so energy is conserved.

Example: Applying the passive sign convention to the following circuit gives the results in the table below.

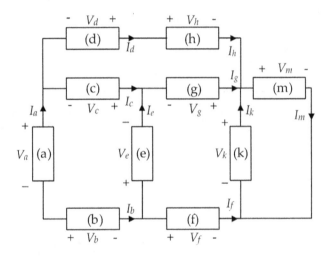

Element	v	i	PSC	$p = svi$
(a)	V_a	I_a	$s = -1$	$p_a = -V_a \cdot I_a$
(b)	V_b	I_b	$s = +1$	$p_b = +V_b \cdot I_b$
(c)	V_c	I_c	$s = -1$	$p_c = -V_c \cdot I_c$
(d)	V_d	I_d	$s = -1$	$p_d = -V_d \cdot I_d$
(e)	V_e	I_e	$s = +1$	$p_e = +V_e \cdot I_e$
(f)	V_f	I_f	$s = +1$	$p_d = +V_f \cdot I_f$
(g)	V_g	I_g	$s = -1$	$p_g = -V_g \cdot I_g$
(h)	V_h	I_h	$s = +1$	$p_h = +V_h \cdot I_h$
(k)	V_k	I_k	$s = -1$	$p_k = -V_k \cdot I_k$
(m)	V_m	I_m	$s = +1$	$p_h = +V_m \cdot I_m$

It is important to note that the passive sign convention is applied based on the way elements are labeled, not on the numerical values assigned to the labeled variables.

For example, if $V_d = -12$ V and $I_d = 2$ A in the above circuit, $p_d = -V_d \cdot I_d = -(-12) \cdot (2) = 24$ W. So this element absorbs power even though the sign on the power expression $p_d = -V_d \cdot I_d$ is negative. As the flashlight example shows, the sign on the computed numeric value for power determines whether the element absorbs or generates power.

2.5 Circuit Elements

Electric circuits are commonly composed of a variety of basic circuit elements. These elements are combined to perform some useful function. Beyond the basic circuit elements considered here, there is a seemingly infinite number of integrated circuits (ICs) that contain thousands to billions of circuit elements that include semiconductor devices. The study of semiconductor devices and the basic circuit elements contained within ICs are covered in other courses. The goal of this text is to provide the knowledge and skills needed so that semiconductor devices and the electronic circuits formed from them can be studied in later courses. The focus here is on electric circuits and basic circuit elements.

Sources (Pumps)

For an electric circuit to be useful, there must be some source of electrical power. Without it, a circuit is just a collection of parts doing nothing. Since plumbing is governed by pressure and flow, pumps that provide pressure and pumps that provide flow form the two basic sources of electrical power.

Ideal Voltage Source: An ideal voltage source provides a given voltage (pressure) under all conditions. **The current flowing through an ideal voltage source is solely determined by the circuit connected to the voltage source.** An ideal voltage source is the simplest model for a battery, such as that in a flashlight. When the flashlight is turned on, current flows through the battery. When the flashlight is turned off, no current flows. In either case, the battery voltage remains constant. The circuit connected to the battery determines how much current flows. Ideal voltage sources that have a constant value under all conditions are called DC sources, where DC stands for di-

rect current, meaning that current flows in the same direction all the time. In most instances this means a constant current. In later chapters, ideal AC sources will be considered, where AC stands for alternating current, meaning that current reverses direction or alternates periodically. In still later chapters, dynamic voltage sources will be considered where the voltage produced by the source is some useful function of time.

Ideal Current Source: An ideal current source provides a given current (flow) under all conditions. **The voltage across an ideal current source is solely determined by the circuit connected to the current source.** There is no simple natural device that can be modeled by an ideal current source. As a result, the current source does not benefit from the kind of intuition gained from thinking about a voltage source being like a battery. Nevertheless, ideal current sources are a fundamental building block for modeling circuits. Current sources are classified into DC, AC, and dynamic sources just as voltage sources are.

DC and AC	
DC	**Direct Current:** constant current flows in the same direction at all times.
AC	**Alternating Current:** current reverses direction or alternates periodically.

The symbols used for voltage and current sources are circles as shown in the table below. The voltage source has a polarity assigned to it by the (+) and (−) labels and a voltage value identified by the accompanying variable or numerical value appearing next to the source. The current source has a polarity assigned to it by the arrow pointing in the direction of current flow and a current value identified by the accompanying variable or numerical value appearing next to the source.

Ideal Voltage Source	Ideal Current Source
i ⬆ $\left(\begin{smallmatrix}+\\-\end{smallmatrix}\right)$ V_s	$+$ v $(\uparrow)$ I_s $-$
V_s is fixed, i is determined by the circuit where the source appears.	I_s is fixed, v is determined by the circuit where the source appears.

Resistors

When you think about fluid flow, the simplest concept is that it is possible to restrict or resist flow. When a water faucet is off, flow is completely restricted. When a water faucet is fully opened, flow is largely unrestricted. The water flow is limited by the resistance due to the friction between water and the interior surface of the piping supplying the faucet. So resistance to flow is a basic phenomenon in fluid systems.

In electrical circuits, resistance to flow is modeled by a resistor as shown in the following figure. The amount of current that passes through a resistor is directly proportional to the voltage applied across it. The greater the voltage, the greater the flow through the resistor.

$$\xrightarrow[+ \quad v \quad -]{\overset{R \quad i}{\wedge\wedge\wedge}}$$

The relationship between the voltage across and current through a resistor is called **Ohm's law**. When the passive sign convention is true, Ohm's law is written as

$$v = iR$$

where R is the standard variable denoting the resistance of the resistor in ohms (Ω), v is the voltage across the resistor, and i is the current through the resistor. When the passive sign convention is not true, a negative sign must be introduced, e.g., $v = -iR$, just as it was in the expression for power earlier.

Ohm's Law			
$i \downarrow$ $R \lessgtr$ $+ \; v \; -$	$v = iR$ $i = \dfrac{v}{R}$ $R = \dfrac{v}{i}$	$i \uparrow$ $R \lessgtr$ $+ \; v \; -$	$v = -iR$ $i = \dfrac{-v}{R}$ $R = \dfrac{-v}{i}$
PSC = True		PSC = False	

So, what is R?: For a uniformly shaped solid block such as that shown below,

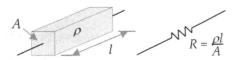

its resistance R is given by

$$R = \frac{\rho l}{A}$$

where ρ is the resistivity of the material making up the block in ohm·meters (Ω·m), l is the length of the solid between its terminals in meters (m), and A is the cross-sectional area through which current flows in meters squared (m²). Resistivity is a fundamental property of materials just as density, melting point, and hardness are.

Therefore resistance is directly proportional to length l, and inversely proportional to cross-sectional area A. This makes intuitive sense. For water pipes, the larger the cross-sectional area of the pipe, the less restrictive it is to water flow, and the longer the pipe is, the greater the total resistance because there is a greater length of pipe having friction on its interior surfaces.

Wire Resistance: It is interesting to use the resistance expression to compute the resistance of wire typically found in cables such as USB and HDMI cables. One common way to specify wire is American Wire Gauge (AWG). USB and HDMI cables are made up of wires that range from 24 to 28 AWG. Using 26 AWG as an example, its cross-sectional area is $1.288 \cdot 10^{-7}$ m² The resistivity of copper at room temperature is about 17 nΩ·m or $1.7 \cdot 10^{-8}$ Ω·m. If the cable has length $l = 1$ m, the resistance of the wire is

$$R = \frac{\rho l}{A}$$

$$R = \frac{1.7 \cdot 10^{-8} \cdot 1}{1.288 \cdot 10^{-7}} = 0.132 \, \Omega = 132 \text{ m}\Omega$$

Given that typical resistances used in electric circuits that process signals are in the kiloohm (kΩ) to megaohm (MΩ) range, the resistance of wire is truly negligible. One meter of 26 AWG wire has a resistance that is a million to a billion times smaller than the circuit resistances the wire is connected to. This is true for the conductors on a printed circuit board (PCB) as well. On a printed circuit board, the conductor cross-sectional area is much smaller, but so is the conductor length. The length is commonly centimeters rather than meters. As a result, the conductor resistance is in the milliohm (mΩ) range as well. Because conductor resistance is so small, it is ignored when solving circuits by setting it to zero and not including it in circuit diagrams or analysis.

To confirm this fact in another way, electric circuits used to process information typically have voltages up to about ten volts in amplitude and currents that range from nanoamperes (nA) to milliamperes (mA). If a current $i = 1$ mA flows through a resistance $R = 1$ mΩ, Ohm's law gives the resulting voltage v across the resistance as

$$v = iR = \left(1 \cdot 10^{-3}\right) \cdot \left(1 \cdot 10^{-3}\right) = 1 \cdot 10^{-6} = 1 \ \mu V$$

Compared to voltages on the order of volts, microvolts are negligible because they are one million times smaller.

Short Circuits and Open Circuits: The terms short circuit and open circuit are frequently used. A short circuit is a length of perfect conductor, *i.e.*, a conductor having zero resistivity, $\rho = 0$. Another way to think about it, is that it is what happens inside a light switch when you turn it on. Turning it on provides an unrestricted path for current to flow. So a short circuit has zero resistance,

$$R_{short} = \frac{\rho l}{A} = \frac{0 \cdot l}{A} = 0 \ \Omega$$

As a result, the voltage across a short circuit is zero,

$$v_{short} = iR_{short} = i \cdot 0 = 0 \ V$$

A short circuit has zero resistance and zero volts across it.

An open circuit is the opposite. It is what happens inside a light switch when you turn it off. Turning it off breaks the circuit, so no current flows. It is a path having infinite resistivity $\rho = \infty$ and infinite resistance,

$$R_{open} = \frac{\rho l}{A} = \frac{\infty \cdot l}{A} = \infty \ \Omega$$

As a result, the current through an open circuit is zero,

$$i_{open} = \frac{v}{R_{open}} = \frac{v}{\infty} = 0 \ A$$

An open circuit has infinite resistance and zero current flowing through it.

Short Circuit		Open Circuit
$+$ v $R = 0$ $-$	$+$ $v = 0$ $-$	i $i = 0$ $R = \infty$

Resistors and Power: When a resistor is labeled by the passive sign convention,

$$\underset{+ \ \ v \ \ -}{\overset{R \quad i}{\longrightarrow\!\!\!\!\!\!\!\text{—/\\/\\—}}}$$

the power in the resistor is

$$p = v \cdot i = v \cdot \left(\frac{v}{R}\right) = \frac{v^2}{R}$$

or

$$p = v \cdot i = (iR) \cdot i = i^2 R$$

so there are three ways to express the power in a resistor

$$p = v \cdot i = \frac{v^2}{R} = i^2 R > 0$$

The expressions involving the square of the voltage and the square of the current show that a resistor always absorbs power because power is always positive for a resistor. Squaring the voltage or current always produces a positive quantity and resistance is a positive quantity.

Resistors and Power
$\underset{+ \ \ v \ \ -}{\overset{R \quad i}{\text{—/\\/\\—}}}$
$p = v \cdot i = \dfrac{v^2}{R} = i^2 R > 0$

Resistors do not generate power; they always absorb power. The power in a resistor is always positive.

Example: To get an understanding of the power levels involved in electric circuits used to process information, let the voltage across a resistor R be 1 volt, $v = 1$ V. Then the associated current i and power p in various resistor values are

R	1 kΩ	10 kΩ	100 kΩ	1 MΩ
$i = \dfrac{v}{R} = \dfrac{1}{R}$	1 mA	100 µA	10 µA	1 µA
$p = \dfrac{v^2}{R} = \dfrac{1^2}{R}$	1 mW	100 µW	10 µW	1 µW

Resistor values in circuits used to process information are typically in the range from 10 kΩ to 1 MΩ. Resistor values less than 1 kΩ needlessly consume too much power. Resistor values greater than 1 MΩ are generally avoided when environmental issues such as humidity and condensation make it difficult to maintain such high resistance values.

Combining Resistors

Resistors in Series: The expression for resistance $R = \rho l / A$, provides insight into how resistors combine when they are connected in series and when they are placed in parallel. As shown in the figure below, let the length of the uniformly shaped solid block be divided at some point along its length into two pieces having length l_1, and l_2, where the total length is $l = l_1 + l_2$.

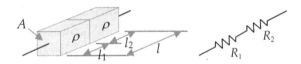

This forms two resistors in series where the resistances of the individual pieces are

$$R_1 = \frac{\rho l_1}{A}$$

and

$$R_2 = \frac{\rho l_2}{A}$$

respectively, and the resistance of the entire block R_{eq} is related to R_1 and R_2 by addition,

$$\frac{\rho l}{A} = \frac{\rho(l_1 + l_2)}{A} = \frac{\rho l_1}{A} + \frac{\rho l_2}{A}$$
$$R_{eq} = R_1 + R_2$$

Therefore, when resistors are connected in series, the equivalent resistance R_{eq} is simply the sum of the individual resistances. Using the water analogy, this is equivalent to connecting two garden hoses together end to end. The total resistance to water flow is the sum of that from each hose. This is true even if the individual sections of hose have different diameters. In general any number of resistors can be connected in series. In this case, when there are N resistors in series, the equivalent resistance is

$$R_{eq} = R_1 + R_2 + \cdots + R_N = \sum_{k=1}^{N} R_k$$

where R_k is the kth resistance.

It is vitally important to note that the equivalent resistance R_{eq} is always greater than the largest resistance in series,

$$R_{eq} > \max_k (R_k)$$

It should be obvious that **magnitude scaling** applies to resistors in series. That is, multiplying resistances by a constant α gives

$$R_{eq} = R_1 + R_2$$
$$\alpha R_{eq} = \alpha R_1 + \alpha R_2$$

For example, since $8 + 10 = 18$ Ω, then it follows that $8\,k + 10\,k = 18\ k\Omega$.

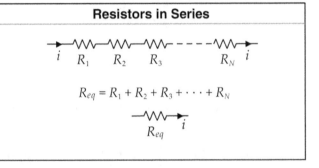

Resistors in Parallel: As shown in the figure below, let the cross section of the uniformly shaped solid block be divided into two fractional areas A_1 and A_2 where the total area is $A = A_1 + A_2$.

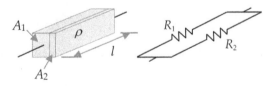

The resistors formed by these individual areas are in parallel with each other because they share the same two nodes. The individual resistances are given by

$$R_1 = \frac{\rho l}{A_1}$$

and

$$R_2 = \frac{\rho l}{A_2}$$

Because their denominators are not equal, these do not add to form an equivalent total resistance R_{eq}.

That is,

$$R_{eq} = \frac{\rho l}{A} \neq \frac{\rho l}{A_1} + \frac{\rho l}{A_2}$$

$$R_{eq} \neq R_1 + R_2$$

In this case, their inverses add

$$\frac{1}{R_{eq}} = \frac{A}{\rho l} = \frac{A_1 + A_2}{\rho l} = \frac{A_1}{\rho l} + \frac{A_2}{\rho l}$$

$$\frac{1}{R_{eq}} = \frac{1}{R_1} + \frac{1}{R_2}$$

Therefore, when resistors are connected in parallel, the inverses of the resistances add to become the inverse of the equivalent resistance. In general, any number of resistors can be connected in parallel and they combine to form an equivalent resistance by adding inverses. When there are N resistors in parallel, the equivalent resistance is

$$\frac{1}{R_{eq}} = \frac{1}{R_1} + \frac{1}{R_2} + \cdots + \frac{1}{R_N} = \sum_{k=1}^{N} \frac{1}{R_k}$$

where R_k is the kth resistance. It is vitally important to note that the equivalent resistance R_{eq} is always smaller than the smallest resistance in parallel,

$$R_{eq} < \min_{k}(R_k)$$

This is true because combining resistors in parallel increases the total area through which current flows. When area increases, resistance decreases because resistance is inversely proportional to area. Using the water analogy, combining resistors in parallel is similar to filling a bucket from two separate garden hoses. The bucket fills faster because there are two hoses, each supplying water to the bucket.

Just as magnitude scaling applies to resistors connected in series, it does as well with resistors connected in parallel. That is, starting with two resistors in parallel and multiplying both by a constant α gives

$$\frac{1}{R_{eq}} = \frac{1}{R_1} + \frac{1}{R_2}$$

$$\frac{1}{\alpha R_{eq}} = \frac{1}{\alpha R_1} + \frac{1}{\alpha R_2}$$

So, if R_1 and R_2 are multiplied by a constant α, the resulting equivalent resistance R_{eq} is also multiplied by α. For example, given that 40 Ω in parallel with 10 Ω is 8 Ω, then 40 kΩ in parallel with 10 kΩ is 8 kΩ.

Resistors in Parallel

$$\frac{1}{R_{eq}} = \frac{1}{R_1} + \frac{1}{R_2} + \frac{1}{R_3} + \cdots + \frac{1}{R_N}$$

Because it is the inverses of resistances that add when resistors are in parallel, it is worthwhile studying this in greater depth.

First, it is convenient to consider the very common case where two resistors R_1 and R_2 are in parallel.

The standard notation for denoting resistors in parallel is to use the symbol of two vertical parallel lines, such as

$$R_{eq} = R_1 \| R_2$$

This says that the parallel combination of resistors R_1 and R_2 is equal to R_{eq}. For this common case, it is possible to simplify the expression for R_{eq} as follows

$$\frac{1}{R_{eq}} = \frac{1}{R_1} + \frac{1}{R_2}$$

Create a common denominator on the right side,

$$\frac{1}{R_{eq}} = \frac{1}{R_1}\left(\frac{R_2}{R_2}\right) + \frac{1}{R_2}\left(\frac{R_1}{R_1}\right)$$

$$\frac{1}{R_{eq}} = \frac{R_2}{R_1 R_2} + \frac{R_1}{R_2 R_1}$$

$$\frac{1}{R_{eq}} = \frac{R_2 + R_1}{R_1 R_2}$$

Inverting this last expression gives the final result

$$R_{eq} = R_1 \| R_2 = \frac{R_1 R_2}{R_1 + R_2}$$

When two resistors are in parallel, the equivalent resistance is simply the product of the two resistances divided by their sum.

This form for two resistors in parallel is easily remembered, but it can lead to an incorrect result if one assumes that the same form applies to three resistors in parallel. **The following is NOT correct.**

$$R_{eq} \neq \frac{R_1 R_2 R_3}{R_1 + R_2 + R_3}$$

$$\text{ohms} \neq \frac{\text{ohms}^3}{\text{ohms}} = \text{ohms}^2$$

This points to one of the easiest ways to spot an error in any expression: perform a dimensional analysis. If the units are incorrect, there is an error.

Sometimes two resistors in parallel have values that are related by a scale factor N, *i.e.*, R and R/N. In this case, the resulting equivalent resistance R_{eq} is easy to remember,

$$\frac{1}{R_{eq}} = \frac{1}{R} + \frac{1}{R/N} = \frac{1}{R} + \frac{N}{R} = \frac{N+1}{R}$$

Inverting this expression gives the useful result

$$R_{eq} = R \parallel \frac{R}{N} = \frac{R}{N+1}$$

This fact is easy to remember and it makes it possible to compute many parallel resistances without a calculator. For example,

$$40\,\text{k} \parallel 10\,\text{k} = 40\,\text{k} \parallel \frac{40\,\text{k}}{4} = \frac{40\,\text{k}}{4+1} = \frac{40\,\text{k}}{5} = 8\,\text{k}\Omega$$

$$30\,\text{k} \parallel 15\,\text{k} = 30\,\text{k} \parallel \frac{30\,\text{k}}{2} = \frac{30\,\text{k}}{2+1} = \frac{30\,\text{k}}{3} = 10\,\text{k}\Omega$$

$$24\,\text{k} \parallel 8\,\text{k} = 24\,\text{k} \parallel \frac{24\,\text{k}}{3} = \frac{24\,\text{k}}{3+1} = \frac{24\,\text{k}}{4} = 6\,\text{k}\Omega$$

This expression also proves that the equivalent resistance of resistors in parallel is always less than the smallest resistance in parallel because, for any $N > 1$

$$R_{eq} = R \parallel \frac{R}{N} = \frac{R}{N+1} < \frac{R}{N} < R$$

or, stated in the opposite order for greater visual clarity,

$$R > \frac{R}{N} > \frac{R}{N+1}$$

The $N = 1$ case also provides the useful result

$$R \parallel \frac{R}{1} = \frac{R}{1+1} = \frac{R}{2}$$

or

$$R_{eq} = R \parallel R = \frac{R}{2}$$

Two equal valued resistors in parallel have an equivalent resistance equal to one half the resistor values. For example, $10\,\text{k} \parallel 10\,\text{k} = 5\,\text{k}\Omega$.

Scaling $R \parallel (R/N)$ by N gives an alternative expression for the same relationship. Let $R_n = N \cdot R$ and substitute R_n into the preceding relationship for R. Doing so gives

$$R \parallel \frac{R}{N} = \frac{R}{N+1}$$

$$N R_n \parallel \frac{N R}{N} = \frac{N \cdot R}{N+1} = \frac{N}{N+1} R$$

or more succinctly

$$N R \parallel R = \frac{N}{N+1} R$$

This expression makes it easy to answer the question, *"How large must a resistance be so that when it is placed in parallel with R the parallel equivalent resistance is one percent less than R?"* One percent less than R is

$$R - 0.01 R = (1 - 0.01) \cdot R = 0.99 \cdot R = \frac{99}{100} R$$

Comparing this result to the right hand side of the previous resistance relationship with $N = 99$ gives

$$N R \parallel R = \frac{N}{N+1} R$$

$$99 R \parallel R = \frac{99}{99+1} R = \frac{99}{100} R = 0.99 R$$

A resistor 99 times larger in value than R, when placed in parallel with R, creates an equivalent parallel resistance one percent lower than R. Resistances larger than $99R$ have even less impact on the equivalent resistance.

The significance of this fact leads to the **rule of thumb** that a resistance $100R$ or more in parallel with a resistance R has negligible impact on the parallel equivalent resistance, *i.e.*, $100R \parallel R \approx R$.

For example, $10\,\text{k}\Omega \parallel 100\,\Omega \approx 100\,\Omega$ because the ratio $10\,\text{k}\Omega/100\,\Omega = 100$, which is greater than 99.

This fact also provides guidance regarding the largest feasible resistor values that can be used in a practical circuit. When soldered on a printed circuit board, a resistor may be exposed to humidity, condensation, or other environmental contaminants. These contaminants can provide a conductive, but highly resistive, path for current flow in parallel around the resistor. As long as the parasitic parallel resistance provided by this conductive path is at least 100 times greater than the resistance of the chosen resistor, the parasitic parallel resistance will have negligible affect on the operation of the circuit. Parasitic resistances limit the upper value for usable resistor values to about $1\,M\Omega$ for many applications. In a clean and dry environment, usable resistor values to about $10\,M\Omega$ may be acceptable.

Two Resistors in Parallel

$$R_1 \parallel R_2 = \frac{R_1 R_2}{R_1 + R_2}$$

$$R \parallel \frac{R}{N} = \frac{R}{N+1}$$

$$N R \parallel R \approx R \quad \text{for} \quad N \geq 100$$

Graphical Solution: In the days before calculators, computing the equivalent resistance of resistors in parallel was time consuming, especially when this computation was needed several times when analyzing a single circuit. It was customary at that time to find a graphical solution, so that one can just read the result from a plot or nomogram. While nomograms are no longer needed because one can quickly compute equivalent resistances, the nomogram for computing parallel resistances provides valuable insight that helps one minimize errors.

The nomogram graphical solution for two resistors in parallel is shown in the following figure. Two intersecting diagonal lines are drawn. One starts at R_1 on the left and goes to zero on the right; the other starts at zero on the left and goes to R_2 on the right. Surprisingly, the intersection of the two lines marks the parallel equivalent resistance R_{eq}.

This graphical solution provides simple and intuitive insight into how two resistors combine in parallel. Perhaps most importantly, it visually confirms that the equivalent parallel resistance must be less than the smaller of the two resistors. The intersection

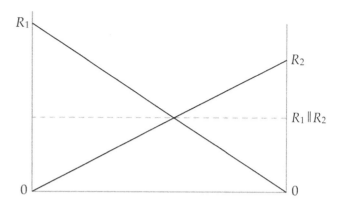

of the two lines cannot be greater than the vertical axis intersection of either line, which occur at R_1 and R_2. Several numerical examples are shown in the following figures.

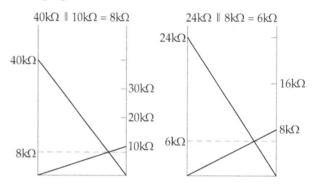

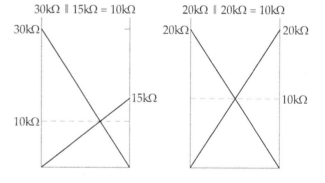

Conductance

Because the inverse of resistance appears often in circuit analysis, it is convenient to define it as a new quantity. That quantity is called conductance because the inverse of "resist" is "conduct." The standard variable for conductance is G,

$$G = \frac{1}{R}$$

where the units of conductance is 1/ohms, which at one time was somewhat humorously denoted by spelling ohms backward as "mhos" and flipping the resistance units symbol Ω upside down. Since 1971, the standard units for conductance are siemens (S).

Using conductance, resistors in parallel can be rewritten simply as

$$\frac{1}{R_{eq}} = \frac{1}{R_1} + \frac{1}{R_2} + \cdots + \frac{1}{R_N} = \sum_{k=1}^{N} \frac{1}{R_k}$$

$$G_{eq} = G_1 + G_2 + \cdots + G_N = \sum_{k=1}^{N} G_k$$

Conductances add when resistors are connected in parallel. Resistances add when resistors are connected in series.

2.6 Invalid Circuits

It is very easy to draw an electric circuit that does not obey either KVL or KCL. Circuits that violate either of these do not exhibit conservation of energy, and therefore they cannot be built in the world we inhabit. **Circuits that violate KVL or KCL are said to be invalid circuits.** Obviously, circuits that obey KVL and KCL are valid and do exhibit conservation of energy.

The simplest invalid circuits are those constructed of ideal voltage and current sources. For example, two ideal voltage sources can be connected in series as shown below. In this case, the two voltage sources can be replaced by one voltage source having a value equal to the sum of the two as determined by applying KVL.

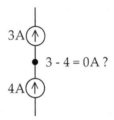

However, two voltage sources having different values cannot be connected in parallel as shown below. Applying KVL to the loop formed by the two voltage sources gives $10 - 5 = 0$ V or 10 V $= 5$ V. Clearly this is invalid.

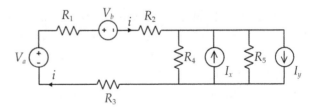

Two current sources can be connected in parallel. When they are, the two sources can be replaced by one current source having a value equal to the sum of

the two as determined by applying KCL as shown in the following circuits.

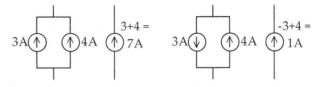

However, two current sources having different values cannot be connected in series as shown below. Applying KCL to the node between the two sources yields $3 - 4 = 0$ A or 3 A $= 4$ A. Clearly this is invalid.

In addition to these two fundamental invalid cases, it is possible to draw more complicated circuits that violate KVL or KCL as well. Since invalid circuits cannot exist, they only appear when circuits are drawn incorrectly either because of a mistake or because they are posed as a tricky academic exercise.

2.7 Simplifying Circuits

In the process of solving a circuit for voltages and currents, it is common to rearrange or combine circuit elements to create an equivalent circuit that is easier to solve. For example, it is common to combine resistors in series and replace them with a single resistor having the equivalent resistance. The same can be done with resistors in parallel—simply replace them with a single resistor having the equivalent resistance. As has been shown, voltage sources in series can be replaced by a single source equal to their sum. Similarly, current sources in parallel can be replaced by a single source equal to their sum.

Sometimes it is possible to rearrange a circuit without violating KVL and KCL, so that circuit elements can be combined using these rules. For example, consider the following circuit.

The resistors R_1, R_2, and R_3 and voltage sources V_a and V_b are in series because they share the same current i as shown. The resistors R_4 and R_5 are in parallel with the current sources I_x and I_y because they share the same two nodes.

After labeling resistor voltages, KVL can be applied to the loop formed from the series components and R_4 as shown below.

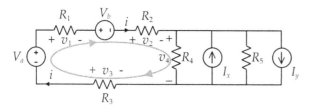

Starting in the lower left and applying KVL, the sum of all voltage rises is

$$V_a - v_1 - V_b - v_2 - v_4 + v_3 = 0$$

The validity of this equation is unchanged if it is rearranged as

$$V_a - V_b - v_1 - v_2 + v_3 + v_4 = 0$$

This equation describes KVL applied to the circuit with similarly rearranged circuit elements as shown below. Starting in the lower left and applying KVL to the loop, leads to the above KVL equation.

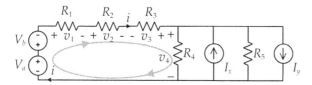

Now, the circuit has two voltage sources in series that can be combined, and three resistors in series that can be combined. Performing these steps simplifies the following circuit.

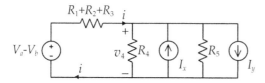

The current i in this circuit is unchanged from the original circuit because it passes through the equivalent combined series voltage sources and the equivalent combined series resistors. Likewise, the voltage v_4 is unchanged. This example demonstrates that when elements are in series, their order can be rear-

ranged as desired so that the circuit can be simplified. In this case, five circuit elements have been combined and reduced to just two.

The resistors R_4 and R_5 that are in parallel with the current sources I_x and I_y can also be rearranged. After labeling resistor currents, KCL can be applied to the top right node labeled (X) as shown below.

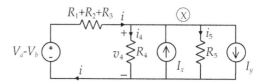

Writing the KCL equation for node (X) gives

$$-i + i_4 - I_x + i_5 + I_y = 0$$

This KCL equation can be rearranged as

$$-i + i_4 + i_5 - I_x + I_y = 0$$

This equation describes KCL applied to the circuit with similarly rearranged circuit elements as shown below.

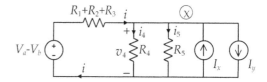

Now, the circuit has two resistors in parallel that can be combined and two current sources in parallel that can also be combined. Performing these steps simplifies the following circuit.

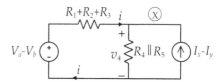

The current i in this circuit is unchanged from the original circuit. Likewise, the voltage v_4 is unchanged because it appears across the equivalent of the original circuit. This example demonstrates that when elements are in parallel, their order can be rearranged as desired so that the circuit can be simplified.

Simplifying Circuits
Elements in **series** can be rearranged as desired so that circuit elements can be combined.
Elements in **parallel** can be rearranged as desired so that circuit elements can be combined.

2.8 Brute Force Solution

Given DC voltage sources, DC current sources, and resistors, as well as KVL and KCL it is now possible to solve all valid circuits containing these items. Solving the circuit means finding the voltage across and current through each element in the circuit. This is the brute force approach to solving a circuit. It is time consuming and prone to errors because of the relatively large number of variables and equations involved. More importantly it does not provide much useful insight into circuit operation. Using brute force is similar to using a circuit analysis computer program to solve a circuit. The computer solution provides results, but not much insight. The material in this text focuses on developing insight.

The brute force solution is best demonstrated by an example. So, consider the following circuit.

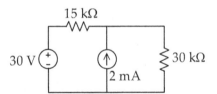

There are two essential nodes, one nonessential node, one essential loop and one nonessential loop in this circuit. They are labeled as shown in the following circuit.

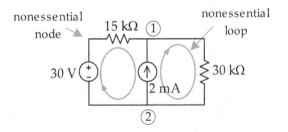

To solve this circuit, the unknown voltages and currents must be labeled. Since the 30 V source and 15 kΩ resistors are in series, they share the same current. Since the 2 mA source and 30 kΩ resistor are in parallel, they share the same voltage. Labeling the es-

sential nodes, essential loop, and unknown voltages and currents leads to the following circuit.

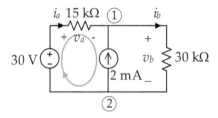

The voltages and currents were labeled so that the passive sign convention is true for both resistors. The polarities chosen are arbitrary. The numerical results will simply be negative values if the labeled polarities differ from that of the results.

There are four unknowns in this circuit, v_a, i_a, v_b, and i_b. Therefore, four independent equations are needed. Writing the Ohm's law relationship for each resistor provides two equations,

$$v_a = 15\,\text{k} \cdot i_a$$
$$v_b = 30\,\text{k} \cdot i_b$$

There are two essential nodes, so writing KCL equations for both of them gives

$$\text{KCL @(1):} \quad -i_a - 2\text{m} + i_b = 0$$
$$\text{KCL @(2):} \quad i_a + 2\text{m} - i_b = 0$$

These two equations differ by a sign change, so they are dependent on each other. As a result, only one of them provides unique or independent information.

One more equation is needed. There are no more KCL equations, but there is an essential loop available. Starting in the lower left hand corner of this loop and writing the KVL equation gives

$$30 - v_a - v_b = 0$$

There are now have four equations in four unknowns. To solve them it is convenient to place them in matrix form. To do so, it is useful to rewrite them in terms of the unknowns v_a, i_a, v_b, and i_b.

First Ohm's law equation:

$$v_a = 15\text{k} \cdot i_a$$
$$v_a - 15\text{k} \cdot i_a = 0$$
$$1 \cdot v_a - 15\text{k} \cdot i_a + 0 \cdot v_b + 0 \cdot i_b = 0$$

Second Ohm's law equation:

$$v_b = 30k \cdot i_b$$
$$v_b - 30k \cdot i_b = 0$$
$$0 \cdot v_a + 0 \cdot i_a + 1 \cdot v_b - 30k \cdot i_b = 0$$

The first KCL equation:

$$-i_a - 2m + i_b = 0$$
$$0 \cdot v_a - 1 \cdot i_a + 0 \cdot v_b + 1 \cdot i_b = 2m$$

The KVL equation:

$$30 - v_a - v_b = 0$$
$$-1 \cdot v_a + 0 \cdot i_a - 1 \cdot v_b + 0 \cdot i_b = -30$$

Each equation is now written in terms of all four unknowns. The resulting set of equations becomes

$$1 \cdot v_a - 15k \cdot i_a + 0 \cdot v_b + 0 \cdot i_b = 0$$
$$0 \cdot v_a + 0 \cdot i_a + 1 \cdot v_b - 30k \cdot i_b = 0$$
$$0 \cdot v_a - 1 \cdot i_a + 0 \cdot v_b + 1 \cdot i_b = 2m$$
$$-1 \cdot v_a + 0 \cdot i_a - 1 \cdot v_b + 0 \cdot i_b = -30$$

Translating these to matrix form gives

$$
\begin{bmatrix}
1 & -15k & 0 & 0 \\
0 & 0 & 1 & -30k \\
0 & -1 & 0 & 1 \\
-1 & 0 & -1 & 0
\end{bmatrix}
\cdot
\begin{bmatrix}
v_a \\ i_a \\ v_b \\ i_b
\end{bmatrix}
=
\begin{bmatrix}
0 \\ 0 \\ 2m \\ -30
\end{bmatrix}
$$

The solution to this set of equations is

$$
\begin{bmatrix}
v_a \\ i_a \\ v_b \\ i_b
\end{bmatrix}
=
\begin{bmatrix}
-10\,V \\ -667\,\mu A \\ 40\,V \\ 1.33\,mA
\end{bmatrix}
$$

The two voltages are integer values, so they are expressed as exact integer values. The two noninteger currents are expressed with three significant digits.

The voltage and current associated with the 15 kΩ resistor are both negative. If the polarity for both of these variables where flipped, these values would be positive. In any case, there is no need to change the assigned polarities and recompute the results. Negative values are fine.

Given these results, the power in each of the circuit elements can be computed. Doing so gives

15 kΩ resistor:

$$p_{15k} = v_a \cdot i_a = (-10) \cdot (-666.7\,\mu) = 6.67\,mW$$
$$p_{15k} = i_a^2 \cdot 15k = (-666.7\,\mu)^2 \cdot 15k = 6.67\,mW$$
$$p_{15k} = \frac{v_a^2}{15k} = \frac{(-10)^2}{15k} = 6.67\,mW$$

30 kΩ resistor:

$$p_{30k} = v_b \cdot i_b = (40) \cdot (1.333\,m) = 53.3\,mW$$
$$p_{30k} = i_b^2 \cdot 15k = (1.333\,m)^2 \cdot 30k = 53.3\,mW$$
$$p_{30k} = \frac{v_b^2}{15k} = \frac{40^2}{30k} = 53.3\,mW$$

30 V source (PSC is false, s = -1)

$$p_{30} = (-1) \cdot 30 \cdot i_a = -30 \cdot (-666.7\,m) = 20\,mW$$

2 mA source (PSC is false, s = -1)

$$p_{2m} = (-1) \cdot v_b \cdot 2m = -1 \cdot 40 \cdot 2m = -80\,mW$$

Four significant digits were used in the above calculations so that the results are accurate to the desired three significant digits.

The subscripts for each of power equations were chosen to give them a direct association with their respective circuit elements.

The sum of the powers in the components is zero as required for a valid circuit with a correct solution,

$$p_{15k} + p_{30k} + p_{30} + p_{2m} = ?$$
$$6.667\,m + 53.33\,m + 20\,m - 80\,m = ?$$
$$60\,m + 20\,m - 80\,m = ?$$
$$80\,m - 80\,m = 0\,W$$

It is interesting that the power in the 30 V source is positive. Since power is positive when an element absorbs power, the 30 V source is not generating power in this circuit; rather, it is absorbing power. The 2 mA source dominates it, forcing 667 µA into its positive terminal. This should not be surprising, since this is what happens when a battery is being charged.

The brute force solution was fairly straightforward for this example. However, as more circuit elements, nodes, and loops are added, this approach becomes tedious and prone to errors because of the increasingly large number of variables involved. In addition, one seldom needs to know all the voltages and all the currents in a circuit. For these reasons, other techniques have been developed that speed the solution process and minimize the chance for errors. The next chapter covers many of these techniques.

2.9 Summary

Fundamental Uses of Electricity

Generation, transmission, and consumption of **energy**. (Maximizing efficiency is most important.)

Generation, transmission, and consumption of **information**. (Minimizing power consumption is important.)

Fluid Analogy

"Voltage is Pressure"

"Current is Flow Rate"

Voltage

Voltage is measured between two points. The two measurement points must be identified with plus (+) and minus (–) labels so that the voltage polarity is uniquely identified. If the voltage value between these two labels is positive, the voltage increases or rises from the negative terminal to the positive terminal, otherwise it decreases or drops.

Current

Current is measured at a point. Measuring current requires that a circuit be broken so that the desired current flows through the meter being used. This generally makes measuring current more difficult than measuring voltage, which just requires access to two measurement points. An operating circuit requires modification to measure current, but generally does not to measure voltage.

Electric Circuit Fundamental Features

Node	The conducting paths or connections between circuit elements. Nodes are separated from each other by circuit elements.
Loop	Any closed path that starts at one node and takes a path through a sequence of circuit elements back to the initial node and does not cross any node more than once.

Kirchhoff's Voltage Law (KVL)

The sum of all voltage **rises**, *i.e.*, voltage increases, around a loop is zero.

A voltage drop or voltage decrease is equal to a negative voltage rise.

KVL holds at all times and around every loop.

Kirchhoff's Current Law (KCL)

The sum of all currents **leaving** a node is zero.

Current entering a node is equal to a negative current leaving the node.

KCL holds at all times and at every node.

Nonessential Loops and Nodes

Loop	A nonessential loop is one composed of only two circuit elements.
Node	A nonessential node is one formed where only two circuit elements are connected to each other.

Series and Parallel

Series	Two circuit elements are in **series** if they share the same current. Two elements are in **series** if they share a nonessential node.
Parallel	Two circuit elements are in **parallel** if they share the same voltage. Two circuit elements are in **parallel** if they form a nonessential loop.

Passive Sign Convention (PSC)

PSC = True	PSC = False
$p = +vi$	$p = -vi$

current enters the side labeled +	current enters the side labeled −

DC and AC

DC **Direct Current:** constant current flows in the same direction at all times.

AC **Alternating Current:** current reverses direction or alternates periodically.

Ideal Voltage Source / Ideal Current Source

Ideal Voltage Source	Ideal Current Source
V_s is fixed, i is determined by the circuit where the source appears.	I_s is fixed, v is determined by the circuit where the source appears.

Ohm's Law

	PSC = True		PSC = False
	$v = iR$ $i = \dfrac{v}{R}$ $R = \dfrac{v}{i}$		$v = -iR$ $i = \dfrac{-v}{R}$ $R = \dfrac{-v}{i}$

Short Circuit / Open Circuit

Short Circuit	Open Circuit
$R = 0$ $v = 0$	$R = \infty$ $i = 0$

Simplifying Circuits

Elements in **series** can be rearranged as desired so that circuit elements can be combined.

Elements in **parallel** can be rearranged as desired so that circuit elements can be combined.

Resistors and Power

$$p = v \cdot i = \frac{v^2}{R} = i^2 R > 0$$

Resistors do not generate power; they always absorb power. The power in a resistor is always positive.

Resistor values in circuits that are used to process information are typically in the range from $10\,\text{k}\Omega$ to $1\,\text{M}\Omega$. Resistor values less than $1\,\text{k}\Omega$ needlessly consume too much power. Resistor values greater than $1\,\text{M}\Omega$ are generally avoided when environmental issues such as humidity and condensation make it difficult to maintain such high resistance values.

Resistors in Series

$$R_{eq} = R_1 + R_2 + R_3 + \cdots + R_N$$

Resistors in Parallel

$$\frac{1}{R_{eq}} = \frac{1}{R_1} + \frac{1}{R_2} + \frac{1}{R_3} + \cdots + \frac{1}{R_N}$$

Two Resistors in Parallel

$$R_1 \parallel R_2 = \frac{R_1 R_2}{R_1 + R_2}$$

$$R \parallel \frac{R}{N} = \frac{R}{N+1}$$

$$N R \parallel R \approx R \quad \text{for} \quad N \geq 100$$

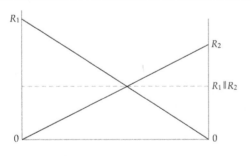

Rule of thumb: a resistance $100R$ or more in parallel with a resistance R has negligible impact on the parallel equivalent resistance, *i.e.*, $100R \parallel R \approx R$.

2.10 Problems

2.1 For each of the following circuits, identify the (i) essential nodes, (ii) nonessential nodes, (iii) essential loops, and (iv) nonessential loops.

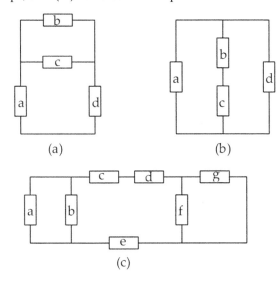

(a)   (b)

(c)

2.2 For each of the following circuits, write KCL equations for each of the nodes.

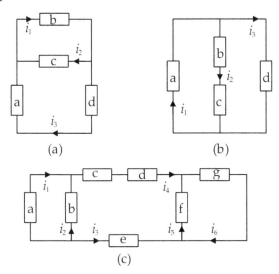

(a)   (b)

(c)

2.3 For each of the following circuits, write KVL equations for each of the labeled loops.

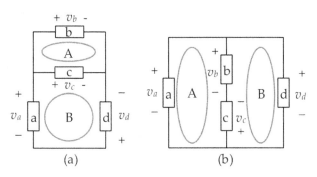

(a)   (b)

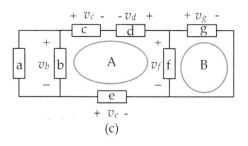

(c)

2.4 For each of the following circuits, identify which elements obey the passive sign convention (PSC) and write expressions for the power in each circuit element.

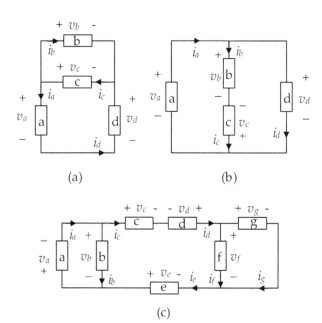

(a)   (b)

(c)

2.5 For each of the following circuits, find the power in each circuit element. Which elements are absorbing power and which ones are generating power? Does the total power in each circuit equal zero?

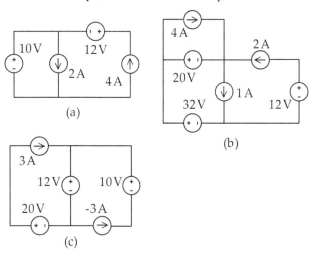

(a)

(b)

(c)

2.6 For each of the following circuits, write expressions for each of the labeled equivalent resistances. Then evaluate each expression to find the corresponding numerical values.

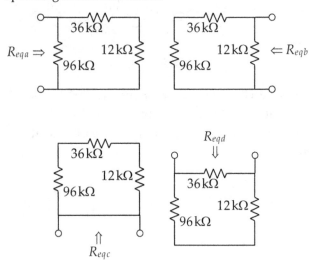

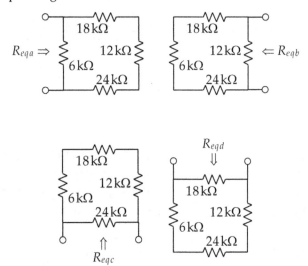

2.7 For each of the following circuits, write expressions for each of the labeled equivalent resistances. Then evaluate each expression to find the corresponding numerical values.

2.8 For each of the following circuits, find the value of R_x so that the equivalent resistance R_{eq} has the given desired value. Note that resistance cannot be negative. If it could be negative, resistors would generate power!

2.9 For each of the following circuits, use the brute force approach to solve for the unknown element voltages and currents.

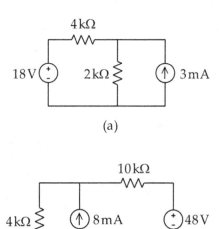

(a)

(b)

3 Circuit Analysis

This chapter covers all the important fundamental techniques for analyzing electric circuits. To start, resistors in series and in parallel are considered again. Then a general purpose circuit analysis technique called modified nodal analysis or simply nodal analysis is covered. This technique eliminates much of the detail associated with the brute force approach covered in Chapter 2. All major software programs that perform circuit analysis use modified nodal analysis because it is straightforward to implement and applies to any circuit. Finally, a number of useful specialized concepts and techniques are covered.

3.1 Resistors in Series and Voltage Division

In the last chapter, we showed that when resistors are in series they can be replaced by an equivalent resistor having a resistance equal to the sum of those in series,

$$R_{eq} = R_1 + R_2 + \cdots + R_N = \sum_{k=1}^{N} R_k$$

where the resistances R_k are those of the resistors in series and R_{eq} is the equivalent resistance.

Consider the following circuit where there are three resistors in series and a known voltage V_{tot} across the entire circuit.

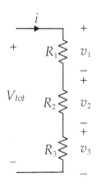

Applying KVL to the circuit gives

$$V_{tot} = v_1 + v_2 + v_3$$

Given the current i, the voltage across each resistor is given by Ohm's law,

$$v_k = i R_k \quad \text{for} \quad k = 1, 2, 3$$

Substituting these into the KVL equation gives

$$V_{tot} = v_1 + v_2 + v_3$$
$$V_{tot} = i R_1 + i R_2 + i R_3$$
$$V_{tot} = i \left(R_1 + R_2 + R_3 \right)$$
$$V_{tot} = i R_{eq}$$

where R_{eq} is equal to the sum of the resistors in series. This once again shows that when resistors are in series, their values simply add to become the resistance of the equivalent series resistor.

Solving this last equation for the current i gives

$$i = \frac{V_{tot}}{R_{eq}}$$

and substituting this into the equations for the voltages across each resistor leads to

$$v_k = i R_k = \left(\frac{V_{tot}}{R_{eq}} \right) R_k = \frac{R_k}{R_{eq}} V_{tot}$$

This last equation describes how the total voltage across the combined resistors in series **divides** among the individual resistors.

For the case where there are N resistors in series, this generalizes to

$$v_k = \frac{R_k}{R_{eq}} V_{tot} \quad \text{for} \quad k = 1, 2, \cdots, N$$

where R_{eq} is the sum of all N resistors. This is called **voltage division**.

The resistor ratio R_k/R_{eq} plays an important role here. First, it is important to note that

$$0 < v_k < V_{tot}$$

because the R_k/R_{eq} is bounded between zero and one,

$$0 < \frac{R_k}{R_{eq}} < 1$$

This is true because R_{eq} is the sum of all the resistances including R_k. Second, the resistor having the largest value has the largest voltage across it because the numerator R_k is largest for this particular resistor.

Voltage division is an often used and very important tool for both analysis and design.

Resistors in Series and Voltage Division

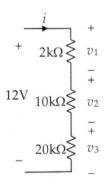

$$R_{eq} = R_1 + R_2 + \cdots + R_N = \sum_{k=1}^{N} R_k$$

$$v_k = \frac{R_k}{R_{eq}} V_{tot} \quad \text{for} \quad k = 1, 2, \cdots, N$$

$$0 < v_k < V_{tot}$$

The **largest** resistance value
has the largest voltage across it.

Example: Consider the following circuit with three resistors in series.

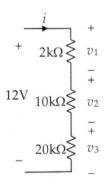

The equivalent series resistance is

$$R_{eq} = 2k + 10k + 20k = 32 k\Omega$$

and the voltages across each of the resistors are

$$v_1 = \frac{R_1}{R_{eq}} V_{tot} = \frac{2k}{32k} 12 = 0.75 V = 750 \text{ mV}$$

$$v_2 = \frac{R_2}{R_{eq}} V_{tot} = \frac{10k}{32k} 12 = 3.75 \text{ V}$$

$$v_3 = \frac{R_3}{R_{eq}} V_{tot} = \frac{20k}{32k} 12 = 7.5 \text{ V}$$

As expected, the largest resistor, $R_3 = 20 k\Omega$, has the largest voltage across it. The 10 kΩ resistor has a voltage one half of that of the 20 kΩ. The 2 kΩ resistor has a voltage one tenth of that of the 20 kΩ.

Applying KVL is one way to check the validity of the solution,

$$V_{tot} = v_1 + v_2 + v_3$$
$$12 V = 0.75 + 3.75 + 7.5$$

So the answer is correct since the sum of the three resistor voltages is equal to the total voltage.

While the voltage across the 20 kΩ is expressed in two significant digits, 7.5 V is an exact value. Had it been expressed as 7.50 V, one may believe that 7.50 V was the result of rounding to three significant digits, rather than be an exact value. Therefore, it is customary to express exact values in fewer than three significant digits when possible. In this case, when a value is expressed in less than three significant digits, it is assumed to be exact.

Voltage Division Design

The voltage division expression

$$v_k = \frac{R_k}{R_{eq}} V_{tot} \quad \text{for} \quad k = 1, 2, \cdots, N$$

is an analysis equation. It describes the voltage across resistor R_k given R_{eq} and V_{tot}. It is not uncommon for the problem to be reversed. That is, knowing V_{tot} and a desired voltage v_k, choose resistors so that v_k is achieved. This is a design problem that has no unique answer.

Consider the following circuit.

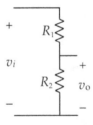

Using the voltage division relationship, the output voltage v_o is related to the input voltage v_i by

$$v_o = \frac{R_2}{R_1 + R_2} v_i$$

When v_o and v_i are known, the goal is to find values for R_1 and R_2 that satisfy this equation. Rather than simply repeatedly guess and check until an acceptable result is found, it is much more productive to rearrange this equation to gain more insight.

Moving v_i to the other side of the equal sign gives,

$$\frac{v_o}{v_i} = \frac{R_2}{R_1 + R_2}$$

simplifying the right hand side leads to,

$$\frac{v_o}{v_i} = \frac{R_2}{R_1 + R_2} \cdot \frac{\left(\frac{1}{R_2}\right)}{\frac{1}{R_2}} = \frac{1}{1 + \frac{R_1}{R_2}}$$

and solving for the ratio R_1/R_2 by inverting both sides,

$$\frac{v_i}{v_o} = 1 + \frac{R_1}{R_2}$$

then rearranging this result gives the desired relationship,

$$\frac{R_1}{R_2} = \frac{v_i}{v_o} - 1$$

To check this result, consider the case where voltage is divided in half, $e.g.$, $v_i = 10$ V and $v_o = 5$ V, then

$$\frac{R_1}{R_2} = \frac{10}{5} - 1 = 2 - 1 = 1$$

So the resistances are equal to each other when voltage is divided in half. Going back to the original voltage division equation

$$v_o = \frac{R_2}{R_1 + R_2} v_i$$

and letting $R_1 = R_2$ gives

$$v_o = \frac{R_2}{R_2 + R_2} v_i = \frac{R_2}{2 R_2} v_i = \frac{v_i}{2}$$

This confirms that the design equation is valid. It also confirms that there is no unique answer. As long as $R_1 = R_2$ is true, voltage is divided in half. $R_1 = R_2 = 1\ \Omega$ works just as well as $R_1 = R_2 = 1\ M\Omega$.

There are two things that provide guidance in choosing the scale of the resistor values. The first is power consumption. **When processing information,**

the goal is to minimize power consumption. The power absorbed by the voltage division circuit is

$$p = \frac{v_i^2}{R_{eq}} = \frac{v_i^2}{R_1 + R_2}$$

so the larger the resistor values are, the less power is absorbed by the resistors. This promotes using the largest possible resistances.

The other issue that determines the scale of the resistors is **"loading."** Loading refers to the impact of a load on the circuit. The output of the voltage divider provides an input to another part of the larger circuit the voltage divider is part of. **Therefore, the voltage divider is often loaded by an effective load resistor R_L as shown in the following circuit. R_L represents the equivalent resistance of the circuit connected to the voltage divider.**

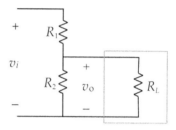

The presence of R_L changes the voltage division relationship to

$$\frac{v_o}{v_i} = \frac{R_{2eq}}{R_1 + R_{2eq}}$$

where $R_{2eq} = R_2 \| R_L$. From Chapter 2, we know that if R_L is at least 100 times larger than R_2, $R_{2eq} = R_2$ with less than 1% error. Conversely, as long as R_2 is more than 100 times smaller than R_L, we can ignore the influence of R_L on the value of v_o.

In the example being considered, if $R_L = 1\ M\Omega$, then R_2 can be at most $R_L/100 = 10\ k\Omega$. Choosing this value for the voltage divider resistances makes the power absorbed by the resistors

$$p = \frac{v_i^2}{R_1 + R_2} = \frac{10^2}{10\,k + 10\,k} = \frac{100}{20\,k} = 500\ \mu W$$

which is generally a very reasonable amount.

Effect of Tolerances: Before moving on, it is worthwhile to consider the influence of resistor tolerances on the result. Common resistors are specified with a ±5% tolerance, meaning that the actual value of the resistance can range from 95% of the nominal value to 105% of the nominal value.

In the example being considered, $v_i = 10$ V, the nominal output voltage is $v_{onom} = 5$ V when $R_1 = R_2 = 100$ kΩ. When R_1 has its smallest value and R_2 has its largest value, the output voltage becomes

$$v_{omax} = \frac{1.05 \cdot R_2}{\left(0.95 \cdot R_1\right) + \left(1.05 \cdot R_2\right)} v_i = \frac{105\,k}{95\,k + 105\,k} 10 = 5.25 \text{ V}$$

Similarly when R_1 has its largest value and R_2 has its smallest value, the output voltage becomes

$$v_{omin} = \frac{0.95 \cdot R_2}{\left(1.05 \cdot R_1\right) + \left(0.95 \cdot R_2\right)} v_i = \frac{95\,k}{105\,k + 95\,k} 10 = 4.75 \text{ V}$$

For this case the tolerance is

$$v_{omin} \le v_{onom} \le v_{omax}$$

$$\frac{v_{omin}}{v_{onom}} \le 1 \le \frac{v_{omax}}{v_{onom}}$$

$$\frac{4.75}{5} \le 1 \le \frac{5.25}{5}$$

$$95\% \le 1 \le 105\%$$

Therefore, the output of this voltage divider also has a ±5% tolerance.

It is possible to show that the resistor tolerance and the output voltage tolerance are equal to each other when voltage is divided by two. However, this fact does not hold for other voltage division ratios.

Next let $v_i = 10$ V, and let $R_1 = 10$ kΩ and $R_2 = 90$ kΩ be resistors having a ±5% tolerance. By voltage division, the nominal output voltage is

$$v_{onom} = \frac{90\,k}{90\,k + 10\,k} 10 = \frac{90\,k}{100\,k} 10 = 9 \text{ V}$$

The maximum output voltage is

$$v_{omax} = \frac{1.05 \cdot 90\,k}{\left(1.05 \cdot 90\,k\right) + \left(0.95 \cdot 10\,k\right)} 10 = 9.08 \text{ V}$$

and the minimum output voltage is

$$v_{omin} = \frac{0.95 \cdot 90\,k}{\left(0.95 \cdot 90\,k\right) + \left(1.05 \cdot 10\,k\right)} 10 = 8.91 \text{ V}$$

For this case, the tolerance is

$$\frac{v_{omin}}{v_{onom}} \le 1 \le \frac{v_{omax}}{v_{onom}}$$

$$99\% \le 1 \le 101\%$$

A ±5% resistor tolerance leads to a ±1% tolerance on the output voltage when the voltage ratio is $v_o/v_i = 9/10$. The output voltage has five times greater precision than the resistor values.

Alternatively, flipping the previous example around produces yet different results. Let $v_i = 10$ V, and let $R_1 = 90$ kΩ, $R_2 = 10$ kΩ be resistors having a ±5% tolerance. The nominal output voltage is

$$v_{onom} = \frac{10\,k}{90\,k + 10\,k} 10 = \frac{10\,k}{100\,k} 10 = 1 \text{ V}$$

the maximum voltage is

$$v_{omax} = \frac{1.05 \cdot 10\,k}{\left(1.05 \cdot 10\,k\right) + \left(0.95 \cdot 90\,k\right)} 10 = 1.09 \text{ V}$$

and the minimum voltage is

$$v_{omin} = \frac{0.95 \cdot 10\,k}{\left(0.95 \cdot 10\,k\right) + \left(1.05 \cdot 90\,k\right)} 10 = 0.913 \text{ V}$$

and the tolerance is given by

$$\frac{v_{omin}}{v_{onom}} \le 1 \le \frac{v_{omax}}{v_{onom}}$$

$$91\% \le 1 \le 109\%$$

In this case, a ±5% resistor tolerance leads to a ±9% tolerance on the output voltage when the voltage ratio is $v_o/v_i = 1/10$. The output voltage has about one half the precision than the resistor values.

As demonstrated by these three examples, when v_o/v_i decreases from 1/2, the voltage tolerance increases relative to the resistor tolerance. When v_o/v_i is equal to 1/2, the voltage tolerance and the resistor tolerance match each other. And as v_o/v_i increases from 1/2, the voltage tolerance decreases relative to the resistor tolerance.

3.2 Resistors in Parallel and Current Division

In the last chapter, we showed that when resistors are in parallel they can be replaced by an equivalent resistor having a resistance given by the reciprocal relationship

$$\frac{1}{R_{eq}} = \frac{1}{R_1} + \frac{1}{R_2} + \cdots + \frac{1}{R_N} = \sum_{k=1}^{N} \frac{1}{R_k}$$

where the resistances R_k are those of the resistors in parallel and R_{eq} is the equivalent parallel resistance.

Consider the following circuit where there are three resistors in parallel, a voltage v between the two nodes, and a total current of I_{tot}.

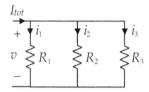

Applying KCL to the top node gives

$$I_{tot} = i_1 + i_2 + i_3$$

Given the voltage v, Ohm's law gives the current through each resistor as

$$i_k = \frac{v}{R_k} \quad \text{for} \quad k = 1,2,3$$

Substituting these into the KCL equation gives

$$I_{tot} = i_1 + i_2 + i_3$$

$$I_{tot} = \frac{v}{R_1} + \frac{v}{R_2} + \frac{v}{R_3}$$

$$I_{tot} = v \cdot \left(\frac{1}{R_1} + \frac{1}{R_2} + \frac{1}{R_3} \right)$$

or more succinctly

$$I_{tot} = v \cdot \left(\frac{1}{R_{eq}} \right)$$

where R_{eq} once again is related to the individual resistors by the parallel resistance equation where the inverses of the resistances add.

Solving this last equation for v gives

$$v = I_{tot} \cdot R_{eq}$$

and substituting this into the equations for the currents through each resistor leads to

$$i_k = \frac{v}{R_k} = \frac{I_{tot} \cdot R_{eq}}{R_k} = \frac{R_{eq}}{R_k} I_{tot}$$

This last equation describes how the total current through the combined resistors in parallel **divides** among the individual resistors.

For the case where there are N resistors in parallel this generalizes to

$$i_k = \frac{R_{eq}}{R_k} I_{tot} \quad \text{for} \quad k = 1,2,\cdots,N$$

where R_{eq} is the equivalent of the N resistors in parallel. This is called **current division**.

The resistor ratio R_{eq}/R_k plays an important role here. First, it is important to note that

$$0 < i_k < I_{tot}$$

because R_{eq}/R_k is bounded between zero and one,

$$0 < \frac{R_{eq}}{R_k} < 1$$

This is true because R_{eq} is smaller than the smallest resistor including R_k. Second, the resistor having the smallest value has the largest current flowing through it because the denominator R_k is smallest for this particular resistor.

Current division is not used as often as voltage division, but it remains very important tool for both analysis and design.

Resistors in Parallel and Current Division

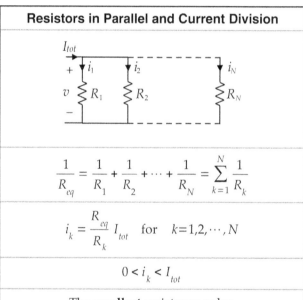

$$\frac{1}{R_{eq}} = \frac{1}{R_1} + \frac{1}{R_2} + \cdots + \frac{1}{R_N} = \sum_{k=1}^{N} \frac{1}{R_k}$$

$$i_k = \frac{R_{eq}}{R_k} I_{tot} \quad \text{for} \quad k=1,2,\cdots,N$$

$$0 < i_k < I_{tot}$$

The **smallest** resistance value
has the largest current flowing through it.

Two Resistor Case

Because the most common case is two resistors in parallel, it is worthwhile to consider this specific case as illustrated in the following.

For two resistors in parallel, the equivalent resistance R_{eq} is commonly written as

$$R_{eq} = \frac{R_1 R_2}{R_1 + R_2}$$

Substituting this into the expression for i_1 gives

$$i_1 = \frac{R_{eq}}{R_1} I_{tot}$$

$$i_1 = \frac{1}{R_1} \left(R_{eq} \right) I_{tot}$$

$$i_1 = \frac{1}{R_1} \left(\frac{R_1 R_2}{R_1 + R_2} \right) I_{tot}$$

which simplifies to

$$i_1 = \frac{R_2}{R_1 + R_2} I_{tot}$$

That is, the current flowing through R_1 is equal to the "other" resistor R_2 divided by the sum of the resistors. Following the same procedure the current flowing through R_2 is

$$i_2 = \frac{R_1}{R_1 + R_2} I_{tot}$$

Note how current division for two resistors is different from voltage division where the expression for v_1 is equal to the "same" resistor R_1 divided by the sum of the resistors. Don't confuse these relationships. If you apply the voltage division ratio to current division or vice versa, the result will be incorrect.

Two Resistors in Parallel and Current Division

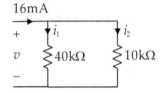

$$R_{eq} = \frac{R_1 R_2}{R_1 + R_2}$$

$$i_1 = \frac{R_2}{R_1 + R_2} I_{tot} \quad \text{and} \quad i_2 = \frac{R_1}{R_1 + R_2} I_{tot}$$

The **smaller** resistance value
has the larger current flowing through it.

Finally, it is interesting to compute the ratio of the two currents by noting that the resistors share the same voltage,

$$v = i_1 R_1 = i_2 R_2$$

Dividing both sides by R_1 gives the result

$$i_1 = \frac{R_2}{R_1} i_2$$

The current i_1 is greater than i_2 if $R_2 > R_1$ and vise versa. For example, if $R_2/R_1 = 4$, then $i_1 = 4i_2$ and the smaller resistor R_1 has four times the current of larger resistor R_2.

Example: Consider the following circuit having two resistors in parallel.

16mA

$+$ $\downarrow i_1$ $\downarrow i_2$

v $\lessgtr 40\text{k}\Omega$ $\lessgtr 10\text{k}\Omega$

$-$

The equivalent parallel resistance is

$$R_{eq} = 40\text{k} \| 10\text{k} = 8\,\text{k}\Omega$$

and the currents through each of the resistors are

$$i_1 = \frac{R_2}{R_1 + R_2} I_{tot} = \frac{10\text{k}}{40\text{k} + 10\text{k}} 16 \text{ mA} = 3.2 \text{ mA}$$

and

$$i_2 = \frac{R_1}{R_1 + R_2} I_{tot} = \frac{40\text{k}}{40\text{k} + 10\text{k}} 16 \text{ mA} = 12.8 \text{ mA}$$

Alternatively, these can be computed with the general current division expression,

$$i_1 = \frac{R_{eq}}{R_1} I_{tot} = \frac{8\text{k}}{40\text{k}} 16 \text{ mA} = 3.2 \text{ mA}$$

$$i_2 = \frac{R_{eq}}{R_2} I_{tot} = \frac{8\text{k}}{10\text{k}} 16 \text{ mA} = 12.8 \text{ mA}$$

As expected the smaller resistor has the larger current since it resists current flow the least. In particular, the $10\,\text{k}\Omega$ resistor conducts $(12.8\text{m}/3.2\text{m}) = 4$ times the current flowing through the $40\,\text{k}\Omega$ resistor. This makes sense since the $40\,\text{k}\Omega$ resistor is 4 times more resistive than the $10\,\text{k}\Omega$ resistor.

Applying KCL is one way to check the validity of the solution,

$$I_{tot} = i_1 + i_2$$

$$16\,\text{mA} = 3.2\,\text{m} + 12.8\,\text{m}$$

So the answer is correct, since the sum of the two resistor currents is equal to the total current.

3.3 Nodal Analysis

The brute force solution technique illustrated in the last chapter is thorough in that the solution includes all the unknown voltages and currents in the circuit. For this reason, once a circuit contains more than a few components, the number of equations and unknowns quickly becomes excessive. This is especially true since at most a few unknowns are usually desired.

To reduce the effort required to solve a circuit, two general solution techniques have been developed, namely nodal analysis and mesh analysis. These two techniques were developed at a time when simultaneous equations had to be solved by hand (which was back when you had to get out of your chair and walk to the TV to change channels). Given the effort and time required to solve three or four simultaneous equations by hand, techniques were sought to minimize the number of equations. When nodal analysis led to fewer equations, it was used. When mesh analysis led to fewer equations, it was used.

Given that simultaneous equations can be easily solved on handheld calculators, using apps or applications, or online, minimizing the number of equations is no longer an issue. Therefore, the choice of method can be determined based on its usefulness to circuit analysis.

In comparing nodal analysis to mesh analysis, nodal analysis solves for voltages, whereas mesh analysis solves for currents. In circuits that process information, voltages are generally much more important than currents. For example, in digital logic circuits, the presence or absence of a voltage determines the two logic states, not the presence or absence of a current. In analog circuits such as amplifiers and filters, the information content is contained in voltages not currents. With these facts in mind, solving for voltages is more useful than solving for currents. The fact that voltages are easily measured in the laboratory and on printed circuit boards, whereas currents are not, also makes solving for voltages more useful. As a result, nodal analysis is much more useful in circuit analysis. Its usefulness is confirmed by the fact that all major software for solving electric circuits utilizes nodal analysis.

Node Voltages

Nodal analysis is based on the concept of **node voltages** rather than circuit element voltages. Node voltages are the voltages at the nodes in a circuit with respect to a single node called the **reference node**.

Consider the automobile tire pressure analogy. The tire gauge always uses the atmosphere as its reference node, so all tire pressures are with respect to the atmosphere. For example, consider the following figure where four tires are shown with their respective tire pressures labeled in each tire.

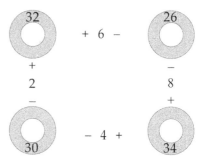

These pressures are all with respect to the atmosphere. The atmosphere is the reference node. The pressure values between the tires are also shown. For example, starting at the tire in the lower left having pressure equal to 30, adding 2 gives the pressure in the tire in the upper left. The pressure values between tires is equivalent to the voltage difference across circuit elements between nodes. The tire pressures themselves are equivalent to node voltages with respect to the atmosphere as the reference node.

It is interesting to note that KVL works for the loop formed by the four tires. That is, starting in the lower left and applying KVL to the pressures between tires gives

$$2 - 6 + 8 - 4 = 0$$

The circuit at the top of the next page illustrates the node voltage concept where the node voltages for nodes ① and ⑥ are measured by the meters shown.

For every node in the circuit, the negative or reference terminal of the meter is connected to the node labeled ⓪, which is also shown having a downward pointing arrow. This arrow is the customary way to label the reference node.

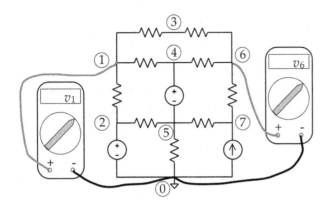

There are seven node voltages in this circuit and twelve component voltages. Nodal analysis computes the node voltages rather than the component voltages. Nodal analysis does not generally compute component currents. Under special circumstances a component current may be computed.

The node voltages are related to the component voltages by KVL. For example, the above circuit has been redrawn below with the component voltages labeled. By letting the voltmeter and its leads form that part of any loop passing through node ⑥, the voltage at node ⑥ is $v_6 = 22$ V with respect to the reference.

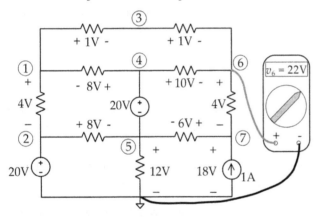

To see why this is true, consider the loop formed by the path shown in bold below.

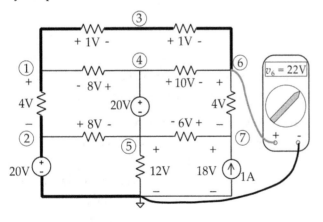

Applying KVL to this loop gives

$$20 + 4 - 1 - 1 - v_6 = 0$$
$$22 = v_6$$

which confirms that $v_6 = 22$ V.

Consider another possible loop formed by the path shown in bold below.

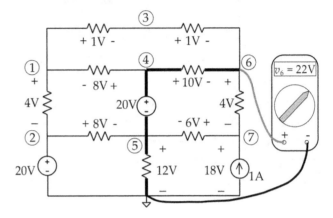

Applying KVL to this loop gives

$$12 + 20 - 10 - v_6 = 0$$
$$22 = v_6$$

which also confirms that $v_6 = 22$ V.

Consider yet another loop formed by the path shown in bold below.

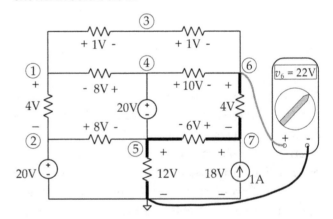

Applying KVL to this loop gives

$$12 + 6 + 4 - v_6 = 0$$
$$22 = v_6$$

which again confirms that $v_6 = 22$ V.

No matter what path is taken to node ⑥, the loop formed with the meter closing the loop leads to the node voltage $v_6 = 22$ V.

Applying KVL by using the fact that voltage must add up, gives the other node voltages as

$$20 + 4 = 24 \text{ v} = v_1$$
$$20 \text{ V} = v_2$$
$$v_1 - 1 = 23 \text{ V} = v_3$$
$$12 + 20 = 32 \text{ V} = v_4$$
$$12 \text{ V} = v_5$$
$$18 \text{ V} = v_7$$

All node voltages are measured with respect to the reference node ⓪. The meter negative (−) or reference lead of the meter stays on the reference node all the time. Using the automobile tire pressure analogy, the tire gauge always uses the atmosphere as its reference node.

Given the node voltages, circuit element voltages can be found by applying KVL using the node voltages on the two sides of a circuit element. For example, consider the following partial circuit where an arbitrary circuit element is connected between nodes (j) and (k).

As labeled, the node voltages are identified as the voltages at the nodes with respect to the reference node. The paths through the circuit from the reference to these nodes are not shown since the node voltages do not depend on the path taken to them as demonstrated in the previous example.

The above circuit forms a loop with three identified voltages. Applying KVL clockwise, starting in the lower left gives

$$v_j - v_x - v_k = 0$$

Solving this for the circuit element voltage v_x gives

$$v_x = v_j - v_k$$

Spoken in words, this statement says, **"the circuit element voltage is equal to the voltage 'here' minus the voltage 'there',"** where 'here' means the (+) side of the circuit element voltage and 'there' means the (−) side of the circuit element voltage.

The node voltage labeling shown above is difficult to apply to a complete circuit because of all the elements in the many paths to all nodes. As a result, the notation shown in the figure below is adopted. The node voltages are simply labeled at the nodes with the understanding that these voltages mean what is seen in the earlier illustration. This approach is easily applied to a complete circuit.

Applying this notation to a resistor connected between two nodes as shown below makes it possible to express the resistor current in terms of the node voltages.

Given that $v_x = v_j - v_k$, Ohm's law and the passive sign convention gives the corresponding currents i_j and i_k as

$$i_j = \frac{v_x}{R} = \frac{v_j - v_k}{R} \quad \text{and} \quad i_k = -i_j = \frac{v_k - v_j}{R}$$

Expressing the voltage and current relationships for a resistor in terms of node voltages forms a vital part of nodal analysis.

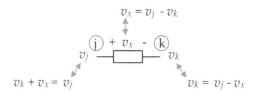

Resistors and Nodal Analysis
$v_x = v_j - v_k$ or $v_k + v_x = v_j$
$i_j = \dfrac{v_x}{R} = \dfrac{v_j - v_k}{R}$ and $i_k = -i_j = \dfrac{v_k - v_j}{R}$

Basic Nodal Analysis Example

Nodal analysis is best explained by demonstration. Therefore, consider the following circuit.

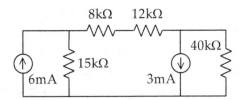

The first step in applying nodal analysis is to label the nodes, starting with the reference node. While the reference node can be any node, it is usually chosen to be the node with the most elements connected to it. Doing this to the circuit above gives the following circuit.

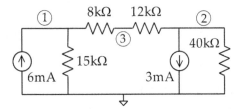

There are three numbered nodes in the circuit, with nodes ① and ② being essential and node ③ being nonessential. The reference node is identified by the downward pointing arrow connected to the node that runs across the bottom of the circuit.

The second step in applying nodal analysis is to write KCL at the labeled nodes using the identified relationship for the resistor currents in terms of the node voltages. **KCL is always applied by its standard convention where the sum of currents leaving the node are set equal to zero.**

Using the nodal analysis relationship for a resistor connected between two nodes, the circuit below identifies the three currents leaving node ①.

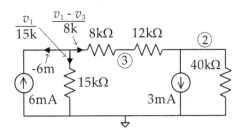

Applying KCL to node ① gives

$$-6\,\mathrm{m} + \frac{v_1}{15\mathrm{k}} + \frac{v_1 - v_3}{8\mathrm{k}} = 0$$

Following the same process, the following circuit identifies the three currents leaving node ②.

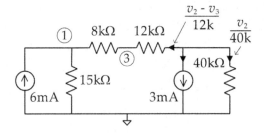

Applying KCL to node ② gives

$$\frac{v_2 - v_3}{12\mathrm{k}} + \frac{v_2}{40\mathrm{k}} + 3\,\mathrm{m} = 0$$

The circuit below shows the two currents leaving node ③.

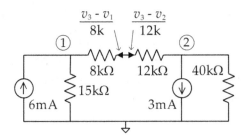

Applying KCL to node ③ gives

$$\frac{v_3 - v_1}{8\mathrm{k}} + \frac{v_3 - v_2}{12\mathrm{k}} = 0$$

By applying KCL systematically as the sum of all currents leaving each node, it is possible to visibly inspect each equation for errors. **For KCL at each node, that node's voltage is positive and appears first in each term where it appears.** If this does not hold, there is an error.

The node voltages are the three unknowns in the above set of three equations. Because there are an equal number of equations and unknowns, this forms a consistent set of equations that can be solved. Rewriting each of the equations to isolate the three unknowns gives

$$\left(\frac{1}{15\mathrm{k}} + \frac{1}{8\mathrm{k}}\right)v_1 + (0)v_2 + \left(\frac{-1}{8\mathrm{k}}\right)v_3 = 6\,\mathrm{m}$$

$$(0)v_1 + \left(\frac{1}{12\mathrm{k}} + \frac{1}{40\mathrm{k}}\right)v_2 + \left(\frac{-1}{12\mathrm{k}}\right)v_3 = -3\mathrm{m}$$

$$\left(\frac{-1}{8\mathrm{k}}\right)v_1 + \left(\frac{-1}{12\mathrm{k}}\right)v_2 + \left(\frac{1}{8\mathrm{k}} + \frac{1}{12\mathrm{k}}\right)v_3 = 0$$

Placing these three equations in matrix form gives

$$\begin{bmatrix} \left(\dfrac{1}{15\,k}+\dfrac{1}{8\,k}\right) & 0 & \left(\dfrac{-1}{8\,k}\right) \\[2mm] 0 & \left(\dfrac{1}{12\,k}+\dfrac{1}{40\,k}\right) & \left(\dfrac{-1}{12\,k}\right) \\[2mm] \left(\dfrac{-1}{8\,k}\right) & \left(\dfrac{-1}{12\,k}\right) & \left(\dfrac{1}{8\,k}+\dfrac{1}{12\,k}\right) \end{bmatrix} \cdot \begin{bmatrix} v_1 \\ v_2 \\ v_3 \end{bmatrix} = \begin{bmatrix} 6\,m \\ -3\,m \\ 0 \end{bmatrix}$$

The solution to this set of equations is

$$\begin{bmatrix} v_1 \\ v_2 \\ v_3 \end{bmatrix} = \begin{bmatrix} 48\,V \\ -8\,V \\ 25.6\,V \end{bmatrix}$$

The first modification to this procedure is to note that node ③ is a nonessential node. Therefore, if the node voltage v_3 is not needed as part of the solution, nonessential node ③ can be left unlabeled as shown in the following circuit.

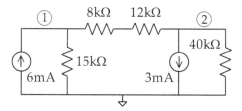

Now when KCL is written for nodes ① and ②, the 8 kΩ and 12 kΩ resistors are treated as one resistance equal to their equivalent series resistance, 8k + 12k.

Using the same procedure used in the analysis of the original circuit, applying KCL to node ① in this revised circuit gives

$$-6\,m + \frac{v_1}{15\,k} + \frac{v_1 - v_2}{8\,k + 12\,k} = 0$$

And applying KCL to node ② in the revised circuit gives

$$\frac{v_2 - v_1}{8\,k + 12\,k} + \frac{v_2}{40\,k} + 3\,m = 0$$

Now there are only two equations in two unknowns, and the set of equations in matrix form becomes

$$\begin{bmatrix} \left(\dfrac{1}{15\,k}+\dfrac{1}{8\,k+12\,k}\right) & \left(\dfrac{-1}{8\,k+12\,k}\right) \\[2mm] \left(\dfrac{-1}{8\,k+12\,k}\right) & \left(\dfrac{1}{8\,k+12\,k}+\dfrac{1}{40\,k}\right) \end{bmatrix} \cdot \begin{bmatrix} v_1 \\ v_2 \end{bmatrix} = \begin{bmatrix} 6\,m \\ -3\,m \end{bmatrix}$$

The solution to this set of equations is

$$\begin{bmatrix} v_1 \\ v_2 \end{bmatrix} = \begin{bmatrix} 48\,V \\ -8\,V \end{bmatrix}$$

which agrees with the previous node voltage solutions for nodes ① and ②.

Nonessential Nodes

Nonessential nodes formed by resistors in series need not be labeled or included in nodal analysis. If they are not included, the resistors in series are simply replaced by their equivalent series resistance when writing the KCL equations.

Nodal Analysis with Voltage Sources

When a voltage source appears in a circuit, a little extra work is sometimes required because the current through a voltage source is an unknown. This unknown current depends on the rest of the circuit. Voltage sources can appear in three ways, (a) between a node and the reference node, (b) between two labeled nodes, or (c) in series with a resistor between nodes. Each of these cases is treated differently.

Consider the following circuit where a voltage source appears between a node and the reference node.

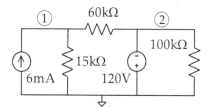

There are two essential nodes in this circuit. Applying KCL to these two nodes will lead to a set of equations to be solved. However, there is no need to write a KCL equation at node ② to find v_2. This voltage is set by the voltage source as $v_2 = -120$ V. The voltage source itself determines this voltage.

Therefore, applying nodal analysis to this circuit gives one equation in one unknown,

$$-6\,m + \frac{v_1}{15\,k} + \frac{v_1 - (-120)}{60\,k} = 0$$

where $v_2 = -120$ V was used in describing the current flowing from node ① to node ② through the 60 kΩ resistor. The solution to the above equation is

$$\left(\frac{1}{15\,k}+\frac{1}{60\,K}\right)v_1 = 6\,m - \frac{120}{60\,k}$$

$$(83.33\,m)v_1 = 6\,m - 2\,m$$

$$v_1 = \frac{6\,m - 2\,m}{83.33\,m} = 48\,V$$

Voltage Source Connected to Reference

When a voltage source appears between the reference node and a labeled node (j), KCL is not required at the labeled node because the voltage there is equal to the voltage source value, $v_j = V_s$.

The next case is when a voltage source appears between two labeled nodes. To study this case, consider the following circuit.

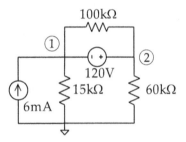

Once again, there are two essential nodes in this circuit. This time, a voltage source is directly connected between nodes ① and ②.

As noted earlier, the current through a voltage source is an unknown that is determined by the rest of the circuit. Since *"I don't $k$now what it is,"* it is another unknown that must be labeled as shown in the following circuit where is it is given as i_{dk}.

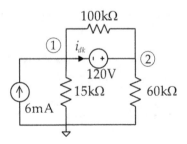

With the current through the voltage source labeled, nodal analysis KCL equations can be written for the two essential nodes.

Applying KCL to node ① gives

$$-6\,m + \frac{v_1}{15\,k} + \frac{v_1 - v_2}{100\,k} + i_{dk} = 0$$

KCL applied to node ② gives

$$\frac{v_2}{60\,k} + \frac{v_2 - v_1}{100\,k} - i_{dk} = 0$$

There are two equations here and three unknowns, v_1, v_2, and i_{dk}. There is no unique solution to this set of equations. Another equation must be added so that there are three equations in three unknowns. Applying KCL at the reference node does not provide a useful equation. Therefore, the use of KCL has been exhausted. That leaves KVL. The relationship between circuit element voltage and node voltages cited earlier and shown in the figure below provides the answer.

$$v_k + v_x = v_j \qquad \text{ⓙ} \overset{+\ v_x\ -}{\rule{2cm}{0.4pt}} \text{Ⓚ} \quad v_k$$

$$v_1 + 120 = v_2 \qquad \text{②} \rule{1.5cm}{0.4pt} \text{①} \quad v_1$$
$$120V$$

In this case node (j) is node ②, v_x is 120 V, and node (k) is node ①. Applying the relationship shown gives

$$v_1 + 120 = v_2 \quad \text{or} \quad v_2 - v_1 = 120$$

This is the third equation in the unknowns. Rewriting all three equations leads to

$$\left(\frac{1}{15\,k}+\frac{1}{100\,k}\right)v_1 + \left(\frac{-1}{100\,k}\right)v_2 + (1)i_{dk} = 6\,m$$

$$\left(\frac{-1}{100\,k}\right)v_1 + \left(\frac{1}{60\,k}+\frac{1}{100\,k}\right)v_2 + (-1)i_{dk} = 0$$

$$(-1)v_1 + (1)v_2 + (0)i_{dk} = 120$$

These can be written in matrix form as

$$\begin{bmatrix} \left(\frac{1}{15\,k}+\frac{1}{100\,k}\right) & \left(\frac{-1}{100\,k}\right) & 1 \\ \left(\frac{-1}{100\,k}\right) & \left(\frac{1}{60\,k}+\frac{1}{100\,k}\right) & -1 \\ -1 & 1 & 0 \end{bmatrix} \begin{bmatrix} v_1 \\ v_2 \\ i_{dk} \end{bmatrix} = \begin{bmatrix} 6\,m \\ 0 \\ 120 \end{bmatrix}$$

The solution to this set of equations is $v_1 = 48$ V, $v_2 = 168$ V, and $i_{dk} = 4$ mA.

This solution technique of creating an additional variable for the unknown current i_{dk} through a voltage source, then writing an additional equation relating the voltage source value to its two node voltages can be used in any nodal analysis problem. Generally, it is not done unless needed.

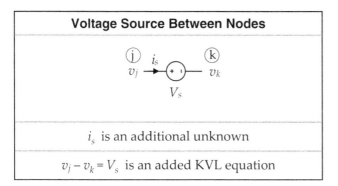

Voltage Source Between Nodes
i_s is an additional unknown
$v_j - v_k = V_s$ is an added KVL equation

The final case to consider is when a voltage source in series with a resistor appears between two nodes as shown in the following circuit.

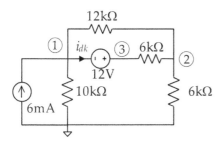

This circuit can be solved the same way as the previous case using the labeled current i_{dk}. However, doing so is not required because an expression for i_{dk} can be written in terms of the node voltages.

The voltage at the nonessential node ③ can be written in terms of the node ① voltage and the voltage source value as

$$v_1 + 12 = v_3$$

Therefore, the node voltages on both sides of the 6 kΩ resistor in series with the source are known. Using the standard expression for resistor current in nodal analysis, i_{dk} is equal to

$$i_{dk} = \frac{v_3 - v_2}{6\,\text{k}}$$

Therefore, substituting the voltage v_3 as identified above gives the current i_{dk} as

$$i_{dk} = \frac{(v_1 + 12) - v_2}{6\,\text{k}}$$

This term appears when KCL is written at node ①, and the negative of it,

$$-i_{dk} = \frac{v_2 - (v_1 + 12)}{6\,\text{k}}$$

appears when KCL is written at node ②. If this technique is used, KCL is not written at node ③.

Solving this circuit simply requires applying KCL to the two essential nodes.

Applying KCL to node ① gives

$$-6\,\text{m} + \frac{v_1}{10\,\text{k}} + \frac{v_1 - v_2}{12\,\text{k}} + \frac{(v_1 + 12) - v_2}{6\,\text{k}} = 0$$

KCL applied to node ② gives

$$\frac{v_2}{6\,\text{k}} + \frac{v_2 - v_1}{12\,\text{k}} + \frac{v_2 - (v_1 + 12)}{6\,\text{k}} = 0$$

Rewriting these equations leads to

$$\left(\frac{1}{10\,\text{k}} + \frac{1}{12\,\text{k}} + \frac{1}{6\,\text{k}}\right)v_1 + \left(\frac{-1}{12\,\text{k}} + \frac{-1}{6\,\text{k}}\right)v_2 = 6\,\text{m} - \frac{12}{6\,\text{k}}$$

$$\left(\frac{-1}{12\,\text{k}} + \frac{-1}{6\,\text{k}}\right)v_1 + \left(\frac{1}{6\,\text{k}} + \frac{1}{12\,\text{k}} + \frac{1}{6\,\text{k}}\right)v_2 = \frac{12}{6\,\text{k}}$$

These can be written in matrix form as

$$\begin{bmatrix} \dfrac{1}{10\,\text{k}} + \dfrac{1}{12\,\text{k}} + \dfrac{1}{6\,\text{k}} & \dfrac{-1}{12\,\text{k}} + \dfrac{-1}{6\,\text{k}} \\ \dfrac{-1}{12\,\text{k}} + \dfrac{-1}{6\,\text{k}} & \dfrac{1}{6\,\text{k}} + \dfrac{1}{12\,\text{k}} + \dfrac{1}{6\,\text{k}} \end{bmatrix} \cdot \begin{bmatrix} v_1 \\ v_2 \end{bmatrix} = \begin{bmatrix} 6\,\text{m} + \dfrac{-12}{6\,\text{k}} \\ \dfrac{12}{6\,\text{k}} \end{bmatrix}$$

Finally, the solution to these equations is $v_1 = 26$ V and $v_2 = 20.4$ V.

Voltage Source in Series with a Resistor
KVL $v_x = v_k + V_s$
$i_j = \dfrac{v_j - v_x}{R} = \dfrac{v_j - (v_k + V_s)}{R}$
$i_k = -i_j = \dfrac{(v_k + V_s) - v_j}{R}$

Symbolic Example

To summarize the implementation of nodal analysis, consider the circuit shown below. All the component values are known, but described symbolically rather than being given numerical values. The voltage v_r and the current i_b are unknown quantities. The reference node is shown as well as labeled essential nodes. No KCL equation is required at node ④ because the voltage at the node is equal to the source value V_a.

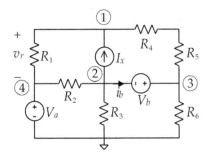

Writing the KCL at node ① gives

$$\frac{v_1 - V_a}{R_1} - I_x + \frac{v_1 - v_3}{R_4 + R_5} = 0$$

KCL applied to node ② gives

$$\frac{v_2 - V_a}{R_2} + I_x + i_b + \frac{v_2}{R_3} = 0$$

KCL applied to node ③ gives

$$\frac{v_3}{R_6} - i_b + \frac{v_3 - v_1}{R_4 + R_5} = 0$$

There are three KCL equations here in four unknowns, v_1, v_2, v_3, and i_b. The last equation is the KVL relationship for the voltage source V_b. As shown earlier, that relationship is

$$v_2 + V_b = v_3$$

Rewriting these four equations to isolate the individual variables gives

$$\left(\frac{1}{R_1} + \frac{1}{R_4 + R_5}\right)v_1 + (0)v_2 + \left(\frac{-1}{R_4 + R_5}\right)v_3 + (0)i_b = I_x + \frac{V_a}{R_1}$$

$$(0)v_1 + \left(\frac{1}{R_2} + \frac{1}{R_3}\right)v_2 + (0)v_3 + (1)i_b = \frac{V_a}{R_2} - I_x$$

$$\left(\frac{-1}{R_4 + R_5}\right)v_1 + (0)v_2 + \left(\frac{1}{R_6} + \frac{1}{R_4 + R_5}\right)v_3 + (-1)i_b = 0$$

$$(0)v_1 + (-1)v_2 + (1)v_3 + (0)i_b = V_b$$

These equations can be written in matrix form as

$$A \cdot \underline{x} = \underline{y}$$

where the matrix A is

$$A = \begin{bmatrix} \left(\dfrac{1}{R_1} + \dfrac{1}{R_4 + R_5}\right) & 0 & \left(\dfrac{-1}{R_4 + R_5}\right) & 0 \\ 0 & \left(\dfrac{1}{R_2} + \dfrac{1}{R_3}\right) & 0 & 1 \\ \left(\dfrac{-1}{R_4 + R_5}\right) & 0 & \left(\dfrac{1}{R_6} + \dfrac{1}{R_4 + R_5}\right) & -1 \\ 0 & -1 & 1 & 0 \end{bmatrix}$$

and

$$\underline{x} = \begin{bmatrix} v_1 \\ v_2 \\ v_3 \\ i_b \end{bmatrix} \quad \text{and} \quad \underline{y} = \begin{bmatrix} I_x + \dfrac{V_a}{R_1} \\ \dfrac{V_a}{R_2} - I_x \\ 0 \\ V_b \end{bmatrix}$$

Given the solution vector denoted $\underline{x}$ above, it is possible to compute other results from the nodal analysis solution. For example, the power in the voltage source V_b is

$$P_{Vb} = s \cdot V_b i_b$$
$$P_{Vb} = -1 \cdot V_b i_b$$

The voltage v_r is found by applying KVL between nodes ④ and ①,

$$V_a + v_r = v_1$$
$$v_r = v_1 - V_a$$

The power in resistor R_5 is found by identifying the current leaving node ① passing through R_4 and R_5,

$$i_{R5} = \frac{v_1 - v_3}{R_4 + R_5}$$

Then the power in resistor R_5 is

$$P_{R5} = i_{R5}^2 \cdot R_5 = \left(\frac{v_1 - v_3}{R_4 + R_5}\right)^2 \cdot R_5$$

In general, once the nodal analysis solution has been found, it is simply a matter of applying circuit analysis techniques such as KCL, KVL, and Ohm's law to find quantities not directly computed by nodal analysis.

Dependent Sources

In addition to the ideal voltage and ideal current sources, there are four other "pumps" that are useful in circuit analysis. The outputs of these sources depend on what is going on elsewhere in the circuit. **As such, they are called dependent sources because their values depend on another voltage or current in the circuit.**

These sources are (a) a voltage controlled voltage source (VCVS), (b) a current controlled voltage source (CCVS), (c) a voltage controlled current source (VCCS), and (d) a current controlled current source (CCCS). Since these pumps differ from the ideal voltage and current sources; they are drawn using diamond-shaped circuit elements as shown below.

The voltage v_x and current i_x in the above illustration are the controlling values. These values, when multiplied by the scale factors or gains, α, r, g, and β, give the voltage or current produced by the source. For example, the voltage produced by the voltage controlled voltage source (VCVS) is equal to $\alpha \cdot v_x$ where α is a constant and v_x is a voltage somewhere else in the circuit.

These sources exist because they model or describe how some common electronic circuit elements such as transistors and op amps behave. As a result, they are useful tools for analyzing circuits.

The introduction of dependent sources was postponed until now because circuits containing them are most easily solved using nodal analysis. These dependent sources are much less common than resistors and the ideal voltage and current sources. Moreover, they most often appear in analytic derivations, not in a circuit with numerically valued components. Only two of these sources are used in this text. They are the voltage controlled voltage source (VCVS) because it models a voltage amplifier, and the current controlled voltage source (CCVS) because it is useful when studying a transformer.

The dependent sources are treated just like their respective ideal sources when using nodal analysis. The two current sources, VCCS and CCCS, provide currents, $g \cdot v_x$ or $\beta \cdot i_x$, which readily become part of KCL. The two voltage source, VCVS and CCVS, are incorporated in exactly the same way ideal voltage sources are treated in nodal analysis, which varies depending on their placement in the circuit.

What sets dependent sources apart from the ideal voltage and current sources are the controlling voltage v_x and controlling current i_x. When writing the KCL equations, these two values will appear as additional unknowns. Therefore, an additional equation is required to get an equal number of equations and unknowns. That equation is simply a KCL or KVL equation relating the voltage v_x or the current i_x to the node voltages.

Example 1: Consider the following circuit where the reference node and essential nodes have been labeled. The circuit contains a VCVS that produces the voltage $\alpha \cdot v_{in}$ where the controlling voltage v_{in} is equal to the node voltage v_1.

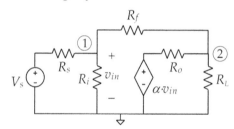

Both voltage sources in this circuit are in series with a resistor, so they can both be treated as demonstrated earlier. Writing KCL at node ① gives

$$\frac{v_1 - V_s}{R_s} + \frac{v_1}{R_i} + \frac{v_1 - v_2}{R_f} = 0$$

and writing KCL at node ② gives

$$\frac{v_2}{R_L} + \frac{v_2 - v_1}{R_f} + \frac{v_2 - \alpha \cdot v_{in}}{R_o} = 0$$

but v_{in} in this case is simply $v_{in} = v_1$, so this equation can be rewritten with this substitution as

$$\frac{v_2}{R_L} + \frac{v_2 - v_1}{R_f} + \frac{v_2 - \alpha \cdot v_1}{R_o} = 0$$

This now gives two equations in the two unknown node voltages. If v_{in} was not so simply defined, this substitution would not have been made, and a third equation relating v_{in} to the node voltages would be written giving three equations in three unknowns.

Rewriting the equations to isolate the unknowns gives

$$\left(\frac{1}{R_s}+\frac{1}{R_i}+\frac{1}{R_f}\right)v_1 + \left(\frac{-1}{R_f}\right)v_2 = \frac{V_s}{R_s}$$

$$\left(\frac{-1}{R_f}+\frac{-\alpha}{R_o}\right)v_1 + \left(\frac{1}{R_L}+\frac{1}{R_f}+\frac{1}{R_o}\right)v_2 = 0$$

And writing the equations in matrix form gives

$$\begin{bmatrix}\left(\dfrac{1}{R_s}+\dfrac{1}{R_i}+\dfrac{1}{R_f}\right) & \left(\dfrac{-1}{R_f}\right) \\[2ex] \left(\dfrac{-1}{R_f}+\dfrac{-\alpha}{R_o}\right) & \left(\dfrac{1}{R_L}+\dfrac{1}{R_f}+\dfrac{1}{R_o}\right)\end{bmatrix}\cdot\begin{bmatrix}v_1 \\ v_2\end{bmatrix} = \begin{bmatrix}\dfrac{V_s}{R_s} \\ 0\end{bmatrix}$$

Example 2: Consider the following circuit where the reference node and essential nodes have been labeled. The circuit contains two CCVSs that produce a voltage controlled by a current.

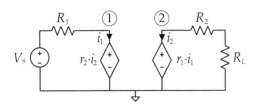

There are no essential nodes in this circuit, but nodal analysis still applies. The two dependent voltage sources have currents i_1 and i_2 flowing through them. Writing KCL at node ① gives

$$\frac{v_1 - V_s}{R_1} + i_1 = 0$$

and writing KCL at node ② gives

$$\frac{v_2}{R_2 + R_L} + i_2 = 0$$

These two equations have four unknowns. The remaining two equations are the KVL equations for the dependent sources,

$$v_1 = r_2 \cdot i_2 \qquad v_2 = r_1 \cdot i_1$$

These two equations can be substituted into the KCL equations for v_1 and v_2. Doing so reduces the prob-

lem to two equations in two unknowns. Alternatively, the four equations in four unknowns can be translated to matrix form and solved. Performing the substitution and rewriting the equation to isolate the variables leads to

$$(1)i_1 + \frac{r_2}{R_1}i_2 = \frac{V_s}{R_1}$$

$$\frac{r_1}{R_1+R_L}i_1 + (1)i_2 = 0$$

Nodal Analysis Summary

Element Voltage to Node Voltage Relationship

$$v_x = v_j - v_k$$

$$v_k + v_x = v_j \qquad\qquad v_k = v_j - v_x$$

Resistors and Nodal Analysis

$$i_j = \frac{v_x}{R} = \frac{v_j - v_k}{R} \quad \text{and} \quad i_k = -i_j = \frac{v_k - v_j}{R}$$

Dependent Sources

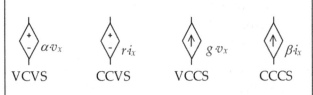

VCVS   CCVS   VCCS   CCCS

Treat dependent sources just like ideal sources. Write an equation for controlling voltage v_x or controlling current i_x in terms of node voltages.

Basic Nodal Analysis Procedure
1. Label reference node and essential nodes.
2. Write KCL at essential nodes.
3. Write KVL equations for voltage sources that have unknown currents.
4. Form matrix equation and solve it.

Detailed Nodal Analysis Procedure
1. Label reference node and essential nodes.
2. Label needed or desired nonessential nodes.
3. Label unknown currents through voltage sources as needed or desired.
4. Write KCL equations for all essential nodes.
5. Write KCL equations for needed nonessential nodes.
6. Write KVL equations for voltage sources with labeled, unknown currents.
7. Write KCL or KVL equations for voltages or currents controlling dependent sources.
8. Form matrix equation and solve it.
9. Use nodal solution to compute other needed results using KVL, KCL, and Ohm's law.

Ideal Voltage Sources

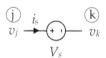

i_s is an additional unknown

$v_j - v_k = V_s$ is an additional KVL equation

$v_j = V_s$, KCL at node (j) is not needed to find v_j.

KVL $\quad v_x = v_k + V_s$

$$i_j = \frac{v_j - v_x}{R} = \frac{v_j - (v_k + V_s)}{R}$$

$$i_k = -i_j = \frac{(v_k + V_s) - v_j}{R}$$

3.4 Superposition

Superposition is **sometimes** a useful property when solving circuits. It is often most useful when performing analytic derivations rather than solving a circuit with numerical values.

There are two separate aspects to superposition. The first is **scaling**. Scaling applies most readily to circuits having a single voltage or current source, such as the following circuit.

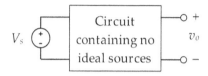

If the circuit is solved to find the output v_o, then scaling says that if the source amplitude doubles to $2V_s$, the output simply doubles as well to $2v_o$. Or, if the source is turned around (scaled by -1), the output goes to $-v_o$. The output simply scales with the source value scaling. Using the water analogy, if I double the water pressure supplying a garden hose, the flow rate from the hose doubles and the bucket fills twice as fast. This makes intuitive sense.

Scaling is useful when the solution to a circuit is known for one source value and the solution is needed for a different source value. The solution, no matter what it is, changes by the ratio of the new source value to the old source value. Scaling is not as useful in circuits having more than one source, because all sources must simultaneously change by the same ratio for scaling to work correctly.

The second aspect of superposition is called **additivity**. Additivity simply means that all sources contribute independently to the solution. The impact of one source on the solution does not alter the impact of any other source on the solution. Using the water analogy, when filling a bucket from multiple garden hoses, how much any one hose contributes to the bucket does not alter what the others contribute. The contributions from all hoses simply add together to form the whole. This too makes intuitive sense.

In circuits, the additivity aspect of superposition means that the solution of a circuit can be found by considering each source individually. That is, the solution can be found with each source acting alone, and all the individual solutions are summed to form the final solution with all sources acting simultaneously. If there are N sources in a circuit, applying superposition in this way means solving the circuit N times, one for each source acting alone. **Having to solve a circuit multiple times is the reason why the additivity aspect of superposition is seldom a good choice for numerically solving a circuit.**

It is important to note that it is not necessary to consider each source individually when applying superposition. Any number of sources can be considered simultaneously. Considering just one source at a time is simply the most common approach.

In solving a circuit N times with each of the N sources acting alone, how does one **"turn OFF"** the other sources so they do not contribute in any way to the solution for the one source acting alone? A first guess would be to simply remove all the other sources not being considered. If those sources are not in the visible circuit, they will certainly not contribute to the solution for the one remaining source being considered. The problem with this idea is that the source must be turned OFF electrically, not visibly. After all, it is the pressure and flow of the sources that must be turned OFF, not their visual appearance.

Voltage and current sources are "turned OFF" by setting their amplitudes or source values to zero as illustrated in the following table.

Shutting OFF Ideal Sources	
$V_s = 0$ short circuit	$I_s = 0$ open circuit

A voltage source becomes a source of zero volts. So, turning OFF a voltage source means replacing it with a short circuit. A current source becomes a source of zero amperes. So, turning OFF a current source means replacing it with an open circuit.

Note: Only ideal sources can be turned OFF. Dependent sources are controlled by the circuit itself, so they cannot be turned OFF. Dependent sources remain active in the circuit under all conditions.

Example: To demonstrate the additivity property of superposition, consider the following circuit where the solution sought is i_o.

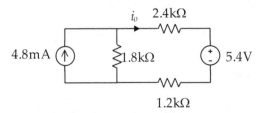

This problem is easily solved using nodal analysis. So, before solving it using superposition, it is beneficial to know what the superposition result should be. Doing so will confirm that superposition is applied properly. Labeling nodes gives the following circuit.

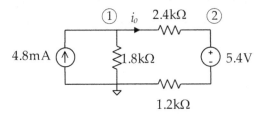

Writing KCL at nodes ① and ② gives

$$-4.8\,\text{m} + \frac{v_1}{1.8\,\text{k}} + \frac{v_1 - v_2}{2.4\,\text{k}} = 0$$

and

$$\frac{v_2 - v_1}{2.4\,\text{k}} + \frac{v_2 - 5.4}{1.2\,\text{k}} = 0$$

where i_o is recognized as

$$i_o = \frac{v_1 - v_2}{2.4\,\text{k}}$$

Rewriting the KCL equations so the variables are isolated gives

$$\left(\frac{1}{1.8\text{k}} + \frac{1}{2.4\text{k}}\right)v_1 + \left(\frac{-1}{2.4\text{k}}\right)v_2 = 4.8\,\text{m}$$

$$\left(\frac{-1}{2.4\text{k}}\right)v_1 + \left(\frac{1}{2.4\text{k}} + \frac{1}{1.2\text{k}}\right)v_2 = \frac{5.4}{1.2\text{k}}$$

which, in matrix form, becomes

$$\begin{bmatrix} \dfrac{1}{1.8\,\text{k}} + \dfrac{1}{2.4\,\text{k}} & \dfrac{-1}{2.4\,\text{k}} \\ \dfrac{-1}{2.4\text{k}} & \dfrac{1}{2.4\,\text{k}} + \dfrac{1}{1.2\,\text{k}} \end{bmatrix} \cdot \begin{bmatrix} v_1 \\ v_2 \end{bmatrix} = \begin{bmatrix} 4.8\,\text{m} \\ \dfrac{5.4}{1.2\,\text{k}} \end{bmatrix}$$

The solution to this set of equations is

$$\begin{bmatrix} v_1 \\ v_2 \end{bmatrix} = \begin{bmatrix} 7.56 \text{ V} \\ 6.12 \text{ V} \end{bmatrix}$$

Then the solution for i_o is

$$i_o = \frac{v_1 - v_2}{2.4 \text{ k}} = \frac{7.56 - 6.12}{2.4 \text{ k}} = 0.6 \text{ mA} = 600 \mu \text{ A}$$

This is the result that superposition must match.

Now apply superposition. First, shutting OFF the 5.4 V source by setting its value to zero converts the source to a short circuit as shown in the circuit below.

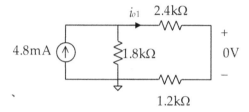

The current i_{o1} is that part of the current i_o that is due to the 4.8 mA source acting alone. This current can be found by applying current division where the 2.4 kΩ and 1.2 kΩ are in series as shown in the revised circuit below.

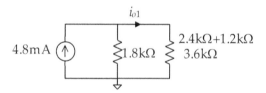

Applying current division gives

$$i_{o1} = \frac{R_{eq}}{R_k} 4.8 \text{ m} = \frac{1.8 \text{ k} \| 3.6 \text{ k}}{3.6 \text{ k}} 4.8 \text{ m} = \frac{1.2 \text{ k}}{3.6 \text{ k}} 4.8 \text{ m} = 1.6 \text{ mA}$$

Next, shutting OFF the 4.8 mA source by setting its value to zero converts the source to an open circuit as shown below.

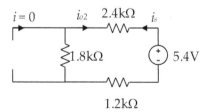

The current i_{o2} is that part of the current i_o that is due to the 5.4 V source acting alone. This current can be found by applying Ohm's law

$$i_{o2} = -i_s = -\frac{5.4}{2.4 \text{ k} + 1.8 \text{ k} + 1.2 \text{ k}} = -\frac{5.4}{5.4 \text{ k}} = -1 \text{ mA}$$

The current i_o is the sum of the two components,

$$i_o = i_{o1} + i_{o2} = 1.6 \text{ m} - 1 \text{ m} = 0.6 \text{ mA} = 600 \text{ } \mu\text{A}$$

This agrees with the earlier nodal analysis solution.

Superposition	
Scaling	When all ideal sources in a circuit are scaled by a constant α, all voltages and currents in the circuit are scaled by α as well.
Additivity	Voltages and currents in a circuit can be found by summing the contribution due to each ideal source acting alone. When a voltage source is shut OFF, it becomes a short circuit. When a current source is shut OFF, it becomes an open circuit. Dependent sources cannot be shut OFF. They remain active at all times.

3.5 Source Transformations

Source transformations are remarkable tools for simplifying circuits. Using a source transformation, a voltage source in **series** with a resistor can be replaced by a current source in **parallel** with a resistor and vice versa as shown below. The two circuits are said to be **equivalent**.

The resistor value R is the same for both circuits and the sources are related by simple Ohm's law relationships, $I_s = V_s/R$ and $V_s = I_s \cdot R$.

Equivalence means that the rest of the circuit has exactly the same voltages and currents as it did before the source transformation was made. The rest of the circuit cannot tell whether it is connected to a voltage source in **series** with a resistor or if it is connected to the equivalent current source in **parallel** with a resistor.

There are a number of ways to demonstrate that the two circuits are equivalent when the resistances are equal and the sources are related by Ohm's law. One way is to conduct tests. If the same set of tests conducted on both circuits produces the same results, the two circuits must be equivalent.

Test one is to measure the open circuit voltage V_{oc} across the terminals of both circuits. The open circuit voltage is the voltage that appears when an open circuit exists at the terminals, namely when nothing is connected and the current is zero as shown in the following circuit.

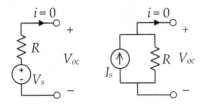

Since the current is zero, the voltage across the resistor in the circuit on the left is also zero, i.e., $0 = 0 \cdot R$. Therefore KVL dictates that

$$V_{oc} = V_s + 0 = V_s$$

Because the current is zero in the right circuit, I_s flows through the resistor R only, so the voltage V_{oc} is given by Ohm's law as

$$V_{oc} = I_s R$$

Equivalence dictates that V_{oc} must be the same for the two circuits, so these two equations must be equal to each other

$$V_{oc} = V_s = I_s R$$

This confirms the relationship between the voltage and current source values.

Test two is to measure the short circuit current I_{sc} that flows through a short circuit connected across the terminals of both circuits as shown below.

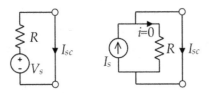

The short circuit current in the circuit on the left is given by Ohm's law as

$$I_{sc} = \frac{V_s}{R}$$

The current through the resistor R in the right circuit is zero because the voltage across it is zero due to the short, $i = 0/R = 0$. Therefore, KCL dictates that

$$I_{sc} = I_s$$

Equivalence dictates that I_{sc} must be the same for both circuits, so these two equations must be equal to each other

$$I_{sc} = I_s = \frac{V_s}{R}$$

This again confirms the relationship between the values for the voltage and current sources.

Test three is to shut OFF the sources in both circuits and measure the equivalent resistance R_{eq} at the terminals as shown in the following circuit.

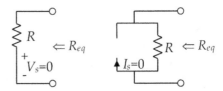

In both circuits, the measured resistance is the same, $R_{eq} = R$, so this confirms that the two resistors have equal value.

These three tests all confirm the relationships between the source transformation circuit elements.

> **Warning:** While no voltages or currents in the rest of the circuit change after making a source transformation, that does not mean that the source transformation elements do not experience change after a source transformation. They do!

As shown below, reconsider the earlier circuits were the open circuit voltage V_{oc} was measured.

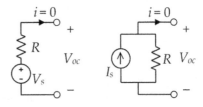

The resistor in the circuit on the left does not absorb any power because the current flowing through it is zero, i.e., $p = i^2 \cdot R = (0)^2 \cdot R = 0$. Since the resistor is not absorbing power, the voltage source is not generating any power either.

However, the resistor in the circuit on the right is absorbing power because it has the current I_s flowing through it, *i.e.*, $p=I_s^2 \cdot R$. Since the resistor is absorbing power, the source is generating it.

So, while the resistor values are identical in both circuits, the two resistors are not absorbing the same power, and the two sources are not creating the same power. The rest of the circuit is unchanged by a source transformation, but the source transformation elements do not have the same power.

Source transformations provide a straightforward way to simplify circuits where voltage sources appear in series with resistors or when current sources appear in parallel with resistors.

Source Transformation

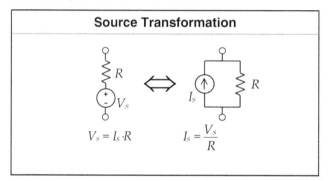

$$V_s = I_s \cdot R \qquad I_s = \frac{V_s}{R}$$

Example: To illustrate the utility of using source transformations, consider the following circuit.

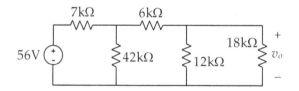

Starting on the left, and performing a sequence of source transformation and simplifications, the circuit simplifies so that v_o is easily found.

Identify a voltage source in series with resistor:

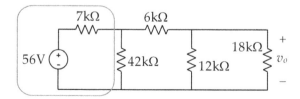

Perform a source transformation:

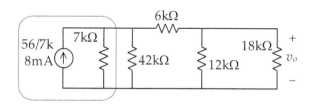

Combine resistors in parallel:

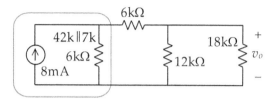

Apply a source transformation:

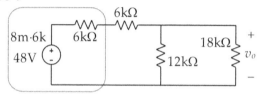

Combine resistors in series:

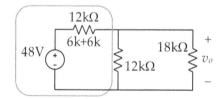

Apply a source transformation:

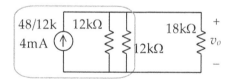

Combine resistors in parallel:

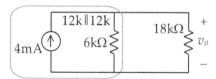

Apply a source transformation:

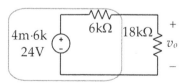

Finally, apply voltage division:

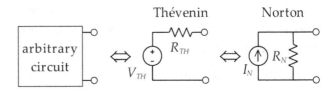

$$v_0 = \frac{18k}{6k+18k} \cdot 24 = 0.75 \cdot 24 = 18V$$

To check this result, the problem can be solved by applying nodal analysis to the following labeled circuit.

Writing KCL at node① gives

$$\frac{v_1 - 56}{7\,k} + \frac{v_1}{42\,k} + \frac{v_1 - v_2}{6\,k} = 0$$

and KCL applied to node ② gives

$$\frac{v_2 - v_1}{6\,k} + \frac{v_2}{12\,k} + \frac{v_2}{18\,k} = 0$$

Rewriting these to isolate the variables gives

$$\left(\frac{1}{7\,k} + \frac{1}{42\,k} + \frac{1}{6\,k}\right)v_1 + \left(\frac{-1}{6\,k}\right)v_2 = \frac{56}{7\,k}$$

$$\left(\frac{-1}{6\,k}\right)v_1 + \left(\frac{1}{6\,k} + \frac{1}{12\,k} + \frac{1}{18\,k}\right)v_2 = 0$$

Rewriting these in matrix form leads to

$$\begin{bmatrix} \left(\frac{1}{7\,k} + \frac{1}{42\,k} + \frac{1}{6\,k}\right) & \left(\frac{-1}{6\,k}\right) \\ \left(\frac{-1}{6\,k}\right) & \left(\frac{1}{6\,k} + \frac{1}{12\,k} + \frac{1}{18\,k}\right) \end{bmatrix} \cdot \begin{bmatrix} v_1 \\ v_2 \end{bmatrix} = \begin{bmatrix} \frac{56}{7\,k} \\ 0 \end{bmatrix}$$

The solution to this set of equations is

$$\begin{bmatrix} v_1 \\ v_2 \end{bmatrix} = \begin{bmatrix} 33\,V \\ 18\,V \end{bmatrix}$$

Since the node ② voltage is equal to the labeled v_0,

$$v_0 = v_2 = 18\,V$$

The source transformation solution is correct.

3.6 Thévenin and Norton Equivalent Circuits

Thévenin and Norton equivalent circuits provide a powerful way to simplify a complicated circuit. A cir-

cuit containing any number of sources and resistors can be replaced by its Thévenin equivalent, which is simply a voltage source in series with a resistor. Likewise, a circuit containing any number of sources and resistors can be replaced by its Norton equivalent, which is simply a current source in parallel with a resistor. The Thévenin and Norton equivalent circuits are just source transformations of each other. The next figure illustrates these equivalent circuits.

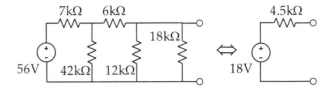

As an example, consider the circuit below. The Thévenin equivalent of the circuit on the left is shown on the right. The more complex circuit on the left is equivalent to the simple circuit on the right.

If you think about it, replacing a complicated circuit with a very simple one is very powerful as shown in the example above. It is amazing that this works.

So, how does one find the Thévenin or Norton equivalent? It turns out that the tests performed earlier to confirm the source transformation relationship work here as well. A complicated circuit can be replaced by a Thévenin or Norton equivalent if any test performed on the complicated circuit has the same result when performed on the equivalent circuits. That is, after all, the definition of equivalent: same tests, same results; therefore equivalent.

Test one is to measure the open circuit voltage V_{oc} across the terminals of all three circuits. The open circuit voltage is the voltage that appears when an open circuit exists at the terminals, namely when nothing is connected and the current is zero. For the Thévenin equivalent, the open circuit voltage is equal to the Thévenin voltage, $V_{oc} = V_{TH}$, as shown in the following figure because zero current through R_{TH} means there is no voltage across it.

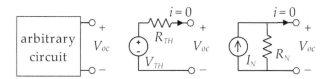

Test two is to measure the short circuit current I_{sc} that flows through a short circuit connected across the terminals of all three circuits. For the Norton equivalent, the short circuit current is equal to the Norton current, $I_{sc} = I_N$, as shown in the figure below because zero voltage across R_N means there is no current flowing through it.

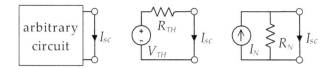

Test three is to shut OFF the ideal sources in all three circuits and measure the equivalent resistance R_{eq} at the terminals. For the Thévenin and Norton equivalent circuits, the equivalent resistance R_{eq} is equal to the Thévenin and Norton resistances respectively, $R_{eq} = R_{TH} = R_N$ as illustrated below.

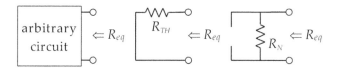

As noted earlier in the discussion of superposition in circuits having dependent sources, it is not possible to shut OFF a dependent source because its value is controlled by some other voltage or current. Therefore, this test of shutting OFF all sources cannot be used in circuits having dependent sources.

Conducting any two of the above tests on the arbitrary circuit is sufficient because there are really only two unknowns since the Thévenin and Norton equivalent circuits are related by source transformation relationships, $V_{TH} = I_N \cdot R_N$ and $R_{TH} = R_N$.

If you compute the open circuit voltage $V_{oc} = V_{TH}$ and the short circuit current $I_{sc} = I_N$, then the Thévenin and Norton resistances are found by applying the source transformation voltage source to current source relationship as follows

$$V_{oc} = I_{sc} \cdot R_{TH}$$

$$\frac{V_{oc}}{I_{sc}} = \frac{V_{TH}}{I_N} = R_{TH} = R_N$$

If you compute the open circuit voltage $V_{oc} = V_{TH}$ and the equivalent resistance $R_{eq} = R_{TH} = R_N$, then the Norton current is

$$I_N = \frac{V_{oc}}{R_{eq}} = \frac{V_{TH}}{R_{TH}}$$

If you compute the short circuit current $I_{sc} = I_N$ and the equivalent resistance $R_{eq} = R_{TH} = R_N$, then the Thévenin voltage is

$$V_{TH} = I_{sc} R_{eq} = I_N R_N$$

Example: Consider the circuit shown earlier and its Thévenin equivalent circuit as shown below.

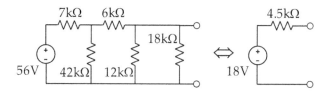

Test one is to measure the open circuit voltage V_{oc} across the terminals of the circuit. This value is easily found by applying nodal analysis.

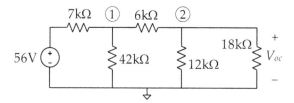

This circuit was solved earlier. The matrix equation was found to be

$$\begin{bmatrix} \left(\dfrac{1}{7\,k} + \dfrac{1}{42\,k} + \dfrac{1}{6\,k}\right) & \left(\dfrac{-1}{6\,k}\right) \\ \left(\dfrac{-1}{6\,k}\right) & \left(\dfrac{1}{6\,k} + \dfrac{1}{12\,k} + \dfrac{1}{18\,k}\right) \end{bmatrix} \cdot \begin{bmatrix} v_1 \\ v_2 \end{bmatrix} = \begin{bmatrix} \dfrac{56}{7\,k} \\ 0 \end{bmatrix}$$

and the solution was

$$\begin{bmatrix} v_1 \\ v_2 \end{bmatrix} = \begin{bmatrix} 33\,V \\ 18\,V \end{bmatrix}$$

Since $V_{oc} = v_2$ in this case, the Thévenin voltage is $V_{TH} = V_{oc} = 18$ V.

Test two is to measure the short circuit current I_{sc} that flows through a short circuit connected across the terminals of the following circuit.

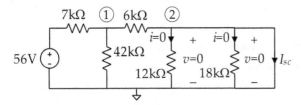

In this case, the added short makes node ② and the reference node be the same node. So $v_2 = 0$. They are connected to each other by a perfectly conducting path through the short. The 12 kΩ and 18 kΩ resistors have been shorted out by the added short, so their voltage is zero as shown. They cannot have any voltage across them. By Ohm's law, the current through them is also zero, $i = v/R = 0/R = 0$.

By KCL, the short circuit current I_{sc} is equal to the current flowing from node ① to node ② through the 6 kΩ resistor. This current is easily found by applying nodal analysis. Applying KCL to node ① gives,

$$\frac{v_1 - 56}{7\,k} + \frac{v_1}{42\,k} + \frac{v_1 - 0}{6\,k} = 0$$

Rewriting this equation to isolate v_1 gives

$$\left(\frac{1}{7\,k} + \frac{1}{42\,k} + \frac{1}{6\,k}\right)v_1 = \frac{56}{7\,k}$$

The solution to this equation is $v_1 = 24$ V.

The Norton current is equal to the short circuit current, which is given by

$$I_N = I_{sc} = \frac{v_1}{6\,k} = \frac{24}{6\,k} = 4\,\text{mA}$$

Given the Thévenin voltage $V_{TH} = 18$ V and the Norton current $I_N = 4$ mA, the Thévenin and Norton resistances are

$$R_{TH} = R_N = \frac{V_{TH}}{I_N} = \frac{18}{4\,m} = 4.5\,k\Omega$$

This value is easily confirmed by applying **test 3**, which is to shut OFF the ideal sources in the circuit and measure the equivalent resistance R_{eq} seen at the terminals as illustrated in the following circuit.

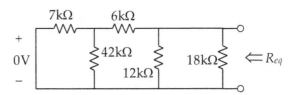

This circuit is simplified by collapsing the circuit toward the measurement point by combing resistors in series and resistors in parallel appropriately. To start, the 7 kΩ resistor is in parallel with the 42 kΩ, so they can be combined as shown below.

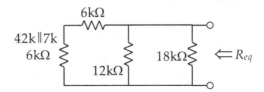

Next, the two 6 kΩ resistors are in series and can be combined as shown below.

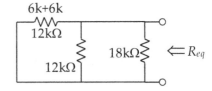

Finally, the two 12 kΩ resistors and the 18 kΩ resistor are all in parallel. Therefore, $R_{eq} = R_{TH} = R_N$ is

$$R_{eq} = \left(12\,k \| 12\,k\right) \| 18\,k = 6\,k \| 18\,k = 4.5\,k\Omega$$

That completes this example. All three tests were conducted and the results were in agreement with each other.

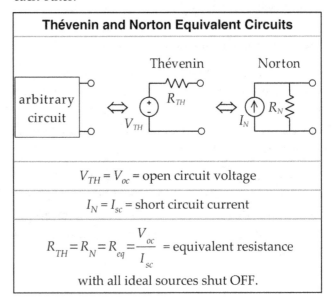

Thévenin and Norton Equivalent Circuits

$V_{TH} = V_{oc}$ = open circuit voltage

$I_N = I_{sc}$ = short circuit current

$$R_{TH} = R_N = R_{eq} = \frac{V_{oc}}{I_{sc}} = \text{equivalent resistance}$$

with all ideal sources shut OFF.

Real World Example: Analytically, there is no harm done when a short is connected across the output to measure the short circuit current. However, in the real world, it might not be possible to measure the short circuit current. Therefore, some other way of finding the Norton current must be found.

In addition, it is easy to shut OFF sources analytically and find the equivalent resistance R_{eq}. Once again, this might not be possible in the real world. Therefore, the equivalent resistance must be found by some other technique.

An example where both of these issues appears is when finding the Thévenin equivalent of a battery, such as a conventional 12 V automotive battery. There is no internal circuitry to analyze in this case, but clearly the battery has a Thévenin equivalent model as shown below.

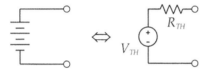

In this case, it is possible to measure the open circuit voltage of the battery, but not its short circuit current. Doing so will discharge the battery quickly and could damage the battery or cause it to overheat. Similarly, it is not possible to measure the equivalent resistance of the battery, because it is not possible to shut OFF the source of voltage inside the battery.

The open circuit voltage across the battery terminals when nothing is connected to it gives the Thévenin voltage V_{TH}. Another test must be conducted to find the Thévenin resistance R_{TH}. In this case, instead of placing a short across the battery terminals, a known, significant, but safe, load that creates a measurable difference in the battery terminal voltage is needed. From this information, the Thévenin resistance R_{TH} can be found. These two tests are shown visually in the following circuits.

Knowing $V_{oc} = V_{TH}$, R_L and V_L, the Thévenin resistance R_{TH} can be found by applying KVL to the loaded Thévenin circuit shown below.

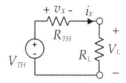

Using Ohm's law, the Thévenin resistance is

$$R_{TH} = \frac{v_x}{i_x}$$

The voltage v_x is found by applying KVL in its form that voltage must add up, namely

$$V_L + v_x = V_{TH}$$

or

$$v_x = V_{TH} - V_L$$

The current i_x is given by Ohm's law as

$$i_x = \frac{V_L}{R_L}$$

Combining the expressions for v_x and i_x gives the Thévenin resistance as

$$R_{TH} = \frac{v_x}{i_x} = \frac{V_{TH} - V_L}{\dfrac{V_L}{R_L}}$$

or more succinctly as

$$R_{TH} = \frac{V_{TH} - V_L}{V_L} R_L$$

Using typical data for a typical automotive battery, $V_{oc} = V_{TH} = 12.6$ V. With the headlights turned ON, $R_L = 1.5\ \Omega$, and $V_L = 12.4$ V. Substituting these values into the above expression, gives a Thévenin resistance of

$$R_{TH} = \frac{V_{TH} - V_L}{V_L} R_L = \frac{12.6 - 12.4}{12.4} 1.5 = 24.2\,\text{m}\Omega$$

This may seem like a very small resistance, but it is not when you compute the battery's short circuit current,

$$I_{sc} = I_N = \frac{V_{TH}}{R_{TH}} = \frac{12.6}{24.2\,\text{m}} = 521\,\text{A}$$

This value is well within the range of a typical automotive battery.

An Engineer's Proof of the Thévenin Equivalent

Normally proofs are not part of engineering courses. They tend to have greater importance in mathematics courses. However, sometimes a proof demonstrates a creative thought process that is worth seeing. The following proof of Thévenin fits this scenario because the proof is not mathematical, but rather it uses circuit analysis concepts creatively.

Consider the following arbitrary boxed circuit for which the Thévenin equivalent is desired.

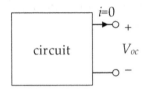

The voltage across the output terminals is the open circuit voltage V_{oc} because there is no current flowing out of the circuit.

Connecting a resistor R in series with one of the output terminals as shown in the following circuit. The open circuit voltage V_{oc} now appears on both sides of the added resistor because there is zero current flowing through it. There is no voltage across the added resistor since there is zero current i flowing through it, i.e., $v = i \cdot R = 0 \cdot R = 0$ V.

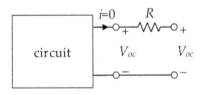

Next placing a voltage source having value V_{oc} across the terminals on the right leads to the circuit below.

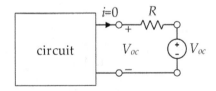

Nothing has changed in this circuit because the voltage remains the same across the terminals on both sides of the resistor R. As a result, the current i remains equal to zero.

Now consider the application of superposition. If **all** sources inside the boxed circuit are turned OFF, the remaining circuit contains resistors only. Therefore, the boxed circuit can be replaced by the equivalent resistance R_{eq} seen looking into the circuit output terminals as shown below.

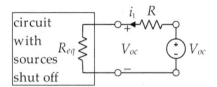

The current i_1 due to the external voltage source V_{oc} acting alone is given by Ohm's law as

$$i_1 = \frac{V_{oc}}{R_{eq} + R}$$

Next turning OFF the external voltage source by setting its value to zero and turning ON all the sources inside the circuit gives the following circuit.

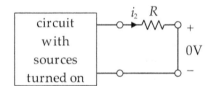

The current i_2 flowing out of the boxed circuit is due to all sources inside the boxed circuit. The current i_2 and the current i_1, due to the external voltage source, must cancel each other out since the current with all sources turned ON was zero, $i = 0$, as shown below.

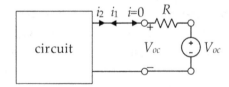

That is, KCL requires that

$$i_2 = i_1 = \frac{V_{oc}}{R_{eq} + R}$$

so that $i = 0$. Using this equation, the boxed circuit can be replaced by the following equivalent circuit.

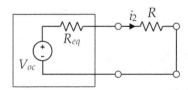

Applying Ohm's law shows that the current i_2 in this equivalent circuit is equal to the preceding current expression.

Therefore, the arbitrary boxed circuit can be replaced by the equivalent circuit shown above. This equivalent circuit is identical to the Thévenin equivalent circuit where $V_{oc} = V_{TH}$ and $R_{TH} = R_{eq}$.

Redrawing the combined circuit as shown below makes it possible to confirm that the current i is zero.

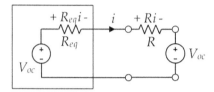

Applying KVL around the loop starting below the voltage source inside the boxed circuit and proceeding clockwise gives

$$V_{oc} - R_{eq}i - Ri - V_{oc} = 0$$
$$V_{oc} - V_{oc} - (R_{eq} + R)i = 0$$
$$(R_{eq} + R)i = 0$$
$$i = 0$$

This confirms that $i = 0$ and V_{oc} is indeed the open circuit voltage.

This proves what we wanted to show. An arbitrary circuit can be replaced by an equivalent voltage source in series with a resistor. This proof did not require mathematics. It just required creative engineering thinking that is useful in the working world.

The Load Line

As should be obvious by now, circuit analysis involves plenty of equations. Because engineers often comprehend material better when it is presented in visual form, it is beneficial to visually illustrate some important equations and relationships. Since the Thévenin equivalent allows an arbitrary circuit to be replaced by a voltage source in series with a resistor, studying the Thévenin equivalent visually is useful.

Consider the following circuit where some arbitrary circuit is replaced by its Thévenin equivalent.

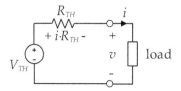

Writing KVL for this circuit having an arbitrary load gives

$$V_{TH} - i \cdot R_{TH} - v = 0$$

Solving this equation for the current i gives,

$$V_{TH} - i \cdot R_{TH} - v = 0$$
$$V_{TH} - v = i \cdot R_{TH}$$
$$\frac{V_{TH} - v}{R_{TH}} = i$$

This last equation can be rewritten in the form of a straight line as

$$i = \left(\frac{-1}{R_{TH}}\right)v + \frac{V_{TH}}{R_{TH}}$$

This equation describes the current i through and voltage v across whatever load is connected to the Thévenin equivalent circuit. This equation also fits the general straight line equation $y = m \cdot x + b$, where m is the slope and b is the y-axis intercept. In this case, the slope is $m = -1/R_{TH}$ and the y-axis intercept is $b = V_{TH}/R_{TH} = I_N$. In addition, the x-axis intercept occurs when $i = 0$, which occurs when $v = V_{TH}$,

$$i = \left(\frac{-1}{R_{TH}}\right)v + \frac{V_{TH}}{R_{TH}}$$
$$0 = \left(\frac{-1}{R_{TH}}\right)V_{TH} + \frac{V_{TH}}{R_{TH}}$$

Given this information, this line can be plotted as shown in the following figure.

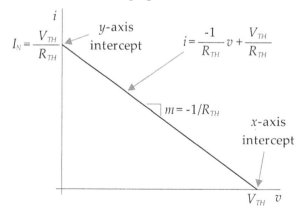

This line describes the current i through and the voltage v across the load no matter what the load is. As a result, this is called the **load line**. Once a load has been chosen, the specific current $i = i_o$ and voltage $v = v_o$ for the load can be found somewhere along this line where a plot of the load i-v characteristic crosses the load line.

Resistor: For example, let the load be a resistor R as shown in the following circuit.

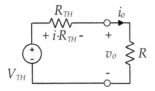

Ohm's law for the resistor gives

$$i = \frac{v}{R} = \left(\frac{1}{R}\right) v$$

This is the equation for a line having positive slope $m = 1/R$ that passes through the origin, $i = 0$, $v = 0$. The smaller the resistance R, the greater the slope of this line and vise versa. The following plot illustrates this resistor characteristic on top of the load line.

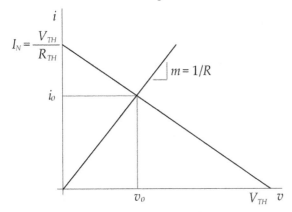

The intersection of the load line and the resistor line $i = v/R$ gives the current i_o through the resistor and voltage v_o across it. These values are called the **operating point**.

LED: Another example is an LED load. The i-v characteristic of an ideal LED is given by

$$i = I_o \left[e^{\frac{qv}{nkT}} - 1 \right]$$

where I_o, q, n, k, and T are all parameters associated with the LED material and its construction. These parameters are discussed in other courses. Because the exponential has a positive argument, the current i through the diode grows exponentially. The following plot illustrates this LED characteristic on top of the load line. The intersection of the load line and the

LED curve gives the operating point current i_o through the LED and voltage v_o across it.

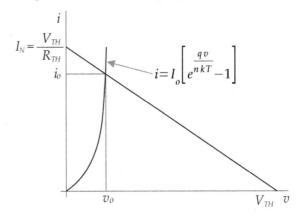

Voltage Source: Yet another example is a voltage source. Its characteristic is simply $v = V_s$. with current i_o determined by the rest of the circuit. The following plot illustrates this characteristic on top of the load line.

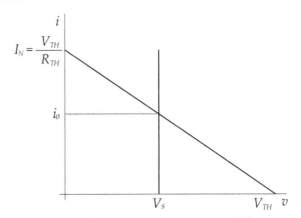

Current Source: Finally consider a current source, $i = I_s$, whose voltage v_o is determined by the rest of the circuit. The following plot illustrates this characteristic on top of the load line.

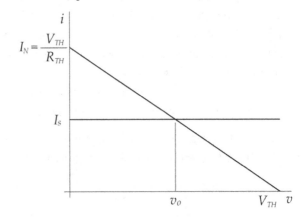

Power: As described here, the load line plot describes the relationship between the current through

and voltage across a load. Because the load is labeled in agreement with the passive sign convention, the power in the load is simply

$$p = v \cdot i$$

For some constant power $p = P_o$, the relationship between current i and voltage v is

$$i = \frac{P_o}{v}$$

A plot of this characteristic is a plot of constant power P_o as a function of i and v. For example, if $P_o = 8$ mW, then points on this plot include the following data.

Constant Power Data for P_o = 8 mW	
i, (mA)	v, (V)
1/2	16
1	8
2	4
4	2
8	1
16	1/2

Plots of constant power for various P_o values form equilateral hyperbolas as shown in the following figure.

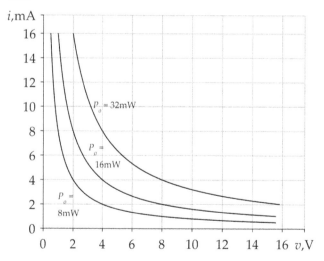

While it may be obvious, it is important to note that as the power increases, the hyperbolas move away from the origin. This occurs because power increases with increasing voltage and current. Therefore, the further away a constant power hyperbola is from the origin, the greater the constant power is.

Combining the load line, a resistor load, and constant power curves on the same plot provides very useful insight. In particular, it is useful to consider three load resistor values, $R = R_{TH}/2$, $R = R_{TH}$, and $R = 2R_{TH}$. The circuit in this case is shown below.

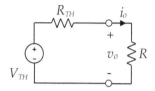

The following plot shows the three lines emanating from the origin describing $i = v/R$ for each of the three resistance values. In addition, the constant power curves passing through the operating points for each resistance value are also shown.

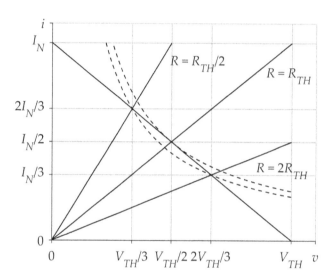

The dashed lines on the plot are the constant power hyperbolas that pass through the operating points. When $R = R_{TH}/2$ or $R = 2R_{TH}$, the power is less than that when $R = R_{TH}$, because the constant power curves for $R = R_{TH}/2$ and $R = 2R_{TH}$, are closer to the origin than that for $R = R_{TH}$. The fact that the power in R is maximum when $R = R_{TH}$ is a statement of the maximum power transfer theorem.

3.7 Maximum Power Transfer and Maximum Efficiency

When an arbitrary circuit is replaced by its Thévenin circuit and some load resistance R_L is connected to the circuit, one **academic** question that can be asked is, *"What value must the load resistance value be to absorb maximum power from the Thévenin equivalent circuit?"* This problem is called the maximum power transfer theorem. The following circuit illustrates this problem.

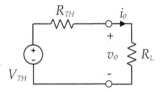

From the preceding load line presentation, the answer is that setting $R_L = R_{TH}$ absorbs maximum power from the circuit. This can be proven using calculus as well. The power in the load resistor R_L is

$$p = v_o \cdot i_o$$

$$p = \left(\frac{R_L}{R_{TH} + R_L} V_{TH} \right) \cdot \left(\frac{V_{TH}}{R_{TH} + R_L} \right)$$

$$p = \left(\frac{V_{TH}}{R_{TH} + R_L} \right)^2 R_L$$

The power p cannot be negative, since negative power means the generation of power by the passive sign convention. Resistors only absorb power, so $p \geq 0$ must hold.

From calculus it is known that the slope of the power expression with respect to R_L is zero at the power maximums and minimums. In this case, there are two minimums. When R_L is zero, the load is a short circuit that does not absorb any power. Likewise when R_L is removed, effectively making $R_L = \infty$, the power is also zero since there is no resistor there to absorb it. Somewhere between these two minimums lies a maximum.

It is an academic exercise to compute the derivative of the power p with respect to R_L, set it equal to zero, and then solve for the value of R_L that is required. That value is $R = R_{TH}$. For this case, the maximum power is

$$p_{max} = \left(\frac{V_{TH}}{R_{TH} + R_{TH}} \right)^2 R_{TH} = \left(\frac{V_{TH}}{2 R_{TH}} \right)^2 R_{TH} = \frac{V_{TH}^2}{4 R_{TH}}$$

While it is interesting that setting $R_L = R_{TH}$ absorbs maximum power from the Thévenin equivalent circuit, this choice is seldom made in practice. **It seems that this theorem appears in most electric circuits books more because it is a practical application of calculus, than because its use provides a solution to a practical engineering problem. In reality, this solution seldom makes engineering sense.**

The problem with maximum power transfer is that the solution exhibits poor efficiency. Efficiency measures how much power is delivered to a load compared to how much power is generated to deliver that power. Efficiency is typically expressed using the variable η, i.e., "eta," and is defined by the ratio

$$\eta = \frac{p_L}{p_s}$$

where p_L is the power absorbed by the load and p_s is the total power generated by the source providing power to the load. Because efficiency is a ratio of powers having a value between zero and one, it is often expressed as a percentage.

The efficiency of the Thévenin equivalent circuit with resistive load can be written as

$$\eta = \frac{p_L}{p_s} = \frac{i^2 R_L}{i^2 (R_{TH} + R_L)} = \frac{R_L}{R_{TH} + R_L}$$

Alternatively, efficiency can be written in term of the ratio R_{TH}/R_L as

$$\eta = \frac{R_L}{R_{TH} + R_L} \cdot \left(\frac{\frac{1}{R_L}}{\frac{1}{R_L}} \right) = \frac{1}{1 + \frac{R_{TH}}{R_L}}$$

When the load resistor is chosen to absorb maximum power, i.e., $R_L = R_{TH}$, the efficiency is

$$\eta = \frac{1}{1 + \frac{R_{TH}}{R_{TH}}} = \frac{1}{1 + 1} = \frac{1}{2} = 50 \%$$

So, one half the power generated is wasted or lost when delivering maximum power to the load. This would certainly not apply in the first fundamental use for electricity, i.e., the generation, distribution, and consumption of energy, where efficiency is of utmost importance. Utility power plants would have to generate twice as much power as their customers consume. For example, if customers as a whole consumed 1000 MW, the utility company would have to create 2000 MW, meaning that 1000 MW would be wasted!

Likewise, operating at 50% efficiency would not apply in the second fundamental use for electricity, *i.e.*, the generation, distribution, and consumption of information. In this case, the goal is to minimize overall energy consumption because information content is not related to energy consumed. Energy consumed is simply an undesired burden or expense. So, operating at 50% efficiency consumes twice as much energy as needed and simply adds to cost.

Operating at the maximum power transfer point does occur in radio frequency (RF) circuits where one wants to eliminate standing waves on transmission lines (a topic to be learned in an electromagnetic fields and waves class). However, it is merely a coincidence that eliminating standing waves and maximum power transfer occur under the same conditions.

In most cases, maximizing efficiency is more important than maximizing power transfer. **Efficiency improves as R_L increases and reaches 100% as R_L goes to infinity.**

For example, if $R_L = 4R_{TH}$, efficiency is 80%,

$$\eta = \frac{1}{1 + \dfrac{R_{TH}}{R_L}} = \frac{1}{1 + 1/4} = \frac{1}{5/4} = 4/5 = 80\%$$

and $R_L = 9R_{TH}$, efficiency is 90%,

$$\eta = \frac{1}{1 + \dfrac{R_{TH}}{R_L}} = \frac{1}{1 + 1/9} = \frac{1}{10/9} = 9/10 = 90\%$$

The problem with the maximum power transfer theorem is that it is the wrong question to ask. The more important and useful question to ask is, *"What value should the Thévenin resistance of a circuit be to maximize the efficiency at which power can be extracted?"* The answer to this question does not require calculus. The Thévenin resistance R_{TH} is zero when efficiency is 100%. That is, when $R_{TH} = 0$,

$$\eta = \frac{1}{1 + \dfrac{R_{TH}}{R_L}} = \frac{1}{1 + \dfrac{0}{R_L}} = \frac{1}{1} = 100\%$$

It is useful to plot both the power in the load resistor R_L and efficiency on the same set of axes. To do so, it is very convenient to plot normalized power,

which is the power for any given R_L divided by the maximum power p_{max} when $R_L = R_{TH}$. The normalized power is given by

$$p_{norm} = \frac{p}{p_{max}} = \frac{\left(\dfrac{V_{TH}}{R_{TH} + R_L}\right)^2 R_L}{\dfrac{V_{TH}^2}{4R_{TH}}}$$

This can be rewritten and simplified as

$$p_{norm} = \left(\frac{V_{TH}}{R_{TH} + R_L}\right)^2 R_L \cdot \left(\frac{4R_{TH}}{V_{TH}^2}\right)$$

$$p_{norm} = \frac{4R_{TH}R_L}{\left(R_{TH} + R_L\right)^2}$$

$$p_{norm} = \frac{4R_{TH}R_L}{\left(R_{TH} + R_L\right)^2} \cdot \left(\frac{\dfrac{1}{R_L^2}}{\dfrac{1}{R_L^2}}\right)$$

$$p_{norm} = 4\frac{\dfrac{R_{TH}}{R_L}}{\left(1 + \dfrac{R_{TH}}{R_L}\right)}$$

When power is expressed in this way, values for both the normalized power and the efficiency vary between zero and one and they can both be plotted on the same axes. The following plot illustrates the relationship between power and efficiency.

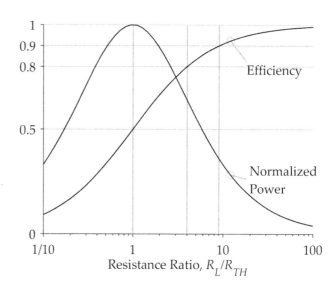

Because the resistance ratio covers such a wide range of values, the x-axis of the above plot has logarithmic scaling. As illustrated in the following figure, in logarithmic scaling, the data points are separated on the horizontal axis based on the common logarithm of their values, rather than the values themselves. Because of this, each factor of ten in resistance ratio occupies the same length along the axis, since $\log(1/10) = -1$, $\log(1) = 0$, $\log(10) = 1$, and $\log(100) = 2$,

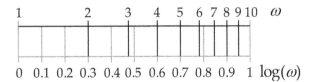

The plotted curves confirm the analysis performance in this section. The normalized power has its peak value of one when the load resistance R_L is equal to the Thévenin resistance R_{TH}. For this value, the efficiency is 50%.

Efficiency steadily increases as the load resistance increases relative to the Thévenin resistance. The plot also confirms the two points found earlier where it was shown that efficiency is equal to 80% efficiency when $R_L = 4R_{TH}$, and that it is equal to 90% when $R_L = 9R_{TH}$.

In conclusion, efficiency is generally much more important than maximum power transfer. This section focused on finding the value of R_L that absorbs maximum power, when a better question is finding the value of R_{TH} that maximizes power and efficiency simultaneously. For a given amount of power, minimizing R_{TH} maximizes efficiency. The ideal value for R_{TH} is zero because any amount of power can be extracted at 100% efficiency.

Maximum Power Transfer and Efficiency
Maximum power is transferred when the load resistance is equal to the Thévenin resistance. However, because this choice results in 50% efficiency, this value is seldom chosen.
For a given amount of power, maximum efficiency is achieved when the Thévenin resistance is as small as possible.

3.8 Summary

Resistors in Series and Voltage Division
(circuit diagram with resistors R_1, R_2, R_3, ..., R_N in series)
$$R_{eq} = R_1 + R_2 + \cdots + R_N = \sum_{k=1}^{N} R_k$$
$$v_k = \frac{R_k}{R_{eq}} V_{tot} \quad \text{for} \quad k = 1, 2, \cdots, N$$
$$0 < v_k < V_{tot}$$
The **largest** resistance value has the largest voltage across it.

Resistors in Parallel and Current Division
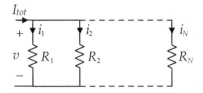
$$\frac{1}{R_{eq}} = \frac{1}{R_1} + \frac{1}{R_2} + \cdots + \frac{1}{R_N} = \sum_{k=1}^{N} \frac{1}{R_k}$$
$$i_k = \frac{R_{eq}}{R_k} I_{tot} \quad \text{for} \quad k = 1, 2, \cdots, N$$
$$0 < i_k < I_{tot}$$
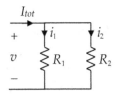
$$R_{eq} = \frac{R_1 R_2}{R_1 + R_2}$$
$$i_1 = \frac{R_2}{R_1 + R_2} I_{tot} \quad \text{and} \quad i_2 = \frac{R_1}{R_1 + R_2} I_{tot}$$
The **smallest** resistance value has the largest current through it.

Basic Nodal Analysis Procedure

1. Label reference node and essential nodes.

2. Write KCL at essential nodes.

3. Write KVL equations for voltage sources that have unknown currents.

4. Form matrix equation and solve it.

Detailed Nodal Analysis Procedure

1. Label reference node and essential nodes.

2. Label needed or desired nonessential nodes.

3. Label unknown currents through voltage sources as needed or desired.

4. Write KCL equations for all essential nodes.

5. Write KCL equations for needed nonessential nodes.

6. Write KVL equations for voltage sources with labeled, unknown currents.

7. Write KCL or KVL equations for voltages or currents controlling dependent sources.

8. Form matrix equation and solve it.

9. Use nodal solution to compute other needed results using KVL, KCL, and Ohm's law.

Element Voltage to Node Voltage Relationship

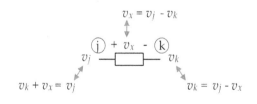

Resistors and Nodal Analysis

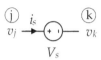

$$i_j = \frac{v_x}{R} = \frac{v_j - v_k}{R} \quad \text{and} \quad i_k = -i_j = \frac{v_k - v_j}{R}$$

Ideal Voltage Sources and Nodal Analysis

i_s is an additional unknown

$v_j - v_k = V_s$ is an additional KVL equation

$v_j = V_s$, KCL at node (j) is not needed to find v_j.

$$\text{KVL} \quad v_x = v_k + V_s$$

$$i_j = \frac{v_j - v_x}{R} = \frac{v_j - (v_k + V_s)}{R}$$

$$i_k = -i_j = \frac{(v_k + V_s) - v_j}{R}$$

Dependent Sources and Nodal Analysis

 $\alpha \cdot v_x$ $r \cdot i_x$ $g \cdot v_x$ $\beta \cdot i_x$

VCVS   CCVS   VCCS   CCCS

Treat dependent sources just like ideal sources. Write an equation for controlling voltage v_x or controlling current i_x in terms of node voltages.

Shutting OFF Ideal Sources

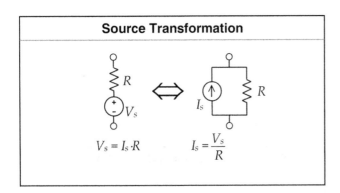

short circuit

open circuit

Superposition

Scaling	When all ideal sources in a circuit are scaled by a constant α, all voltages and currents in the circuit are scaled by α as well.
Additivity	Voltages and currents in a circuit can be found by summing the contribution due to each ideal source acting alone. When a voltage source is shut OFF, it becomes a short circuit. When a current source is shut OFF, it becomes an open circuit. Dependent sources cannot be shut OFF. They remain active at all times.

Source Transformation

$$V_s = I_s \cdot R \qquad I_s = \frac{V_s}{R}$$

Thévenin and Norton Equivalent Circuits

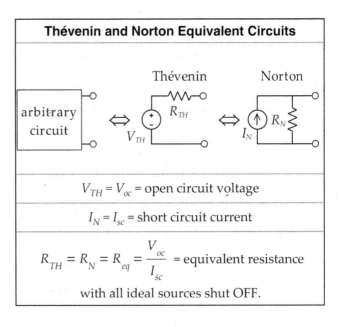

Thévenin   Norton

arbitrary circuit

$$V_{TH} = V_{oc} = \text{open circuit voltage}$$

$$I_N = I_{sc} = \text{short circuit current}$$

$$R_{TH} = R_N = R_{eq} = \frac{V_{oc}}{I_{sc}} = \text{equivalent resistance}$$

with all ideal sources shut OFF.

3.9 Problems

3.1 Find i_s and v_o in the circuit below.

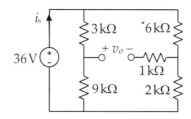

3.2 Find i_x, i_y, and v_o in the circuit below.

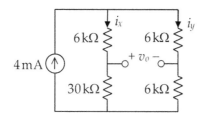

3.3 Find v_x, v_y, and v_o in the circuit below.

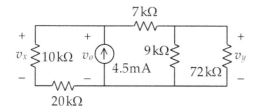

3.4 Find i_s and v_o in the circuit below.

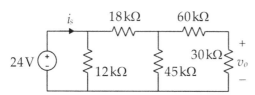

3.5 Find R_1 and R_2 in the circuit below so that $v_1 = 30$ V and $v_2 = 0$ V when the switch is OPEN and $v_1 = v_2 = 20$ V when the switch is CLOSED.

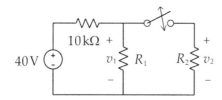

3.6 Find R_1 and R_2 in the following circuit so that $i_s =$ 22.5 mA when the switch is OPEN and $i_s = 32.5$ mA when the switch is CLOSED.

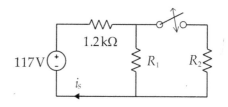

3.7 Find i_s, i_x, and i_y in the circuit below.

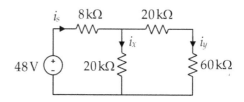

3.8 Find the power in the 48 kΩ resistor and the 20 V source in the circuit below.

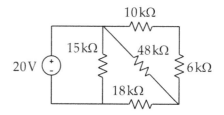

3.9 The resistors in the circuits below have ±5% tolerances. Find the corresponding tolerances on the output voltage v_0.

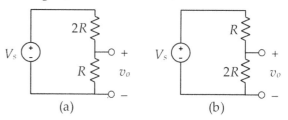

3.10 Find the node voltages in the circuit below by applying KVL between the reference node and each numbered node by several paths to confirm that node voltages are not dependent on the path taken.

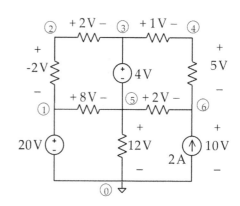

3.11 Using nodal analysis, find the power in the 60 V source in the circuit below.

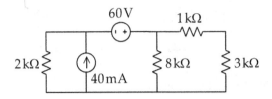

3.12 Using nodal analysis, find i_x and v_o in the circuit below.

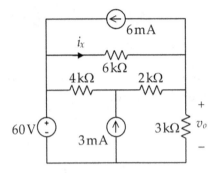

3.13 All component values in the circuit below are known quantities. Using the nodes as labeled, write the nodal analysis equations required to solve the circuit. Be sure to have as many equations as you have unknowns.

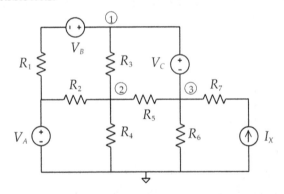

3.14 Find v_o in the circuit below by using (a) nodal analysis, (b) superposition, and (c) a sequence of source transformations and simplifications.

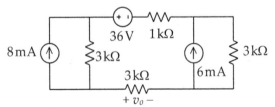

3.15 Find i_o in the following circuit by using (a) nodal analysis, (b) superposition, and (c) a sequence of source transformations and simplifications.

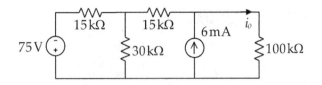

3.16 Find the Thévenin equivalent of the circuit on the left below. Note that $V_{TH} \neq V_s$.

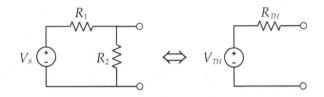

3.17 Find the power in R_L in the circuit below when it takes on the values $R_L = 1\,k\Omega$, $2\,k\Omega$, $4\,k\Omega$, $8\,k\Omega$, $12\,k\Omega$, $16\,k\Omega$, and $24\,k\Omega$.

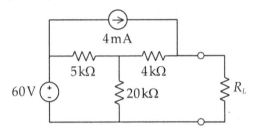

3.18 Find the Thévenin and Norton equivalent circuits for the circuit below (a) by finding the open circuit voltage V_{oc}, short circuit current I_{sc}, and equivalent resistance R_{eq} seen looking into the terminals with the source shut OFF, and (b) by applying a sequence of source transformations and simplifications until the circuit becomes the desired results.

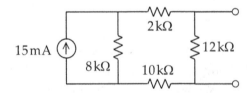

3.19 Find the Thévenin and Norton equivalent circuits for the circuit below by finding the open circuit voltage V_{oc}, short circuit current I_{sc}, and equivalent resistance R_{eq} seen looking into the terminals with the sources shut OFF.

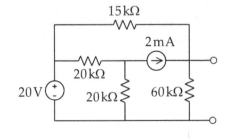

4 Op Amps

When a phrase contains many syllables, it is common for engineers to abbreviate it in some descriptive way or to use an acronym. In this case, "op amp" refers to **operational amplifier**. Operational amplifiers are the basic building blocks for analog circuits that process signals containing information. They are the analog counterpart to logic gates, the basic building blocks for digital circuits. Even though op amps are electronic circuits containing transistors, they can be studied and understood without knowledge of the transistors.

Op amps generally perform two important tasks that are implied by their full name "operational amplifier." The first task and term "operational" refers to the fact that op amps can be used to perform mathematical operations, namely addition and subtraction. That is, op amps can add and subtract signals. The second task and term "amplifier" means that op amps can be used to amplify signals, meaning to change their amplitude. These signals are commonly voltages that contain information.

Op amps were first constructed using vacuum tubes prior to the existence of integrated circuits. Later, they were among the first commercialized integrated circuits and have been in common usage since the late 1960s. The internal schematic of one of the most popular op amps of all time, the 741 op amp, is shown below. This op amp is one of thousands in production today.

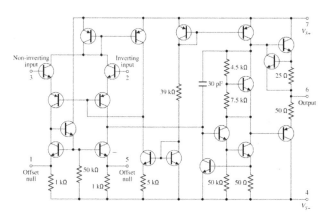

The analysis of op amps can proceed in three different ways. First, the general behavior of op amps can be studied intuitively using only basic principles. Second, they can be analyzed using the circuit analysis concepts covered in Chapter 3. And finally, they can be studied in detail at the transistor level, which is beyond the scope of this text.

Rather than jump directly into rigorous analysis using Chapter 3 material, it is useful to develop an understanding at the intuitive level. Doing so helps to minimize misunderstandings and errors.

4.1 Op Amp Behavior

The Potentiometer

The behavior of an op amp starts with voltage division as illustrated in the following circuit. The output voltage v_0 is some fraction of the total voltage V_s.

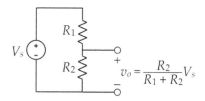

In this case, let $R_1 = (1 - \alpha)R$ and $R_2 = \alpha R$, where α is an adjustable parameter between zero and one. Then voltage division gives the output voltage v_0 as

$$v_o = \frac{R_2}{R_1 + R_2} V_s$$

$$v_o = \frac{\alpha R}{\alpha R + (1 - \alpha)R} V_s$$

$$v_o = \frac{\alpha R}{(\alpha + 1 - \alpha)R} V_s$$

$$v_o = \frac{\alpha R}{R} V_s$$

$$v_o = \alpha V_s$$

Therefore as α varies over its range, $0 \leq \alpha \leq 1$, the output voltage varies between 0 and V_s. For example, when $\alpha = 0$, $v_0 = 0 V_s = 0$. When $\alpha = 1$, $v_0 = 1 V_s = V_s$. And when $\alpha = 1/2$, $v_0 = (1/2)V_s = V_s/2$.

The need to provide a variable voltage in this way appears in many applications. As a result, the above two resistors are implemented in a single device called a potentiometer, or simply a "pot." The schematic symbol for a pot is shown on the left in the figure below. The lead with the arrow tip is called the wiper, which in practice is a mechanically movable electrical connection to the underlying resistance. When the wiper moves to the top of the resistance, $\alpha = 1$, and when the wiper moves to the bottom of the resistance, $\alpha = 0$. Movement of the wiper from one end to the other implements $0 \leq \alpha \leq 1$.

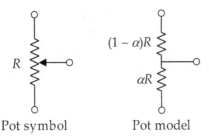

Pot symbol   Pot model

Voltage division using a pot as implemented above only permits positive output voltages. Obviously, if the voltage source is flipped over, the output would permit only negative voltages. By using two voltage sources, the output voltage v_o can take on negative values in addition to positive voltages. For example, consider the following circuit.

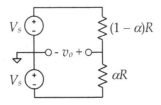

Now consider the $\alpha = 1$ case shown in the following circuit. With the upper resistance equal to zero, the upper source is directly connected across the terminals in a polarity that matches v_o, so $v_o = V_s$.

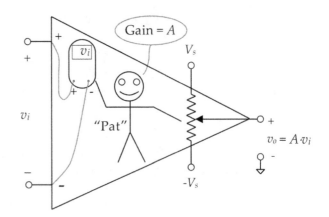

When $\alpha = 0$ as shown in the following circuit, the lower resistance is equal to zero, and the lower source is directly connected across the terminals in a polarity that is the opposite of that for v_o, so $v_o = -V_s$.

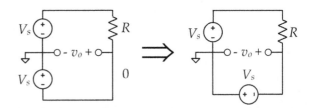

So, as the pot wiper is moved from one end to the other, the output voltage varies from $-V_s$ to V_s, i.e., $-V_s \leq v_o \leq V_s$. When the wiper is at the top, $v_o = V_s$, and when the wiper is at the bottom, $v_o = -V_s$. This circuit is said to produce **bipolar output**.

Rather than draw this circuit with the voltage sources as shown earlier, it is simpler and more common to draw it using node voltage labeling as shown in the following circuit simplifications.

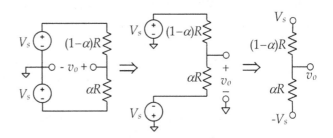

4.2 Op Amp Models

The "Pat" Model

The above voltage divider circuit producing bipolar output can be used to draw the first op amp model as shown below. In this circuit, a nonanatomically drawn person named "Pat" reads the input voltage v_i using the voltmeter. Then "Pat" multiplies the input value by the gain A that "Pat" has in mind. This value tells "Pat" where to place the wiper on the pot so that the desired output is reached, $v_o = A v_i$.

This simple model describes basic op amp behavior. Gain is created by moving the wiper on the pot in direct response to the input voltage. The input voltage directs what the output voltage should be. Both positive and negative output voltages can be produced. However, the output cannot exceed the power supply limits $\pm V_s$. You cannot produce a voltage greater than that available. This is a fundamental and inherent limitation. Thinking about the analogy between voltage and pressure, you cannot inflate a tire to a pressure greater than that available from the pump being used.

The Circuit Analysis Model

The "Pat" op amp model leads to the circuit analysis model shown below where "Pat" is replaced by a voltage controlled voltage source (VCVS) implementing "Pat's" actions.

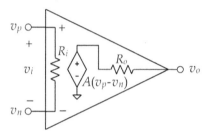

That is, the output of the VCVS is equal to the product of the gain A and the input voltage $v_i = v_p - v_n$, where v_p and v_n are the input node voltages with respect to the reference node. In addition, the input is given a finite resistance R_i, and the voltage source is given an additional Thévenin resistance R_o. The power supply connections have been excluded for clarity only. All amplifiers require external power because power cannot be created out of nothing. Conservation of energy must hold, so all power consumed must be supplied from some source. In this case, the power supply provides power to the voltage controlled voltage source and establishes the reference node. As long as the output voltage remains within the bounds set by the power supply voltages, the power supply does not affect normal operation.

The above op amp model contains two known circuit element types, and the circuit can be solved by applying nodal analysis. This model provides greater clarity about op amp behavior. What remains is determining values for the three components. These

components do not exist in real op amps, but rather they model the transistors inside the op amp. In any case, it is important to know appropriate values for the components so that the model has validity in solving real problems.

Appropriate resistor values are straightforward to identify. The voltage across the input terminals must be measured. No current is required to do so. Any current flowing into the op amp simply creates needless power loss in R_i that must be absorbed by the op amp. **Therefore, the input resistance R_i should be as high as possible.**

When a load resistor R_L is connected at the output, the output voltage is reduced by the voltage divider formed by the output resistance R_o and the load resistor R_L. Furthermore, any current flowing out of the op amp makes R_o needlessly absorb power. **Therefore, the output resistance R_o should be as small as possible.**

What is a good value for the gain A? Certainly the gain needs to take on different values for different applications. So, one possibility is to create a whole collection of op amps having different gains, in much the same way that resistors have a variety of standard values. If this were done, one would just select the op amp with the correct gain for each application.

It turns out that this is not the best idea. **A far better idea is to make the gain A as large as possible**, then use only that amount of A needed for each application. In doing so, there is no need to stock a variety of op amps each having different gains. A single op amp can provide any desired gain up to the internal op amp gain A.

The process of making the overall circuit gain, denoted G, a value smaller than A is called **feedback**. In feedback, the op amp output is fed back to the input, where it acts to subtract or reduce the gain. In practice, this means adding a resistor between the output of the op amp and the negative (–) input terminal. As will be shown next, the use of this "feedback" resistor reduces the gain A to a desired gain G.

The gain A is called the **open loop gain**, whereas the net circuit gain G is called the **closed loop gain** because feeding back the output forms what is called a closed loop.

The following table summarizes the values for the three components in this circuit analysis model for the op amp. In addition to the general size of the components, ideal values, and those of typical op amps are given.

Op Amp Parameter Values			
	R_i	R_o	A
size	large	small	large
ideal	∞	0	∞
typical	$10^6\,\Omega - 10^{12}\,\Omega$	$10^2\,\Omega$	$10^5 - 10^6$

4.3 Op Amp Analysis

Solve and then Simplify

Now that the relative sizes of the three op amp parameters are known, op amp circuits can be constructed and analyzed. Consider the following op amp circuit or configuration where R_f is the feedback resistor connected between the output terminal and the negative input terminal (–), v_s is the source voltage to be amplified, R_s is a source resistor, and R_L is the equivalent resistance of whatever load is attached to the output of the op amp. As is customary, the op amp is drawn with the positive (+) input terminal toward the bottom of the circuit.

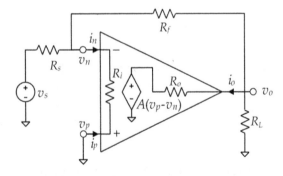

Note that the two input node voltages with respect to the reference node are labeled v_n and v_p for the negative (–) and positive (+) terminals respectively. v_o is the output node voltage with respect to the reference node. In this case, $v_p = 0$ since this node is directly connected to the reference node. The op amp currents i_n, i_p, and i_o have been labeled for analysis purposes.

There are two essential nodes in this circuit, one at the negative (–) terminal and one at the output terminal. Noting that $v_p = 0$, using nodal analysis, and applying KCL to these two nodes leads to

$$\text{KCL @ } v_n: \quad \frac{v_n - v_s}{R_s} + \frac{v_n - v_o}{R_f} + \frac{v_n - 0}{R_i} = 0$$

$$\text{KCL @ } v_o: \quad \frac{v_o - v_n}{R_f} + \frac{v_o}{R_L} + \frac{v_o - A(0 - v_n)}{R_o} = 0$$

These equations form two symbolic equations in the two unknowns v_n and v_o. All the other values are known. If numerical values are given for the known values, these equations are easily solved. However, solving these equations symbolically provides a great deal of insight. Doing so involves solving one equation for v_n, and then substituting this relationship into the other equation to eliminate v_n. What remains is the desired gain relationship between the input voltage v_s and the output voltage v_o. Performing these steps by hand is tedious and prone to error. However, with the help of symbolic algebra software, clear results can be obtained. In this case, the net or closed loop gain relationship is

$$G = \frac{v_o}{v_s} = \frac{\dfrac{-R_f}{R_s} - \left(\dfrac{1}{A}\right)\dfrac{R_o}{R_s}}{1 - \left(\dfrac{1}{A}\right)\left[\left(1+\dfrac{R_o}{R_L}\right)\cdot\left(1+\dfrac{R_f}{R_s}+\dfrac{R_f}{R_i}\right)+\dfrac{R_o}{R_s}+\dfrac{R_o}{R_i}\right]}$$

To a mathematician this is beautiful; to an engineer it is overly complicated. At least the units work out. The closed loop gain G must be dimensionless since it is a ratio of voltages. The open loop gain A is dimensionless and all resistances appear in ratios. Therefore, the right hand side is dimensionless as required.

In practice, the closed loop gain G is commonly between one and one hundred. The added resistors R_f and R_s are typically in the kiloohm (kΩ) range. Making them smaller simply increases the power absorbed in them, which serves no useful purpose when processing information. Making them very large leads to problems due to humidity, condensation, and in other environmental situations. Similarly, the load resistor R_L is commonly in the kiloohm range as well since op amps are commonly used to process voltages containing information.

To get a sense of the gain G, it is useful to substitute typical values. So, consider the case where $R_i = 10^6\,\Omega$, $R_o = 10^2\,\Omega$, $A = 10^6$, $R_s = 10^3\,\Omega$, $R_f = 10^4\,\Omega$, and $R_L = 10^4\,\Omega$. The gain G then becomes

$$G = \frac{v_o}{v_s} = \frac{\dfrac{-10^4}{10^3} - \left(\dfrac{1}{10^6}\right)\dfrac{10^2}{10^3}}{1 - \left(\dfrac{1}{10^6}\right)\left[\left(1 + \dfrac{10^2}{10^4}\right)\cdot\left(1 + \dfrac{10^4}{10^3} + \dfrac{10^4}{10^6}\right) + \dfrac{10^2}{10^3} + \dfrac{10^2}{10^6}\right]}$$

$$G = \frac{v_o}{v_s} = \frac{-10 - 10^{-7}}{1 - 10^{-6}\left[\left(1 + 10^{-2}\right)\cdot\left(1 + 10 + 10^{-2}\right) + 10^{-1} + 10^{-4}\right]}$$

Using these typical parameter values, many of the terms in the above equation are negligible, especially when one requires only three significant digits for the solution. Using the terms shown in the above equation, the closed loop gain G in 14 significant digits is

$$G = -10.000\ 112\ 303\ 260$$

To five significant digits, the gain is $G = -10$. The largest term in the numerator above is -10 and the largest term in the denominator is the leading term 1. The ratio of these two terms is $-10/1 = -10$, which is equal to the closed loop gain G to five significant digits.

Consider the exact gain expression again,

$$G = \frac{v_o}{v_s} = \frac{\dfrac{-R_f}{R_s} - \left(\dfrac{1}{A}\right)\dfrac{R_o}{R_s}}{1 - \left(\dfrac{1}{A}\right)\left[\left(1 + \dfrac{R_o}{R_L}\right)\cdot\left(1 + \dfrac{R_f}{R_s} + \dfrac{R_f}{R_i}\right) + \dfrac{R_o}{R_s} + \dfrac{R_o}{R_i}\right]}$$

The fact that the open loop gain A is very large, coupled with the relative sizes of the other resistors, makes the two terms containing $1/A$ in the above equation negligible. Therefore, setting these terms to zero gives an approximate expression for the closed loop gain G as

$$G = \frac{\dfrac{-R_f}{R_s} - 0}{1 - 0} = -\frac{R_f}{R_s}$$

Substituting the earlier values $R_s = 10^3\,\Omega$ and $R_f = 10^4\,\Omega$ into this gain expression gives $G = -10$, which is the correct value to 5 significant digits. As a result, as long as the open loop gain A is very large, one need not use the exact gain expression. The simpler expression $G = -R_f/R_s$ is sufficient for engineering purposes. This is particularly true when one considers the fact that common resistor values have a $\pm 5\%$ tolerance. For this tolerance, the resistor ratio

R_f/R_s itself does not have three significant digits of accuracy. For the resistor values considered, the gain G varies between the minimum magnitude

$$G_{min} = -\frac{0.95\,R_f}{1.05\,R_s} = -\frac{0.95\cdot 10^4}{1.05\cdot 10^3} = -9.05$$

and the maximum magnitude

$$G_{max} = -\frac{1.05\,R_f}{0.95\,R_s} = -\frac{1.05\cdot 10^4}{0.95\cdot 10^3} = -11.1$$

Since the gain varies over the range

$$-9.05 \le G \le -11.1$$

due to resistor tolerances alone, it is silly to use the exact gain expression for computing G. Even if resistors having $\pm 1\%$ tolerance are used, it is silly to use the exact gain expression.

In hindsight, it was not necessary to go through all the effort to derive the exact gain expression. Rather than derive the exact gain expression, and then eliminate the negligible terms, it is much easier to eliminate the negligible terms first, and then solve the circuit. In other words, do the process in the reverse order: simplify and then solve.

Before simplifying the circuit it is beneficial to identify expressions for two other variables. First, in addition to solving the two symbolic KCL equations for the gain, they can be symbolically solved for the voltage at the negative (–) terminal. Doing so gives

$$v_n = \frac{1 + \dfrac{R_o}{R_L} + \dfrac{R_o}{R_f}}{A + \dfrac{R_o}{R_f}}\, v_o$$

All three resistor ratios in this expression are negligible for typical resistor values, so this expression can be simplified to

$$v_n \approx \frac{v_o}{A}$$

Since the output voltage v_o is commonly less than 10 volts and A is on the order of 10^6, the voltage at the negative (–) terminal is in the microvolt (μV) range. This is about a million times smaller than the input and output voltages, so it can be approximated as zero, $v_n \approx 0$.

The other parameter to consider is the current entering the negative (–) terminal, i_n. Using the simplified expression for v_n, Ohm's law gives i_n as

$$i_n = \frac{v_n}{R_i} = \frac{v_o}{A R_i}$$

Since A and R_i are both on the order of 10^6, this current is on the order of 10^{-12}, which means that i_n is in the picoampere (pA) range! Clearly, this can be neglected when other currents are in the milliampere (mA) range, a billion or 10^9 times greater in magnitude.

To summarize this analysis, the current flowing into the negative terminal i_n is for all practical purposes equal to zero, as is the voltage v_n at the terminal.

Simplify and then Solve

With the developed understanding, reconsider the op amp circuit as shown below.

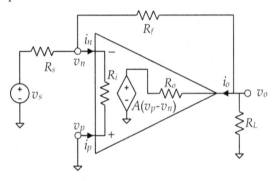

Using the approximations $v_n = 0$ and $i_n = 0$, applying KCL at the negative (–) terminal gives

$$\frac{v_n - v_s}{R_s} + \frac{v_n - v_o}{R_f} + i_n = 0$$

$$\frac{0 - v_s}{R_s} + \frac{0 - v_o}{R_f} + 0 = 0$$

The KCL equation at the output node is not needed since the above expression can be solved for the closed loop gain as follows

$$\frac{-v_s}{R_s} + \frac{-v_o}{R_f} = 0$$

$$\frac{v_o}{R_f} = \frac{-v_s}{R_s}$$

$$v_o = \frac{-R_f}{R_s} v_s$$

which agrees with the expression found earlier. This simple expression

$$G = \frac{v_o}{v_s} = -\frac{R_f}{R_s}$$

is the closed loop gain of this op amp configuration. The gain is not a function of any of the op amp parameters R_i, R_o, or A as long as these parameters have reasonably nominal values. It is also not a function of the load resistance R_L that models whatever is connected to the op amp output. This is really amazing! This property is largely due to the wisdom of making the open loop gain A as large as possible. The closed loop gain G is determined solely by the two added resistors. Because the internal op amp parameters do not play a role in determining the gain, op amp circuits are commonly drawn without any of the internal structure as shown in the following circuit.

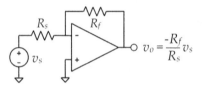

The above op amp configuration is called the **inverting amplifier**. It has this name because the gain is negative. The polarity of the output is the opposite of that of the input. If v_s is positive, v_o is negative, and vice-versa.

The Ideal Op Amp

The above analysis does not appear in most textbooks. Rather, the introduction to op amps starts with the ideal op amp whose parameters are cited in the previous table, namely $R_i = \infty$, $R_o = 0$, and $A = \infty$. Analysis using these parameters leads to the same accurate and simplified gain results given in the preceding section, but the results are not easily accepted largely because it is difficult to believe that the open loop gain A could ever be infinite in practice.

Consider what happens to the general gain expression when the open loop gain A becomes infinite,

$$G = \frac{v_o}{v_s} = \frac{\dfrac{-R_f}{R_s} - \left(\dfrac{1}{\infty}\right)\dfrac{R_o}{R_s}}{1 - \left(\dfrac{1}{\infty}\right)\left[\left(1 + \dfrac{R_o}{R_L}\right)\cdot\left(1 + \dfrac{R_f}{R_s} + \dfrac{R_f}{R_i}\right) + \dfrac{R_o}{R_s} + \dfrac{R_o}{R_i}\right]}$$

In this case, the same two terms that were dropped earlier because they were negligible are now identically equal to zero because they are divided by ∞.

$$G = \frac{v_o}{v_s} = \frac{-\left(\dfrac{R_f}{R_s}\right) - 0}{1 - 0} = -\frac{R_f}{R_s}$$

So, assuming that the op amp has infinite open loop gain has the same effect as dropping negligible terms because the negligible terms are so close to zero.

Infinite open loop gain also provides values for the voltage and current flowing into the negative (–) terminal. The voltage at the output of the dependent voltage source is

$$v = A \cdot \left(v_p - v_n\right)$$

When $A = \infty$, the voltage v is infinite if the term in parentheses is any nonzero value. Therefore, the only way the voltage v and the resulting op amp output voltage v_o can be finite and reasonable is if the term in parentheses is zero,

$$v_p - v_n = 0$$

This says that

$$v_p = v_n$$

must hold for the op amp to work properly. The voltage at the negative terminal is equal to the voltage at the positive terminal. This agrees with the earlier derivation where we showed that $v_n \approx 0$ when the positive terminal is connected to the reference node and $v_p = 0$.

Using this result, and writing Ohm's law for the input resistor R_i gives,

$$i_n = \frac{v_n - v_p}{R_i} \approx \frac{0}{R_i} = 0$$

which is equal to its value as determined earlier.

Assuming that an op amp has ideal properties eliminates the need for approximations in analyzing op amp circuits. As a result, as long as the closed loop gain G is much less than the open loop gain A, it is both convenient and more than sufficiently accurate to simply assume ideal op amp properties from the start. These properties are summarized in the following table.

Analyzing Ideal Op Amp Circuits	
$v_p = v_n$	equal voltages at input terminals
$i_p = i_n = 0$	zero current into input terminals
KCL @ v_n	analysis equation required to find the closed loop gain G

The information above makes it possible to analyze all common op amp configurations. For the ideal op amp, $v_p = v_n$ and $i_p = i_n = 0$ are exact expressions, and they are, for all practical purposes, also true when an op amp has typical values. Using these relationships, it is not necessary to consider the internal structure of the op amp.

4.4 Common Op Amp Configurations

Inverting Amplifier

Consider the inverting amplifier that was extensively studied in the previous section. The circuit is repeated in the following.

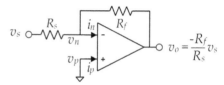

Using the ideal op amp properties, $v_p = v_n$ and $i_p = i_n = 0$, and applying KCL at v_n, gives the relationship

$$\frac{v_n - v_s}{R_s} + \frac{v_n - v_o}{R_f} + i_n = 0$$

but $v_n = v_p = 0$, so

$$\frac{0 - v_s}{R_s} + \frac{0 - v_o}{R_f} + 0 = 0$$

which simplifies to

$$\frac{-v_s}{R_s} + \frac{-v_o}{R_f} = 0$$

$$\frac{v_o}{R_f} = \frac{-v_s}{R_s}$$

$$v_o = \frac{-R_f}{R_s} v_s$$

Once again, the gain of the inverting amplifier is negative and is given by the ratio of the feedback resistance R_f to the source resistance R_s.

Noninverting Amplifier

The natural counterpart to the inverting amplifier is an amplifier that provides positive gain. The circuit in this case moves the input over to the positive (+) terminal and connects the source resistor to reference as shown in the following circuit.

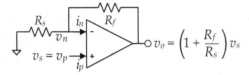

$$v_0 = \left(1 + \frac{R_f}{R_s}\right)v_s$$

Applying KCL at v_n, gives the relationship

$$\frac{v_n}{R_s} + \frac{v_n - v_o}{R_f} + i_n = 0$$

Substituting in the ideal op amp characteristics, $i_n = 0$ and $v_n = v_p$ gives

$$\frac{v_p}{R_s} + \frac{v_p - v_o}{R_f} + 0 = 0$$

Using the fact that $v_p = v_s$ for this configuration, the above expression becomes

$$\frac{v_s}{R_s} + \frac{v_s - v_o}{R_f} + 0 = 0$$

Finally, solving for the gain $G = v_o/v_s$ follows as

$$\frac{v_s}{R_s} + \frac{v_s}{R_f} = \frac{v_o}{R_f}$$

$$v_s\left(\frac{1}{R_s} + \frac{1}{R_f}\right) = \frac{v_o}{R_f}$$

$$v_s\left(\frac{R_f}{R_s} + \frac{R_f}{R_f}\right) = v_o$$

$$v_s\left(\frac{R_f}{R_s} + 1\right) = v_o$$

Therefore the gain expression is

$$v_0 = G v_s = \left(1 + \frac{R_f}{R_s}\right)v_s$$

The closed loop gain G is positive, making the gain noninverting. This is the noninverting amplifier.

Unity Gain Buffer

The gain of the noninverting amplifier is at least equal to one. However, if the feedback resistor R_f is set to zero, i.e., replaced by a short, and the source resistor R_s set to infinity, i.e., removed, the gain becomes one,

$$v_0 = \left(1 + \frac{R_f}{R_s}\right)v_s = \left(1 + \frac{0}{\infty}\right)v_s = v_s$$

and the circuit simplifies to the following

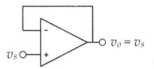

$$v_0 = v_s$$

This circuit is called a unity gain buffer or voltage follower.

At first this may appear to be a useless circuit since all it does is replicate whatever appears at its input. However, knowing that $i_p = 0$, the resistance seen looking into the input terminals R_{eq} is infinity as shown in the following circuit.

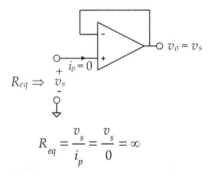

$$R_{eq} = \frac{v_s}{i_p} = \frac{v_s}{0} = \infty$$

As a result, the input to this circuit does not draw any current from whatever circuit it is connected to. That is, the input to this op amp circuit does not load the circuit it receives its input from. **In this context, "load" means to change the voltages or currents in a circuit as a result of connecting another circuit to it.** When connected to the output of another circuit, the unity gain buffer does not load the other circuit down.

To understand the significance of **loading**, consider the voltage division in the following circuit. The voltage across the 72 kΩ resistor is 8 V.

$$v_x = \frac{72\,\text{k}}{72\,\text{k} + 24\,\text{k}}12 = \frac{72\,\text{k}}{96\,\text{k}}12 = 8\,\text{V}$$

Now assume that the output of this circuit is connected to another circuit that has an input resistance of 36 kΩ. The revised circuit is shown below.

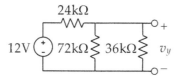

The 36 kΩ resistor **loads** the circuit and changes the output voltage to

$$v_y = \frac{72k\|36k}{72k\|36k+24k}12\,V = \frac{24\,k}{24k+24k}12\,V = 6\,V$$

The voltage across the 72 kΩ resistor dropped from 8 V to 6 V because the 36 kΩ resistor loads the circuit.

This loading problem disappears if a unity gain buffer is placed between the 72 kΩ resistor and the 36 kΩ resistor as shown in the following circuit.

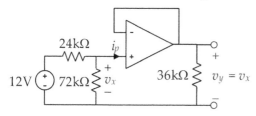

The fact that $i_p = 0$ means that v_x is unchanged from its original value of 8 V. The unity gain buffer replicates v_x at its output, making $v_y = v_x = 8$ V. The unity gain buffer provides a **buffer** between its input and output. The 36 kΩ resistor no longer **loads** the circuit output. **A unity gain buffer eliminates loading.**

Difference Amplifier

Combining the inverting and noninverting amplifiers creates a difference amplifier that computes the difference between two input voltages. The basic difference amplifier is shown in the circuit below where v_1 and v_2 are two input voltages.

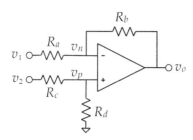

There are several ways to find the output voltage of this circuit. This is one case where superposition works well. The output for v_1 and v_2 each acting alone can be found. Then, by superposition, the total response is the sum of the two partial solutions. An alternative is to simply apply the op amp analysis guidelines presented earlier. The following analysis applies the analysis guidelines.

Since the current flowing into the positive (+) terminal is zero, the voltage at the positive terminal v_p is given by voltage division,

$$v_p = \frac{R_d}{R_c + R_d}v_2$$

In addition, writing KCL at the negative (–) terminal gives

$$\frac{v_n - v_1}{R_a} + \frac{v_n - v_o}{R_b} = 0$$

Solving this for v_o leads to

$$v_n\left(\frac{1}{R_a}+\frac{1}{R_b}\right) - \frac{v_1}{R_a} = \frac{v_o}{R_b}$$

$$\left(\frac{R_b}{R_a}+\frac{R_b}{R_b}\right)v_n - \frac{R_b}{R_a}v_1 = v_o$$

$$\left(1 + \frac{R_b}{R_a}\right)v_n - \frac{R_b}{R_a}v_1 = v_o$$

Since $v_n = v_p$, the above voltage division expression for v_p can be substituted for v_n leading to the result,

$$v_o = \left(1 + \frac{R_b}{R_a}\right)\cdot\left(\frac{R_d}{R_c + R_d}v_2\right) - \left(\frac{R_b}{R_a}\right)v_1$$

$$v_o = \left(1 + \frac{R_b}{R_a}\right)\cdot\left(\frac{R_d}{R_c + R_d}\right)v_2 - \left(\frac{R_b}{R_a}\right)v_1$$

Alternatively, the gain expression is

$$v_o = G_2 v_2 - G_1 v_1$$

where

$$G_2 = \left(1 + \frac{R_b}{R_a}\right)\cdot\left(\frac{R_d}{R_c + R_d}\right) \quad\text{and}\quad G_1 = \left(\frac{R_b}{R_a}\right)$$

The output is a scaled difference between v_2 and v_1. The individual gains G_2 and G_1 for v_2 and v_1 respectively are set by choosing appropriate resistor values.

In many designs the gains G_2 and G_1 are chosen to be equal. That is, if $G_2 = G_1 = G$, then

$$v_o = G\left(v_2 - v_1\right)$$

In this case, the output is the difference between v_2 and v_1 multiplied by the gain G.

The relationship among the resistors required to make the $G_2 = G_1 = G$ can be found by setting G_2 equal to G_1 and simplifying the result,

$$\left(1 + \frac{R_b}{R_a}\right)\frac{R_d}{R_c + R_d} = \frac{R_b}{R_a}$$

$$\frac{R_d}{R_c + R_d} = \frac{\dfrac{R_b}{R_a}}{\left(1 + \dfrac{R_b}{R_a}\right)}$$

$$\frac{R_d}{R_c + R_d}\left(\frac{\dfrac{1}{R_c}}{\dfrac{1}{R_c}}\right) = \frac{\dfrac{R_b}{R_a}}{1 + \dfrac{R_b}{R_a}}$$

$$\frac{\dfrac{R_d}{R_c}}{1 + \dfrac{R_d}{R_c}} = \frac{\dfrac{R_b}{R_a}}{1 + \dfrac{R_b}{R_a}}$$

Inspection of this last expression shows that equality holds if

$$\frac{R_d}{R_c} = \frac{R_b}{R_a}$$

When this is true, $G_2 = G_1 = G = R_b/R_a$, and the output expression becomes

$$v_o = G\left(v_2 - v_1\right) = \frac{R_b}{R_a}\left(v_2 - v_1\right)$$

and the revised circuit is shown below.

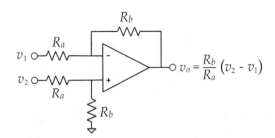

$$v_o = \frac{R_b}{R_a}\left(v_2 - v_1\right)$$

Inverting Summer

Sometimes the sum of two or more voltages is needed. By simply adding source resistors and inputs to the inverting amplifier the sum of multiple voltages can be implemented. This circuit, called the inverting summer, is shown in the following circuit.

Noting that $v_n = v_p = 0$ and applying KCL at v_n gives

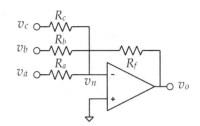

$$\frac{0 - v_a}{R_a} + \frac{0 - v_b}{R_b} + \frac{0 - v_c}{R_c} + \frac{0 - v_o}{R_f} = 0$$

Simplifying this expression leads to the desired result,

$$\frac{v_o}{R_f} = \frac{-v_a}{R_a} + \frac{-v_b}{R_b} + \frac{-v_c}{R_c}$$

$$v_o = \frac{-R_f}{R_a}v_a + \frac{-R_f}{R_b}v_b + \frac{-R_f}{R_c}v_c$$

This result is remarkably simple. The gain from each input voltage is controlled independently by the source resistor connecting that input. That is, only R_a affects the output due to v_a, and so on for the other inputs. The resistor R_a can be changed as desired without changing the output due to v_b or v_c.

In addition, any number of source resistors and input voltages can be added or removed without affecting the gains for the others. For example, if a source voltage v_d and accompanying resistor R_d is added to the above circuit, another term $-(R_f/R_d)v_d$ is added to the expression for v_o.

The only potential disadvantage of the inverting summer is that the gains are negative. There is no simple noninverting summer circuit. The simplest way to change the sign on the result is to multiply it by -1, which is easily accomplished by appending an inverting amplifier with gain equal to -1 to the output as shown in the following circuit.

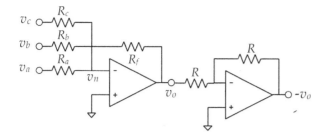

This figure demonstrates how op amps are used as basic building blocks for analog signal processing.

4.5 Practical Considerations

Output Voltage Limitations

The "Pat" op amp model made it clear that the output of an op amp cannot exceed the power supply voltages. In reality, the op amp output voltage cannot reach all the way to either power supply voltage. Many op amps can get no closer than 1 to 2 volts from either power supply voltage. This generally applies to op amps that are designed for ±15 volt power supplies.

Other "rail-to-rail" op amps can get within about 0.1 volts (100 mV) of the power supply voltages. This generally applies to op amps that are designed for lower voltage power supplies or for single power supply operation. In single supply operation, no negative power supply is used. The negative power supply terminal is connected to the circuit reference, and a positive power supply voltage, typically 5 V, is connected from reference to the positive power supply terminal. In this case, the op amp output is limited to positive output voltages only. Single power supply operation is considered in Chapter 9.

Output Current Limitations

Because op amps are almost always used to process information rather than transmit power, most op amps have limited output current capabilities. The current flowing out of or into the op amp output terminal is limited in amplitude by the physical size of the transistors inside the op amp.

For typical op amps, the output current cannot exceed 10 to 20 mA in either direction. Almost all op amps protect themselves if the current in either direction exceeds limits. That is, they lower the amplitude of the output voltage so that the current stays within safe operating limits. Doing so keeps the op amp from overheating and destroying itself.

4.6 Examples

"T" Feedback Configuration

Find the closed loop gain $G = v_0/v_s$ and output current i_0 in the following circuit.

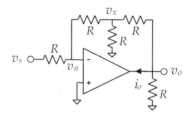

This circuit does not have a single feedback resistor R_f connected from the output to the negative input terminal (–). Instead, it has a structure composed of three resistors formed in the shape of the letter "T". There is no need for all the resistors to have equal values. They were just chosen that way to simplify this problem. Because of the essential node labeled v_x, KCL needs to be applied there as well.

Since the positive input terminal (+) is connected to reference and $v_n = v_p = 0$, KCL at v_n gives

$$\frac{0 - v_s}{R} + \frac{0 - v_x}{R} = 0$$

Multiplying through by R and rearranging this equation gives the relationship,

$$v_x = -v_s$$

Next, writing KCL at the "T" gives

$$\frac{v_x - 0}{R} + \frac{v_x}{R} + \frac{v_x - v_0}{R} = 0$$

Once again multiplying through by R and simplifying gives

$$v_0 = 3v_x$$

Combining the two KCL results gives the desired gain expression,

$$v_0 = 3v_x = 3(-v_s) = -3v_s$$

So the circuit gain G is equal to negative three.

Knowing the output voltage, the current i_0 can be found by writing KCL at the output node

$$\frac{v_0}{R} + \frac{v_0 - v_x}{R} + i_0 = 0$$

Substituting $v_0 = -3v_s$ and $v_x = -v_s$ and simplifying leads to

$$\frac{-3v_s}{R} + \frac{-3v_s - (-v_s)}{R} + i_0 = 0$$

$$\frac{-3v_s - 3v_s + v_s}{R} + i_0 = 0$$

$$\frac{-5v_s}{R} + i_0 = 0$$

So the output current is

$$i_0 = \frac{5v_s}{R}$$

Naturally, the larger the input voltage v_s is the larger the output current i_0 becomes. When the input voltage is positive, the current flows into the op amp. In addition, since the output must provide current for the feedback path, the larger the resistance R is, the smaller the output current is. If there were a load resistor R_L connected to the output, the output current would have to support it as well.

To get an idea of the magnitude of the current, let the input voltage be $v_s = 1$ V and let the resistance be $R = 10$ kΩ. Using these values, the output voltage and current are

$$v_0 = -3v_s = -3 \cdot 1 = -3\,\text{V}$$

$$i_0 = \frac{5v_s}{R} = \frac{5 \cdot (-3)}{10\text{k}} = -1.5\,\text{mA}$$

This current amplitude is acceptable for most op amps. If the output voltage reached $v_0 = \pm 10$ volts, the current would be ± 5 mA, which is still within the limits of most op amps. However, if the resistance is dropped by a factor of ten to $R = 1$ kΩ, the output current would increase by a factor of ten and current limits would easily be exceeded.

Differential Output Creation

In numerous applications, differential signaling is used to minimize the impact of signal interference when sending analog or digital signals down cables or across a PC board. In differential signaling, two signals of opposite polarity are created and sent. For analog signals this means creating the desired signal and the negative of the desired signal as exemplified by the following op amp circuit.

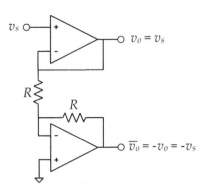

To find the relationship between the input and the two outputs, it is easiest to consider each op amp separately. The voltage at the negative input terminal (–) on the lower op amp is equal to zero because $v_n = v_p$ holds and the positive input terminal (+) is connected to reference. Therefore, the upper op amp can be redrawn equivalently as shown in the following circuit.

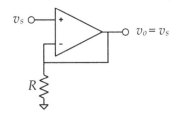

This circuit is a standard noninverting amplifier with a gain equal to $G = (1 + 0/R) = 1$. Therefore the output voltage is equal to the input voltage as shown.

The input terminal voltages of the upper op amp also obey $v_n = v_p$. So, the lower op amp circuit can be redrawn equivalently as shown below.

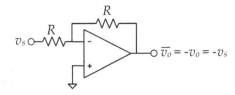

This is a standard inverting amplifier with a gain equal to $G = -R/R = -1$, so the output here is $-v_s$. This output is equal in magnitude and opposite in sign to that of the upper op amp. As a result, the two outputs form the desired differential signal pair, v_s and $-v_s$.

Signal Mathematics

This problem is to design op amp circuits that implement the following mathematical gain statement

$$v_0 = -2v_a + 3v_b - 4v_c$$

where v_a, v_b, and v_c are input voltages and v_o is the desired output voltage. The simplest way to solve this problem is to use and combine the basic op amp circuits.

Four Op Amp Solution: A simple approach to solving this problem starts by creating the needed gains, followed by the mathematics. Because the inverting summer produces negative gains, it is useful to rewrite the desired output as

$$v_o = -\left(2v_a - 3v_b + 4v_c\right)$$

If op amp circuits are used to create each of the terms inside the parentheses, then an inverting summer having unity gain can be used to combine the terms. The positive gain terms are implemented using the noninverting amplifier and the negative gain term is implemented with the inverting amplifier. This solution is shown in the circuit below.

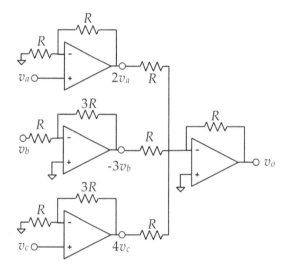

The three op amps on the left produce the three terms inside the parentheses using standard op amp configurations. The outputs of these three op amps are then combined by the inverting summer on the right. The only thing missing from this design is specifying the value for the resistance R. To keep currents safely within the limits of the op amps, the resistance R should be in the range

$$10\,\mathrm{k}\Omega \le R \le 100\,\mathrm{k}\Omega$$

Two Op Amp Solution: The use of four op amps is excessive. It is possible to reduce the number of op amps to two by rewriting the gain statement as

$$v_o = -2v_a - \left(-3v_b\right) - 4v_c$$

When viewed in this form, creating $-v_b$ first, followed by an inverting summer having the needed individual gains produces the desired output. This solution is shown in the circuit below.

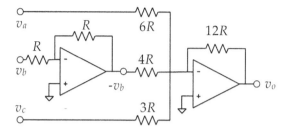

The gain for v_a is $-12R/(6R) = -2$ as desired. The gain for v_b is $-[-12R/(4R)] = 3$ as desired. And the gain for v_c is $-12R/(3R) = -4$ as desired. Once again, the resistance R needs to be in the range cited earlier to avoid excessive op amp currents.

One Op Amp Solution: By combining the difference amplifier and the inverting summer, it is possible to reduce the number of op amps needed to just one as shown in the circuit below.

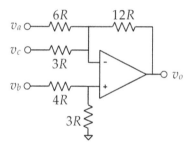

Applying superposition is the easiest way to confirm that the above circuit creates the desired mathematical gain expression. If the voltage v_b is turned OFF by setting it equal to zero, the circuit becomes that shown below.

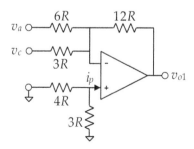

Since the current i_p is zero, the voltage at the positive terminal v_p is also zero because no current flows through either resistor connected to the positive terminal. Therefore, the remaining circuit is an inverting summer circuit having gains of $-12R/(6R) = -2$ for v_a and $-12R/(3R) = -4$ for v_c, leading to the output

$$v_{o1} = -2v_a - 4v_c$$

Next, going back to the original circuit and turning OFF the voltages v_a and v_c gives the following circuit.

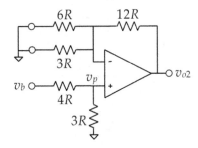

In this circuit, the $6R$ and $3R$ resistors connected to the negative input terminal (–) are in parallel. Using the $R \| R/N = R/(N+1)$ relationship, the equivalent resistance of these two in parallel is

$$R_{eq} = 6R \| 3R = 2R$$

With this substitution, the circuit has the form of a noninverting amplifier with a voltage divider circuit at the positive terminal. Using voltage division, the voltage at the positive terminal is

$$v_p = \frac{3R}{3R + 4R} v_b$$

and the resulting circuit output is

$$v_{o2} = \left(1 + \frac{12R}{R_{eq}}\right) v_p$$

$$v_{o2} = \left(1 + \frac{12R}{2R}\right) \cdot \left(\frac{3R}{3R + 4R} v_b\right)$$

$$v_{o2} = (1 + 6)\frac{3R}{7R} v_b$$

$$v_{o2} = (7)\frac{3}{7} v_b$$

$$v_{o2} = 3v_b$$

The total or net output is then given by the sum

$$v_o = v_{o1} + v_{o2} = -2v_a + 3v_b - 4v_c$$

which is the desired gain expression. As with the other designs, the resistance R should be chosen so that op amp current limits are not exceeded.

Alternative Difference Amplifier

There are several difference amplifier configurations. The problem to be solved in this example is to find the gain expression for the following op amp circuit.

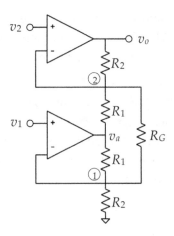

This difference amplifier requires two op amps. One advantage of this configuration over the standard one op amp configuration is that both inputs are connected directly to the positive terminals of the op amps. As a result, since there is no current flowing into the op amps, this circuit does not load the circuitry providing the inputs v_1 and v_2. Connecting these inputs to another circuit does not change the operation of the other circuit.

Because the voltage at the negative input terminal (–) of each op amp is equal to the voltage at the associated positive input terminal (+) of the op amp, the voltages at the nodes labeled ① and ② are equal to v_1 and v_2 respectively. Applying KCL to these two essential nodes gives

$$\frac{v_1}{R_2} + \frac{v_1 - v_a}{R_1} + \frac{v_1 - v_2}{R_G} = 0$$

$$\frac{v_2 - v_o}{R_2} + \frac{v_2 - v_a}{R_1} + \frac{v_2 - v_1}{R_G} = 0$$

In these equations, the input voltages v_1 and v_2 are known, and the two op amp output voltages v_a and v_o are unknown. Moving the term v_a/R_1 to the other side of the equal sign in both equations leads to

$$\frac{v_1}{R_2} + \frac{v_1}{R_1} + \frac{v_1 - v_2}{R_G} = \frac{v_a}{R_1}$$

$$\frac{v_2 - v_o}{R_2} + \frac{v_2}{R_1} + \frac{v_2 - v_1}{R_G} = \frac{v_a}{R_1}$$

Since the right hand sides of both equations are equal, the left hand sides must also be equal. By setting them equal, the output voltage v_a is eliminated from the equations. What remains is the relationship between the two input voltages v_1 and v_2, and the output voltage v_o. Setting the left hand sides of the two equations equal to each other gives

$$\frac{v_2 - v_o}{R_2} + \frac{v_2}{R_1} + \frac{v_2 - v_1}{R_G} = \frac{v_1}{R_2} + \frac{v_1}{R_1} + \frac{v_1 - v_2}{R_G}$$

Moving the term v_o/R_2 to one side of the equal sign and all other terms to the other side gives

$$\frac{v_o}{R_2} = \left(\frac{v_2}{R_2} + \frac{v_2}{R_1} + \frac{v_2 - v_1}{R_G} \right) - \left(\frac{v_1}{R_2} + \frac{v_1}{R_1} + \frac{v_1 - v_2}{R_G} \right)$$

$$\frac{v_o}{R_2} = \frac{v_2}{R_2} + \frac{v_2}{R_1} + \frac{v_2 - v_1}{R_G} - \frac{v_1}{R_2} - \frac{v_1}{R_1} - \frac{v_1 - v_2}{R_G}$$

Grouping terms on the right hand side that share a common denominator leads to

$$\frac{v_o}{R_2} = \frac{v_2 - v_1}{R_2} + \frac{v_2 - v_1}{R_1} + \frac{v_2 - v_1}{R_G} - \frac{v_1 - v_2}{R_G}$$

All terms on the right hand side can be written with the common numerator $v_2 - v_1$ as

$$\frac{v_o}{R_2} = \frac{v_2 - v_1}{R_2} + \frac{v_2 - v_1}{R_1} + \frac{v_2 - v_1}{R_G} + \frac{v_2 - v_1}{R_G}$$

Now, combining terms on the right hand side and simplifying gives

$$\frac{v_o}{R_2} = \left(\frac{1}{R_1} + \frac{1}{R_2} + \frac{2}{R_G} \right) \cdot (v_2 - v_1)$$

$$v_o = \left(\frac{R_2}{R_1} + \frac{R_2}{R_2} + \frac{2 R_2}{R_G} \right) \cdot (v_2 - v_1)$$

or finally

$$v_o = \left(1 + \frac{R_2}{R_1} + \frac{2 R_2}{R_G} \right) \cdot (v_2 - v_1) = G(v_2 - v_1)$$

This is the gain expression for the difference amplifier. By choosing values for R_1, R_2, and R_G, the gain can be set as desired.

Noninverting Summer

The inverting summer has the very beneficial and convenient property that the gains from each input are independent of each other. The same does not hold for the following single op amp noninverting amplifier.

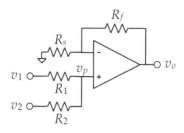

Given the voltage v_p at the positive input terminal (+), the output is given by the noninverting gain

$$v_o = \left(1 + \frac{R_f}{R_s} \right) v_p$$

So finding the gain expression for this configuration is easy once v_p is known. Even though the positive input terminal (+) node is not an essential node, KCL can be written for it as

$$\frac{v_p - v_1}{R_1} + \frac{v_p - v_2}{R_2} = 0$$

This equation can be solved for v_p by multiplying through by the product $R_1 \cdot R_2$ and simplifying,

$$R_1 R_2 \left(\frac{v_p - v_1}{R_1} + \frac{v_p - v_2}{R_2} \right) = 0$$

$$R_2 \left(v_p - v_1 \right) + R_1 \left(v_p - v_2 \right) = 0$$

solving for v_p,

$$\left(R_1 + R_2 \right) v_p = R_2 v_1 + R_1 v_2$$

$$v_p = \frac{R_2}{R_1 + R_2} v_1 + \frac{R_1}{R_1 + R_2} v_2$$

Substituting this result into the previous noninverting gain expression leads to,

$$v_o = \left(1 + \frac{R_f}{R_s} \right) v_p$$

$$v_o = \left(1 + \frac{R_f}{R_s} \right) \cdot \left(\frac{R_2}{R_1 + R_2} v_1 + \frac{R_1}{R_1 + R_2} v_2 \right)$$

$$v_o = \left(1 + \frac{R_f}{R_s} \right) \cdot \left(\frac{R_2}{R_1 + R_2} \right) v_1 + \left(1 + \frac{R_f}{R_s} \right) \left(\frac{R_1}{R_1 + R_2} \right) v_2$$

or finally,

$$v_o = G_1 v_1 + G_2 v_2$$

where

$$G_1 = \left(1 + \frac{R_f}{R_s}\right)\left(\frac{R_2}{R_1 + R_2}\right) \quad G_2 = \left(1 + \frac{R_f}{R_s}\right)\left(\frac{R_1}{R_1 + R_2}\right)$$

From these expressions for the gains G_1 and G_2, it is clear that the gains from the two inputs v_1 and v_2 cannot be independently set by changing a single resistor for each gain term, which was the case for the inverting summer. Here, both R_1 and R_2 influence the gain from both inputs. This makes the design of non-inverting summer amplifiers more involved. This design gets even more involved if there are more than two inputs to be summed.

Design equations for the two input case considered here can be derived by taking the ratio of the two gains

$$\frac{G_1}{G_2} = \frac{\left(1 + \frac{R_f}{R_s}\right)\left(\frac{R_2}{R_1 + R_2}\right)}{\left(1 + \frac{R_f}{R_s}\right)\left(\frac{R_1}{R_1 + R_2}\right)} = \frac{R_2}{R_1}$$

or

$$G_1 R_1 = G_2 R_2$$

If the sum of R_1 and R_2 is chosen to be

$$R_T = R_1 + R_2$$

then

$$R_2 = R_T - R_1$$

Substituting this relationship into the above gain relationship gives an expression for R_1 as

$$G_1 R_1 = G_2 R_2$$
$$G_1 R_1 = G_2 \left(R_T - R_1\right)$$
$$G_1 R_1 = G_2 R_T - G_2 R_1$$
$$G_1 R_1 + G_2 R_1 = G_2 R_T$$
$$\left(G_1 + G_2\right)R_1 = G_2 R_T$$

which simplifies to

$$R_1 = \frac{G_2}{G_1 + G_2}R_T$$

Then, given G_1, G_2, and R_T, R_1 is given by the above equation and R_2 is simply

$$R_2 = R_T - R_1$$

Using these values, the ratio R_f/R_s can be found as

$$G_1 = \left(1 + \frac{R_f}{R_s}\right)\left(\frac{R_2}{R_1 + R_2}\right)$$

$$G_1 = \left(1 + \frac{R_f}{R_s}\right)\left(\frac{R_2}{R_T}\right)$$

$$G_1\left(\frac{R_T}{R_2}\right) = \left(1 + \frac{R_f}{R_s}\right)$$

or simply

$$\frac{R_f}{R_s} = G_1\left(\frac{R_T}{R_2}\right) - 1$$

Example: if $G_1 = 4$, $G_2 = 6$, and $R_T = 100 \text{ k}\Omega$, then

$$R_1 = \frac{G_2}{G_1 + G_2}R_T = \frac{6}{4+6}100\text{k} = \frac{6}{10}100\text{k} = 60\text{k}\Omega$$

$$R_2 = R_T - R_1 = 100\text{k} - 60\text{k} = 40\text{k}\Omega$$

$$\frac{R_f}{R_s} = G_1\left(\frac{R_T}{R_2}\right) - 1 = 4\left(\frac{100\text{k}}{40\text{k}}\right) - 1 = 10 - 1 = 9$$

Therefore

$$R_f = 9 R_s$$

and example values are $R_s = 20 \text{ k}\Omega$ and $R_f = 180 \text{ k}\Omega$.

The circuit below shows the resulting circuit that implements the chosen gain expression

$$v_o = G_1 v_1 + G_2 v_2$$
$$v_o = 4 v_1 + 6 v_2$$

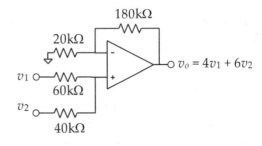

4.7 Summary

Analyzing Op Amp Circuits

$v_p = v_n$	equal voltages at input terminals
$i_p = i_n = 0$	zero current into input terminals
KCL @ v_n	analysis equation required to find the closed loop gain

Inverting Amplifier

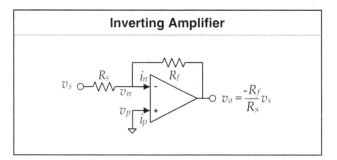

$$v_o = \frac{-R_f}{R_s} v_s$$

Noninverting Amplifier

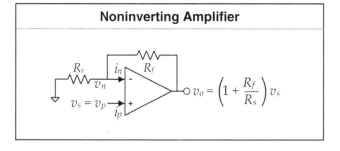

$$v_o = \left(1 + \frac{R_f}{R_s}\right) v_s$$

Unity Gain Buffer

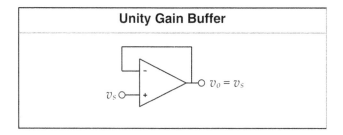

$$v_o = v_s$$

Simple Difference Amplifier

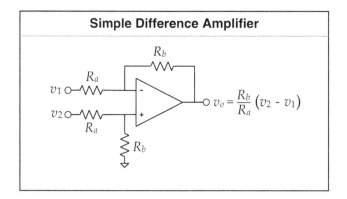

$$v_o = \frac{R_b}{R_a} (v_2 - v_1)$$

Difference Amplifier

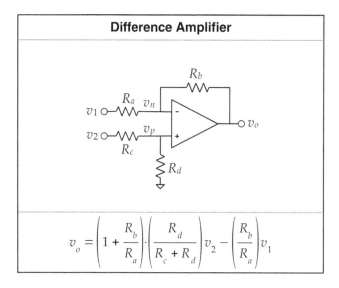

$$v_o = \left(1 + \frac{R_b}{R_a}\right) \cdot \left(\frac{R_d}{R_c + R_d}\right) v_2 - \left(\frac{R_b}{R_a}\right) v_1$$

Alternative Difference Amplifier

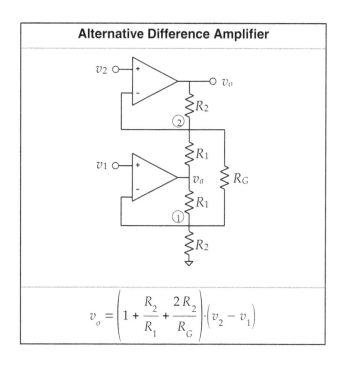

$$v_o = \left(1 + \frac{R_2}{R_1} + \frac{2 R_2}{R_G}\right) \cdot \left(v_2 - v_1\right)$$

Inverting Summer

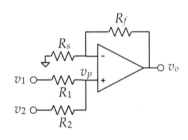

$$v_o = -\sum_{k=1}^{n} \frac{R_f}{R_k} v_k = -\frac{R_f}{R_1} v_1 - \frac{R_f}{R_2} v_2 \cdots - \frac{R_f}{R_n} v_n$$

Noninverting Summer

$$v_o = G_1 v_1 + G_2 v_2$$

$$G_1 = \left(1+\frac{R_f}{R_s}\right) \cdot \left(\frac{R_2}{R_1+R_2}\right)$$

$$G_2 = \left(1+\frac{R_f}{R_s}\right) \cdot \left(\frac{R_1}{R_1+R_2}\right)$$

alternatively, choose $R_T = R_1 + R_2$, then

$$R_1 = \frac{G_2}{G_1 + G_2} R_T$$

$$R_2 = R_T - R_1$$

$$\frac{R_f}{R_s} = G_1 \left(\frac{R_T}{R_2}\right) - 1$$

4.8 Problems

4.1 Using the op amp model below, compute the gain $G = v_o/v_s$ for each of the following cases using the full precision of your calculator, tablet, or computer.

(a) $R_f = 20$ kΩ, $R_s = 10$kΩ, $R_L = 10$ kΩ, $R_i = 1$ MΩ, $R_o = 100$ Ω, $A = 10^6$.

(b) $R_f = 20$ kΩ, $R_s = 10$kΩ, $R_L = \mathbf{1}$ **kΩ**, $R_i = 1$ MΩ, $R_o = 100$ Ω, $A = 10^6$.

(c) $R_f = 20$ kΩ, $R_s = 10$kΩ, $R_L = 10$ kΩ, $R_i = \mathbf{100}$ **kΩ**, $R_o = 100$ Ω, $A = 10^6$.

(d) $R_f = 20$ kΩ, $R_s = 10$kΩ, $R_L = 10$ kΩ, $R_i = 1$ MΩ, $R_o = \mathbf{1}$ **kΩ**, $A = 10^6$.

(e) $R_f = 20$ kΩ, $R_s = 10$kΩ, $R_L = 10$ kΩ, $R_i = 1$ MΩ, $R_o = 100$ Ω, $A = \mathbf{10^4}$.

If each of the above gains are rounded to three significant digits, are they all equal to each other? From these results, how sensitive is the gain G to changes in the load resistance R_L, the input resistance R_i, the output resistance R_o, and the open loop gain A?

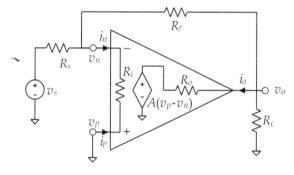

4.2 Find the output voltage v_o and output current i_o for the op amp circuit below.

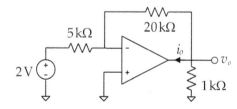

4.3 Find the gain $G = v_o/v_s$ for each of the following op amp circuits.

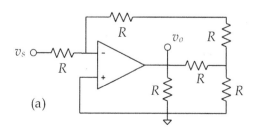

(a)

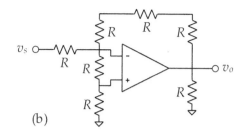

(b)

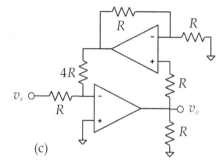

(c)

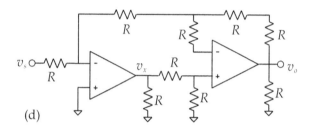

(d)

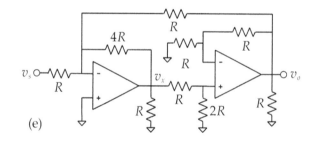

(e)

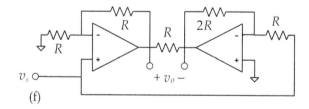

(f)

4.4 Find the value of α so that the gain of the following op amp circuit is equal to $G = v_o/v_s = -4$.

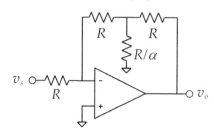

4.5 Choose practical resistor values for the op amp circuits below so that $v_o = 3v_a + 9v_b$.

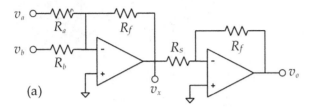

(a)

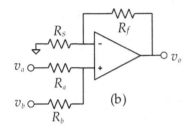

(b)

4.6 Choose practical resistor values for the op amp circuit below so that $v_o = 10(v_2 - v_1)$.

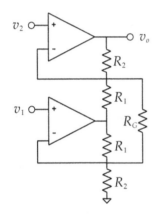

4.7 Find the gain expression $v_o = G_1v_1 + G_2v_2 + G_3v_3$ for the op amp circuit below.

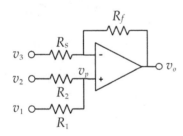

4.8 Derive the gain expression for the common difference amplifier below by using superposition.

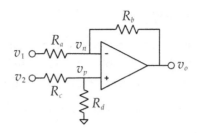

4.9 Design op amp circuits using practical resistor values that implement the following gain expressions:

(a) $v_o = 2v_a - 3v_b + 4v_c$, using two op amps

(b) $v_o = 2v_a - 3v_b + 4v_c$, using one op amp

(c) $v_o = -2v_a - 4v_b - 6v_c$, using one op amp

(d) $v_o = 2v_a + 4v_b + 6v_c$, using two op amps

(e) $v_o = 4v_a + 6v_b$, using one op amp

(f) $v_o = 2(v_a - v_b) + 4(v_c - v_d)$, using two op amps

4.10 (a) Find the gain expression for the general non-inverting summer having n inputs as shown below. This task is most easily accomplished by using source transformations on all inputs, converting them into current sources in parallel with their associated resistors. Then all resistors can be combined into an equivalent resistance R_{eq}. Superposition can then be applied to find the output due to each input source and the sum of the individual outputs gives the desired gain expression. This is a practical example, where both source transformations and superposition make an otherwise difficult problem relatively easy.

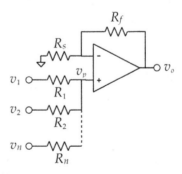

(b) Given the above result, design a noninverting summer circuit with practical resistor values that implements the following gain expression

$$v_o = 2v_a + 3v_b + 4v_c$$

5 Transient Response

Previous chapters focused on basic circuit analysis concepts that apply to all circuits. This work utilized sources that have constant values, *i.e.*, DC sources. Such circuits are static in that voltages and currents throughout the circuit are constants over time. Circuits are much more useful when they are dynamic, meaning when the voltages and currents change with time.

The first dynamic circuits to consider are circuits that have a transient response. This type of response is characterized by a circuit that starts at rest or is static. Then an event occurs to stimulate the circuit and the circuit responds with a transient response. And then, over time, the circuit returns to a resting or static state. As an analogy, this is similar to a dog. The dog is lying quietly on the floor, you walk by and accidentally bump the dog. The dog jumps up and moves to another place, lies down, and after a while, falls back asleep. The dog's movement describes a transient response.

Electric circuits can produce a transient response when they store energy, just as the dog uses its energy to get up and move when bumped. Because resistors absorb energy and do not store it, new circuit elements are needed. These elements, the capacitor and inductor, store energy but do not absorb it permanently. They can be charged and discharged. When charging, they absorb energy; when discharging, they give energy back. Resistors absorb energy and convert it to heat that is lost to its surroundings, so they cannot give it back. It's gone.

Before considering energy storage elements and the transient response of electrical circuits, it is beneficial to develop an intuitive understanding of the transient response that is more substantial than thinking about the movement of a dog.

5.1 Intuition

In mechanical structures, energy can be classified as potential energy or kinetic energy. Potential energy is stored energy and kinetic energy is the energy associated with motion. For example, an above ground tank storing water contains potential energy created by the action of gravity on the water. If a drain valve at the bottom of the tank is opened, kinetic energy is created by the flow of water out of the tank. The potential energy stored in the tank gets converted to kinetic energy. Once the tank is empty, the energy is dissipated, gone.

First Order Transients

Becasue water flow is generally understood and easily visualized, water makes a very good example for developing an intuitive understanding of the transient response of electric circuits.

Consider the water tank, valve, and drain pipe shown below. Before the valve is opened, the water stores potential energy. If the valve is opened at $t = 0$, the water level $h(t)$ drops as the water drains out.

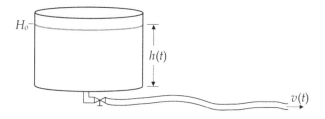

As shown, the initial height of the water is H_o. When the valve opens, the instantaneous height of the water is given by $h(t)$ and the flow rate or velocity of the water is given by $v(t)$. As the tank empties, $h(t)$ decreases to zero, as does $v(t)$.

Several things should be apparent about the operation of this tank:

(1) **The height of the water in the tank does not jump** or change at the instant the valve opens. Mathematically, this says that $h(t)$ is continuous at $t = 0$. This makes sense since it is not possible for some fixed amount of the water in the tank to disappear from the tank instantaneously when the valve opens.

(2) **The flow rate of the water leaving the tank does jump** at the instant the valve opens. Mathematically,

113

this says that $v(t)$ is discontinuous at $t = 0$. Before the valve opens the flow rate is zero; immediately after the valve opens, water begins to flow.

(3) **The time it takes to drain the tank is proportional to tank capacity.** The larger the capacity of the tank, the longer it takes to drain. The smaller the capacity of the tank, the less time it takes to drain.

(4) **The time it takes to drain the tank is inversely proportional to both the diameter of the drainage piping and the friction provided by the piping.** If the tank is the size of a swimming pool and the piping is the size of a drinking straw it takes a long time to drain the tank. If the piping is very long, water experiences more friction along the interior surface of the piping, which slows the time it takes to drain the tank.

(5) **The higher the water level in the tank, the faster the water flow rate is at $t = 0$.** The pressure at the valve is proportional to the weight of the water pressing down on it. So, the higher the water level, the higher the pressure is, so the faster the flow rate is.

Using these facts, the height $h(t)$ and flow rate $v(t)$ have a transient response that resembles the plots shown below.

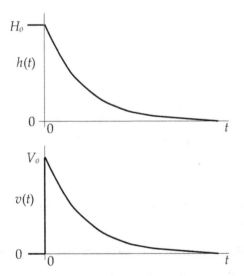

The height is continuous at $t = 0$, starting at H_o and decreasing to zero. The rate at which it falls decreases with increasing time because the pressure pushing down on the water lowers as the height decreases. The flow rate is discontinuous. It starts at zero before $t = 0$, then jumps up to a value V_o immediately after $t = 0$. From there it decreases to zero following the same shape as the height.

This transient response is called the natural response. It describes a process where initial stored energy is released and goes to zero. The tank started with potential energy and ended with none.

The next case to consider is shown in the following figure. Instead of draining a tank, this case considers filling the empty tank on the right from the very large reservoir on the left.

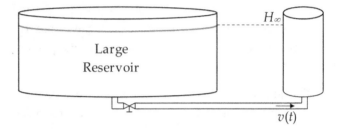

As before, several things are apparent about the operation of this scenario:

(1) **The height of the water in the tank to be filled does not jump at the instant the valve opens.**

(2) **The velocity of the water entering the tank does jump at the instant the valve opens.**

(3) **Tank fill time is proportional to tank capacity.**

(4) **Tank fill time is inversely proportional to both the diameter of the piping and the friction provided by the piping.**

(5) **The higher the water level in the reservoir, the faster the water flow rate is at $t = 0$.**

Using these facts, the water height $h(t)$ in the tank to be filled and the flow rate $v(t)$ have a transient response that resembles the plots shown below.

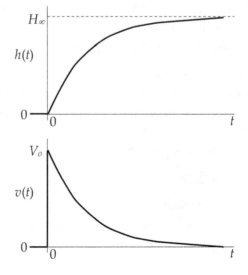

The height is continuous at $t = 0$, starting at 0 and increasing to its final value H_∞. The rate at which the water rises decreases over time because the pressure pushing down on the water in the filling tank increasingly counteracts the pressure from the reservoir as the tank fills.

The flow rate is discontinuous. After the valve opens, it responds to the net pressure experienced by the water. When the water height in the tank matches that of the reservoir, the downward pressure in the tank matches that of the reservoir, making the net pressure on the water zero.

This transient response is called the step or forced response. It describes a process where energy increases from zero and reaches some final value. The tank started empty so it had zero potential energy, and ended with water containing potential energy.

A third situation that could be considered is when the tank connected to the reservoir starts with water height either below the height of the reservoir, $h(t) < H_\infty$, or height above the height of the reservoir, $h(t) > H_\infty$. In both of these cases, opening the valve allows water to pass in whatever direction is necessary so that the water heights match as time evolves, $h(\infty) = H_\infty$. This situation is called the complete response.

The transient response of electric circuits containing a single energy storage element has the same characteristics as those described here. **The natural response occurs when an energy storage element loses its energy. The step response occurs when an energy storage element containing zero energy gains energy. And the complete response occurs when the energy level changes from one value to another.** In addition, just like water height, the primary variable associated with energy storage will be continuous through a switching event. And just like the water flow rate, other variables will be discontinuous through switching events.

Second Order Transients

There are scenarios where either two energy storage devices or two energy storage modes interact with each other in a way that energy alternates repeatedly between the two modes or devices. The simplest way to visualize this phenomenon is to consider a pendulum as shown in the following figure.

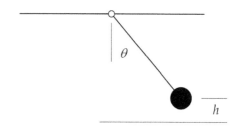

When the pendulum is held in the position shown, it stores potential energy equal to Mgh where M is the mass, g is the acceleration due to gravity, and h is the vertical height the mass is raised relative to its lowest point when $\theta = 0$. If the pendulum mass is released, it falls. The angular velocity about the pivot at the top increases from zero and reaches its peak when θ and h are zero. At this specific point the potential energy is zero, but the kinetic energy, $\frac{1}{2}Mv^2$, is maximum because the linear velocity v is maximum. Then as the pendulum swings in the opposite direction, the kinetic energy decreases and the potential energy once again increases. Depending on the friction at the pivot and the drag caused by air movement, the pendulum oscillates back and forth about $\theta = 0$ and slowly loses energy as illustrated in the following figure.

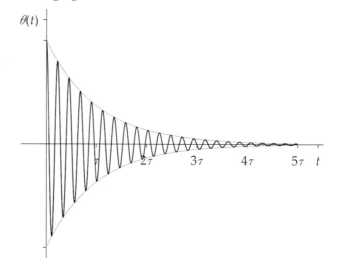

This transient response, called underdamped, also appears in electric circuits when a capacitor and an inductor interact with each other in a circuit. As the energy stored in one element decreases, it increases in the other element and vise versa. Over time, this energy is dissipated by resistors in the circuit, which makes the response decay to zero as illustrated for the pendulum above.

5.2 Dynamic Electric Circuits

Electric circuits are dynamic when they contain switches that change state. For mathematical simplicity, the opening or closing of a switch occurs at time equal to zero, $t = 0$. For example, consider the circuit shown below. The switch in this circuit closes at $t = 0$. Therefore $v_1(t)$ and $v_2(t)$ have different values before and after $t = 0$.

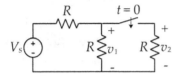

Before $t = 0$ the resistor on the far right is not connected, so the voltage v_2 is zero for $t < 0$. The voltage v_1 across the center resistor is given by voltage division as

$$v_1 = \frac{R}{R + R} V_s = \frac{R}{2R} V_s = \frac{V_s}{2}$$

Once the switch changes state at $t = 0$, the voltages v_1 and v_2 are equal because the two resistors are in parallel. Both v_1 and v_2 become

$$v_1 = v_2 = \frac{R\|R}{R + R\|R} V_s = \frac{R/2}{R + R/2} V_s = \frac{R/2}{3R/2} V_s = \frac{V_s}{3}$$

Plots of the voltages v_1 and v_2 as a function of time are shown below.

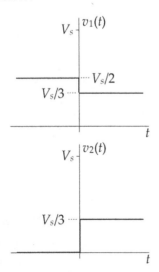

Both of these voltages are discontinuous at $t = 0$ when the switch changes state. As a result, it is not possible to say what the values of the two voltages are exactly at $t = 0$. The voltages $v_1(0)$ and $v_2(0)$ are undefined. However, their values are known at the instant before and the instant after $t = 0$. These two instants are denoted $t = 0^-$ and $t = 0^+$ respectively as shown below.

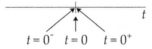

Using this notation, the voltages on either side of $t = 0$ can be written as

$$v_1(0^-) = \frac{V_s}{2} \quad v_1(0^+) = \frac{V_s}{3}$$

$$v_2(0^-) = 0 \quad v_2(0^+) = \frac{V_s}{3}$$

This notation is used extensively in electric circuits.

While circuits containing sources, switches, and resistors are dynamic, they are generally not that interesting because voltages and currents simply change instantaneously. It is much more interesting when energy storage elements are included.

5.3 Capacitors

A capacitor is formed whenever two conductors are separated by an insulator. Capacitors are commonly constructed by forming a sandwich where two sheets of conductor are pressed together on either side of an insulator as shown in the figure below. Conducting leads are connected to each of the two conducting plates as shown.

When a voltage is applied across the capacitor, opposing charges accumulate on the two conducting plates as shown in the following figure. When in this state, the capacitor is said to be charged.

The amount of charge that accumulates on the plates is directly proportional to the applied voltage V_s, the area of the conducting plates, and the inverse of the thickness of the insulating layer. It is also directly proportional to the permittivity or dielectric constant of the material making up the insulating layer. Stated mathematically, in the ideal case, the charge on the plates is given by

$$q = \left(\frac{\varepsilon A}{d}\right) v$$

where q is the charge in coulombs, ε is the insulating material permittivity in farads/meter, A is the area of the plates in square meters, d is the distance between the plates (or the insulating layer thickness) in meters, and v is the applied voltage in volts.

The terms related to the dimensions and material characteristics are collectively called the capacitance, which is denoted as

$$C = \frac{\varepsilon A}{d}$$

which has units of farads, (F). Substituting this expression into the charge equation gives the fundamental relationship

$$q = C v$$

Once a capacitor is charged, the voltage source supplying the charge can be removed. In doing so, the charge remains behind and the voltage across the capacitor terminals remains unchanged. This charge contains potential energy, so a capacitor stores energy. This is analogous to a tank of water storing potential energy. In this case, it is particles of charge rather than water molecules that store energy.

Terminal Characteristics

If a path is provided for the stored charge to move off the plates, the flow rate at which it moves is by definition current. Taking the derivative of the charge relationship gives the capacitor current as

$$i = \frac{dq}{dt} = \frac{d}{dt} C v = C \frac{dv}{dt}$$

This defines the relationship between the voltage across a capacitor and the current flowing through it when the capacitor is labeled by the passive sign convention. Using the standard schematic symbol for a capacitor, this relationship is shown as follows.

The current in a capacitor is related to how fast the voltage is changing. **When the voltage is not changing, the current is zero. This follows from the fact that the derivative of a constant is zero,**

$$i = C \frac{dv}{dt}\bigg|_{v=\text{constant}} = C \cdot 0 = 0$$

Any time the voltage is constant, there is no current, and the capacitor appears as an open circuit as illustrated below.

When the voltage is not constant, the rate the voltage across a capacitor can change is given by moving C to the other side of the capacitor equation

$$\frac{dv}{dt} = \frac{i}{C}$$

The derivative on the left is the rate the capacitor voltage can change. The larger the capacitance C, the slower the voltage can change. From this perspective, **a capacitor attempts to keep its voltage from changing.**

Though it is seldom needed, using simply calculus, it is possible to write the voltage across the capacitor in terms of the current as

$$v(t) = \frac{1}{C}\int_0^t i(\tau)d\tau + v(0)$$

Energy

The energy stored in a capacitor is given by

$$w_C = \frac{1}{2} C v^2$$

with units of energy being joules, J. When the voltage is zero, there is no charge on the capacitor and therefore there is no energy stored. In addition, it does not matter what direction the capacitor is charged. For example, if the voltage is 10 V or –10 V, the energy stored is the same because the voltage is squared in the energy expression. Quite naturally, the energy stored is proportional to the size of the capacitor C, just as a larger water tank stores more potential energy.

It is easy to show that this energy expression is correct by noting that power is the derivative of energy

$$p = \frac{dw}{dt}$$

Substituting the capacitor energy expression into this power expression gives

$$p = \frac{d}{dt}\left(\frac{1}{2}Cv^2\right)$$

$$p = \frac{1}{2}C\frac{d}{dt}\left(v^2\right)$$

$$p = \frac{1}{2}C\,2v\frac{dv}{dt}$$

$$p = v\left(C\frac{dv}{dt}\right)$$

$$p = vi$$

Finding the derivative of the energy leads to the fundamental expression for power $p = vi$ when the passive sign convention holds. Therefore, the energy expression must be correct.

Continuous Voltage

The voltage across a capacitor cannot jump in value. That is, it cannot be discontinuous. If a switching event occurs at $t = 0$, $v(0^-) = v(0^+)$. The voltage cannot be discontinuous because of the basic relationship $q = Cv$. If the voltage v changes instantaneously, the charge q must change instantaneously as well since they are directly proportional to each other. In this case, the current becomes infinite, $i = dq/dt = \infty$, which is impossible. Using the water tank analogy, saying the voltage across a capacitor cannot jump is equivalent to saying that the water height cannot change instantaneously.

While the voltage across a capacitor must be continuous, the current flowing through it is typically discontinuous. This follows from the idea that the flow rate from a water tank goes from zero to some value the instant the valve opens.

Farads

How big is a farad? It turns out that 1 farad is a very large quantity. Capacitors in electric circuits are typically in the range of 1 nF $= 10^{-9}$ farads to 1 mF $= 10^{-3}$ farads. Smaller values typically appear in circuits that process information, and larger values are more common in circuits that process power.

Using the simple and ideal case, consider a capacitor having an area of one square meter, $A = 1$, and a distance between the plates of one micrometer, $d = 10^{-6}$, and let the permittivity be that of air, $\varepsilon = 8.85 \cdot 10^{-12}$ F/m. The capacitance created using these values is

$$C = \frac{\varepsilon A}{d} = \frac{8.85 \cdot 10^{-12} \cdot 1}{10^{-6}} = 8.85 \cdot 10^{-6} = 8.85 \ \mu F$$

One square meter is a large area. If the area A is reduced to a square having one centimeter dimensions, $A = (10^{-2})^2 = 10^{-4}$ m, the capacitance becomes

$$C = \frac{\varepsilon A}{d} = \frac{8.85 \cdot 10^{-12} \cdot 10^{-4}}{10^{-6}} = 8.85 \cdot 10^{-10} = 885 \ pF$$

Series and Parallel

Capacitors are seldom placed in series because the equivalent capacitance of two capacitors in series is

$$\text{Series:} \quad \frac{1}{C_{eqs}} = \frac{1}{C_1} + \frac{1}{C_2}$$

That is, capacitors in series add the way resistors add in parallel. Therefore, the equivalent series capacitance is less than that of either of the two in series. In practice, it seldom makes sense to pay for two larger capacitors to achieve a desired smaller capacitance.

However, capacitors are often placed in parallel. When two capacitors are placed in parallel the equivalent capacitance C_{eqp} is given by

$$\text{Parallel:} \quad C_{eqp} = C_1 + C_2$$

Capacitors in parallel add the way resistors add in series.

While capacitors are often placed in parallel, they are seldom placed in parallel to increase the capacitance. For example, it is common to place a 10 μF capacitor in parallel with a 10 nF capacitor. The equivalent capacitance is then 10.01 μF, which, to three significant digits, is no different from the 10 μF capacitor alone. This is especially true because the 10 μF capacitor will likely have a $\pm 10\%$ tolerance. The important reasons for placing two capacitors having widely varying values in parallel will be covered later in this text.

5.4 Inductors

Common inductors are formed by creating a coil of conductors. Outside of circuit analysis, inductors are commonly called electromagnets. Often times the coil is formed around ferromagnetic material (*e.g.*, steel or ferrite) called a core. However, inductors need not have any core or may have a plastic core. The core material influences the inductor's value in the same way that insulator material influences capacitance.

Capacitors
$\begin{array}{c} + \\ v \\ - \end{array} \dashv\vdash \begin{array}{c} i = C\dfrac{dv}{dt} \\ C \end{array}$
$i=0 \quad + \atop C \dashv\vdash v = \text{constant} \Rightarrow \quad i=0 \quad\text{open} \atop \quad\quad\quad\quad\quad\quad\quad\quad\; \text{circuit}$
v is always continuous, e.g., $v(0^-) = v(0) = v(0^+)$ i is often discontinuous, e.g., $i(0^-) \neq i(0^+)$
$dv/dt = i/C$, a capacitor tries to keep its voltage from changing.
Energy: $w_C = \dfrac{1}{2} C v^2$
Typical values: $1\,\text{nF} \leq C \leq 1\,\text{mF}$

As covered in physics, whenever current flows in a conductor, a magnetic field surrounds the conductor. The presence of this magnetic field is what establishes inductance. When formed into a coil, the magnetic field becomes focused as illustrated in the figure below.

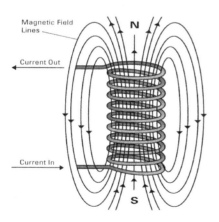

Terminal Characteristics

A measure of the amount of magnetic field that passes through the turns of the coil is called flux linkage, which is defined by

$$\lambda = L\,i$$

where λ is flux linkage in webers, Wb, L is inductance in henries, (H), and i is current in amperes, A.

The significance of flux linkage λ is that Faraday's law says that a voltage is induced or created across the coil terminals equal to the rate at which flux linkage changes with time. That is,

$$v = \frac{d\lambda}{dt} = \frac{d}{dt}Li = L\frac{di}{dt}$$

This expression defines the relationship between the voltage across and the current flowing through an inductor when it is labeled by the passive sign convention. Using the standard schematic symbol for an inductor, this relationship is shown as follows.

$$L \quad v = L\frac{di}{dt}$$

The voltage across an inductor is related to how fast the current is changing. **When the current is not changing, the voltage is zero. This follows from the fact that the derivative of a constant is zero,**

$$v = L\frac{di}{dt}\bigg|_{i=\text{constant}} = L\cdot 0 = 0$$

Any time the current is constant, there is no voltage across the inductor and the inductor appears as a short circuit as illustrated below.

$$L \quad \begin{array}{c} i = \text{constant} \\ + \\ v = 0 \\ - \end{array} \Rightarrow \begin{array}{c} + \\ v = 0 \\ - \end{array} \quad \begin{array}{l} \text{short} \\ \text{circuit} \end{array}$$

When the current is not constant, the rate the current through an inductor can change is given by moving L to the other side of the inductor equation,

$$\frac{di}{dt} = \frac{v}{L}$$

The derivative on the left is the rate the inductor current can change. The larger the inductance L, the slower the current can change. Therefore, **an inductor attempts to keep its current from changing.**

Though it is seldom needed, using simply calculus, it is possible to write the current through the inductor in terms of the voltage as

$$i(t) = \frac{1}{L}\int_0^t v(\tau)\,d\tau + i(0)$$

Energy

The energy stored in an inductor is given by

$$w_L = \frac{1}{2}Li^2$$

with units of energy being joules, J. When the current is zero, there is no magnetic field in the coil and therefore there is no energy stored. In addition, it does not matter what direction the inductor current flows. For example, if the current is 1 A or –1 A the energy stored is the same because the current is squared in the energy expression. Quite naturally, the energy stored is proportional to the size of the inductor L.

The analysis needed to prove that the above expression holds follows exactly what was done earlier for the capacitor.

Continuous Current

The current through an inductor cannot jump in value. That is, it cannot be discontinuous. If a switching event occurs at $t = 0$, $i(0^-) = i(0^+)$. The current cannot be discontinuous because of the basic relationship $\lambda = Li$. If the current i changes instantaneously, the flux linkage λ must change instantaneously as well since they are directly proportional to each other. In this case, the voltage becomes infinite, $v = d\lambda/dt = \infty$, which is impossible.

While current through an inductor must be continuous, the voltage across it is typically discontinuous.

Henries

The computation of inductance involves careful consideration of all the magnetic field flowing through a coil. In most cases, inductance must be approximated numerically. Sufficiently accurate approximate expressions exist for simple geometries.

Inductances in electric circuits are typically in the range of $1\,\text{nH} = 10^{-9}$ henries to about $10\,\text{H} = 10$ henries. Smaller values typically appear in circuits that process information, and larger values are more common in circuits that process power.

Since all conductors have inductance, it is useful to note that the inductance of conductors such as small diameter wire and the conductor traces on PC boards have an inductance of $1\,\text{nH}$ to $20\,\text{nH}$ per centimeter of length.

Series and Parallel

In practice, one seldom places inductors in series or parallel because it is much cheaper to use one inductor of the appropriate size rather than pay for two or more inductors to achieve the same equivalent inductance. The equivalent inductance L_{eqs} of two inductors in series is

$$\text{Series:} \quad L_{eqs} = L_1 + L_2$$

and the equivalent inductance L_{eqp} of two inductors in parallel is

$$\text{Parallel:} \quad \frac{1}{L_{eqp}} = \frac{1}{L_1} + \frac{1}{L_2}$$

These results show that inductances add in the same way that resistors do. You can easily find derivations for the above series and parallel equivalent inductances online.

Inductors
$i \downarrow$ $+$ L $v = L\dfrac{di}{dt}$ $-$
$\downarrow i = $ constant $+$ L $v = 0$ $\Rightarrow$ $\begin{matrix} + \\ v = 0 \\ - \end{matrix}$ short circuit $-$
i is always continuous, $e.g.$, $i(0^-) = i(0) = i(0^+)$ v is often discontinuous, $e.g.$, $v(0^-) \neq v(0^+)$
$di/dt = v/L$, an inductor tries to keep its current from changing.
Energy: $w_L = \dfrac{1}{2}Li^2$
Typical values: $1\,\text{nH} \leq L \leq 10\,\text{H}$

5.5 First Order Transients

The terminal relationships for the capacitor and inductor relate the element voltage and current by differentiation. As a result, derivatives appear when writing KCL and KVL expressions for circuits containing these elements.

While a circuit may contain any number of capacitors and inductors, the fundamental behavior of a circuit having a single capacitor or inductor is vitally important. Writing the KCL or KVL equations for these circuits leads to a first order differential equation because either $i = C\,dv/dt$ or $v = L\,di/dt$ appears in the equations.

The three fundamental responses of first order differential equations that were discussed in Chapter 1, Section 1.14, pages 20–22, are shown in the following tables.

As discussed in Chapter 1, the natural response describes the scenario where some initial energy is dissipated and the response goes to zero. The step response describes the opposite scenario where energy is increased from zero to some final value. And the complete response is where the energy level changes from some nonzero value to another. The complete response is simply the sum of the natural response and the step response.

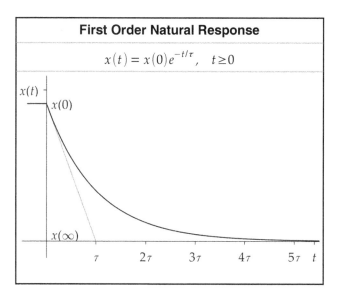

First Order Natural Response

$$x(t) = x(0)e^{-t/\tau}, \quad t \geq 0$$

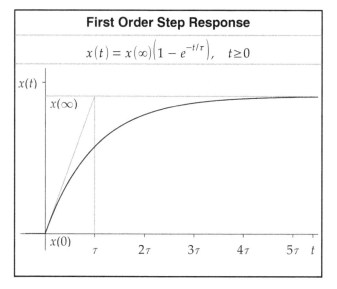

First Order Step Response

$$x(t) = x(\infty)\left(1 - e^{-t/\tau}\right), \quad t \geq 0$$

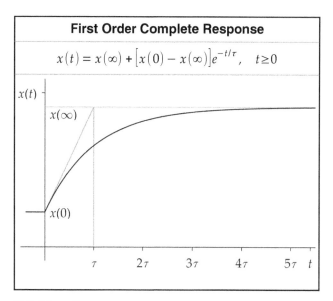

First Order Complete Response

$$x(t) = x(\infty) + \left[x(0) - x(\infty)\right]e^{-t/\tau}, \quad t \geq 0$$

RC Circuits

A circuit containing one capacitor, plus resistors and sources forms what is commonly called an RC circuit. These circuits can be constructed in essentially an infinite number of ways. In all cases, the capacitor dictates the voltages and currents in the circuit. Before considering more complex examples, it is useful to identify the basic properties of the natural, step, and complete responses for circuits containing one capacitor. The capacitor voltage is the primary solution sought since the energy stored in the capacitor is related to its voltage, and the transient response inherently involves the movement of energy. It is often easiest to find other voltages and currents in the circuit by applying circuit analysis after computing the capacitor voltage.

Natural Response: Consider the circuit below where an arbitrary circuit on the left is replaced by its Thévenin equivalent. The switch changes position at $t = 0$. The resistor on the right R_{eq} is the equivalent load resistor seen by the capacitor C after the switch changes state.

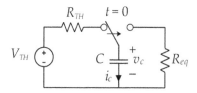

Before the switch changes position, the capacitor is exposed to a source of energy, V_{TH}, whereas after the switch changes position, the capacitor is connected to a resistor. Therefore, the solution to this circuit is a natural response where the capacitor is initially charged and then it gets discharged through the resistor R_{eq}.

It is always assumed that the switch is in its $t < 0$ position for a sufficiently long time that the circuit is at rest. When at rest, the voltages and currents in the circuit are constants. Because the voltage across the capacitor is constant, the capacitor current is zero because the derivative of a constant is zero,

$$i_c = C\frac{dv_c}{dt} = C \cdot (0) = 0, \quad t < 0$$

The capacitor is an open circuit when the voltage across it is constant, as illustrated in the following $t < 0$ circuit.

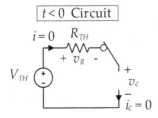

$t < 0$ Circuit

The voltage across R_{TH} is zero because by Ohm's law, $v_R = R_{TH} \cdot i = R_{TH} \cdot (0) = 0$. Therefore, the capacitor voltage for $t < 0$ is equal to the Thévenin voltage V_{TH} by KVL,

$$V_{TH} = v_c + v_R = v_c + 0 = v_c$$

This is the voltage the capacitor is charged to before the switch changes position. In particular, it is the value at $t = 0^-$,

$$v_c(0^-) = V_{TH}$$

This value determines the initial energy stored in the capacitor,

$$w_c(0^-) = \frac{1}{2}C v_c^2(0^-) = \frac{1}{2}C V_{TH}^2$$

There is nothing more to do with the $t < 0$ circuit.

At $t = 0$, the switch changes position, giving the following $t > 0$ circuit.

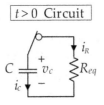

$t > 0$ Circuit

The energy stored in the capacitor can now discharge into the equivalent resistor R_{eq}, where it is converted to heat.

Writing KCL at the top node gives

$$i_c + i_R = 0$$

$$C\frac{dv_c}{dt} + \frac{v_c}{R_{eq}} = 0$$

$$\frac{dv_c}{dt} + \frac{1}{R_{eq}C}v_c = 0$$

This equation is a first order differential equation describing the capacitor voltage. Using the analysis from Chapter 1 or the earlier summary table, the solution to this differential equation is the natural response

$$v_c(t) = v_c(0)e^{-t/\tau}, \quad t \geq 0$$

where

$$v_c(0) = v_c(0^-) = v_c(0^+) = V_{TH}$$

is the initial voltage, since the capacitor voltage cannot change instantaneously, and

$$\tau = R_{eq}C$$

is the time constant.

The response effectively decays to zero in five time constants, 5τ. The time constant $\tau = R_{eq}C$ makes sense. The larger the capacitance, the more charge it holds, so it take longer to discharge. Also, since the power in the equivalent resistance R_{eq}, is $p = v_c^2/R_{eq}$, the larger R_{eq} is, the less power is absorbed by R_{eq}, making the capacitor discharge more slowly.

Given the capacitor voltage, the current through the R_{eq} is discontinuous at $t = 0$ and is given by

$$i_R(t) = -i_c(t) = \begin{cases} 0, & t < 0 \\ \dfrac{v_c(t)}{R_{eq}}, & t \geq 0^+ \end{cases}$$

Before $t = 0$ the resistor R_{eq} is not connected to the rest of the circuit, so it has no current flowing through it. However, the instant the switch changes state, the capacitor and its voltage are connected directly across the resistor. The resistor current is undefined at exactly $t = 0$, but $i_R(0^-) = 0$ and $i_R(0^+) = v_c(0^+)/R_{eq}$.

The following figure shows the capacitor voltage and resistor current.

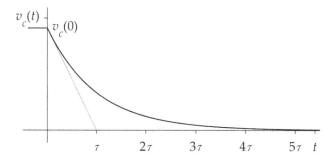

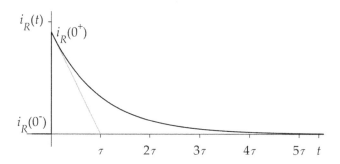

Step Response: Consider the same circuit again, but let the switch go in the opposite direction at $t = 0$.

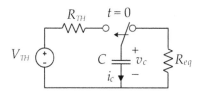

Now, the capacitor starts discharged, $v_c(0^-) = 0$, and becomes charged after the switch changes position. Therefore, this is a step response problem described by the following $t > 0$ circuit.

$$\boxed{t > 0 \ \text{Circuit}}$$

By letting the node on the bottom be the reference node, applying KCL at the upper right node gives

$$i_c + \frac{v_c - V_{TH}}{R_{TH}} = 0$$

$$C\frac{dv_c}{dt} + \frac{v_c}{R_{TH}} = \frac{V_{TH}}{R_{TH}}$$

$$\frac{dv_c}{dt} + \frac{1}{R_{TH}C}v_c = \frac{V_{TH}}{R_{TH}C}$$

Using the analysis provided in Chapter 1, and noting that $v_c(0^-) = v_c(0^+) = 0$, the solution to this differential equation is the step response

$$v_c(t) = v_c(\infty)\left[1 - e^{-t/\tau}\right], \quad t \geq 0$$

where the time constant is

$$\tau = R_{TH}C$$

In this case, R_{TH} is the equivalent resistance seen by the capacitor when the source is shut OFF by setting $V_{TH} = 0$.

The final value of the capacitor voltage $v_c(\infty)$ is found by letting time go to infinity when the circuit is at rest. Once again, the capacitor becomes an open circuit under these conditions, the voltage across and the current through R_{TH} are zero, and the capacitor charges to the source voltage, $v_c(\infty) = V_{TH}$. For the natural response, this was the starting value.

The following figure shows the capacitor voltage and associated capacitor current.

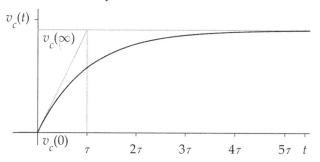

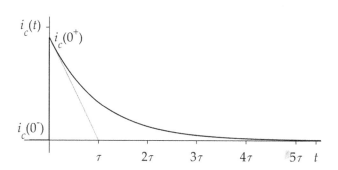

Complete Response: When there is a source of energy in the circuit for both $t < 0$ and $t > 0$, the response is the complete response. The following circuit illustrates a simple complete response example.

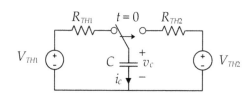

Based on the previous examples, the capacitor voltage starts at $v_c(0) = v_c(0^-) = v_c(0^+) = V_{TH1}$. After the switch changes position, the capacitor then charges to $v_c(\infty) = V_{TH2}$. The time constant is determined by the equivalent resistance seen by the capacitor for $t > 0$. In this case, the time constant is

$$\tau = R_{TH2}C$$

and the response is

$$v_c(t) = v_c(\infty) + \left[v_c(0) - v_c(\infty)\right]e^{-t/\tau}, \quad t \geq 0$$

which is illustrated in the following figure.

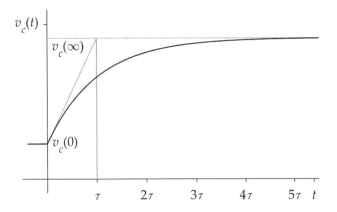

The above content regarding RC circuits was intended to illustrate the three solution types. To solve problems, it is not necessary to derive the differential equation describing the circuit. One just needs to fit the circuit to the differential equation solution.

RL Circuits

A circuit containing one inductor, plus resistors and sources forms what is commonly called an RL circuit. These circuits can be constructed in essentially an infinite number of ways. In all cases, the inductor dictates the form of the voltages and currents in the circuit. Before considering more complex examples, it is useful to identify the basic properties of the natural, step, and complete responses for circuits containing one inductor. The inductor current is the primary solution sought since the energy stored in the inductor is related to its current, and the transient response inherently involves the movement of energy. It is often easiest to find other voltages and currents in the circuit by applying circuit analysis after computing the inductor current.

Natural Response: Consider the following circuit where an arbitrary circuit on the left is replaced by its Norton equivalent. The switch changes position at

$t = 0$. The resistor on the right R_{eq} is the equivalent load resistor seen by the inductor L after the switch changes state.

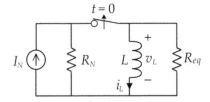

Before the switch changes position, the inductor is exposed to the current source, I_N, whereas after the switch changes position, the inductor is connected to a resistor. Therefore, the solution to this circuit is a natural response where the inductor is initially charged and is discharged through the resistor R_{eq}.

It is always assumed that the switch is in its $t < 0$ position for a sufficiently long time that the circuit is at rest. When at rest, the voltages and currents in the circuit are constants. Because the current through the inductor is constant, the inductor voltage is zero because the derivative of a constant is zero,

$$v_L = L\frac{di_L}{dt} = L\cdot(0) = 0, \quad t < 0$$

The inductor is a short circuit when its current is constant, as shown in the following $t < 0$ circuit.

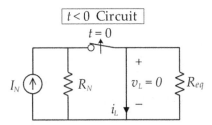

The voltage v_L is also the voltage across both resistors in this circuit. By Ohm's law, the current through these resistors is zero,

$$\frac{v_L}{R_{eq}} = \frac{0}{R_{eq}} = 0$$

$$\frac{v_L}{R_N} = \frac{0}{R_N} = 0$$

Therefore, the current I_N only flows through the inductor prior to $t = 0$. In particular, the value at $t = 0^-$ is

$$i_L(0^-) = I_N$$

This value determines the initial energy stored in the inductor,

$$w_L(0^-) = \frac{1}{2}Li_L^2(0^-) = \frac{1}{2}LI_N^2$$

There is nothing more to do with the $t < 0$ circuit.

At $t = 0$, the switch changes position giving the following $t > 0$ circuit.

| $t > 0$ Circuit |

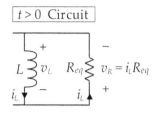

The energy stored in the inductor can now discharge into the equivalent resistor R_{eq}.

Writing KVL around the loop formed gives

$$v_L + v_R = 0$$

$$L\frac{di_L}{dt} + i_L R_{eq} = 0$$

$$\frac{di_L}{dt} + \frac{R_{eq}}{L}i_L = 0$$

This last equation is a first order differential equation describing the inductor current. Using the analysis from Chapter 1, the solution to this differential equation is the natural response

$$i_L(t) = i_L(0)e^{-t/\tau}, \quad t \geq 0$$

where

$$i_L(0) = i_L(0^-) = i_L(0^+) = I_N$$

is the initial current, and

$$\tau = \frac{L}{R_{eq}}$$

is the time constant.

The following figure illustrates the inductor current and its associated voltage. The current is continuous at $t = 0$, but the voltage is not.

The response decays essentially to zero in five time constants, 5τ. The time constant $\tau = L/R_{eq}$ makes sense. The larger the inductance, the stronger the magnetic field it creates, so the longer it takesto discharge the field. **The resistance plays the opposite role here. The smaller the resistance value, the slower the discharge.** Since the power in the equivalent resistance R_{eq} is $p = i_L^2 \cdot R_{eq}$, the smaller R_{eq} is, the

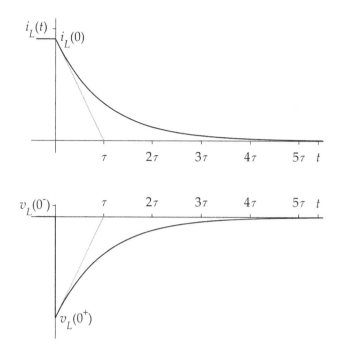

less power is absorbed by R_{eq}, making the inductor discharge more slowly.

Step Response: Consider the same circuit, but let the switch go in the opposite direction at $t = 0$ as shown below.

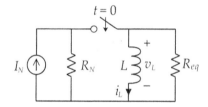

Now, the inductor starts discharged, $i_L(0^-) = 0$, and becomes charged after the switch changes position. Therefore, this is a step response problem described by the following $t > 0$ circuit.

| $t > 0$ Circuit |

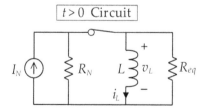

The two resistors are in parallel now. They can be combined into an equivalent $R_{eq2} = R_N \| R_{eq}$ as shown in the following circuit.

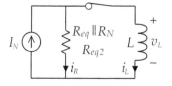

Applying KCL at the upper node gives

$$i_R + i_L - I_N = 0$$

$$\frac{v_L}{R_{eq2}} + i_L = I_N$$

$$\frac{1}{R_{eq2}} L \frac{di_L}{dt} + i_L = I_N$$

$$\frac{L}{R_{eq2}} \frac{di_L}{dt} + i_L = I_N$$

which in standard form becomes

$$\frac{di_L}{dt} + \frac{R_{eq2}}{L} i_L = \frac{R_{eq2}}{L} I_N$$

Using the analysis provided in Chapter 1, and noting that $i_L(0^-) = i_L(0^+) = 0$, the solution to this differential equation is the step response

$$i_L(t) = i_L(\infty)\left[1 - e^{-t/\tau}\right], \quad t \geq 0$$

where the time constant is

$$\tau = \frac{L}{R_{eq2}}$$

In this case, $R_{eq2} = R_N \| R_{eq}$ is the equivalent resistance seen by the inductor when the source is shut OFF by setting $I_N = 0$.

The final value of the inductor current $i_L(\infty)$ is found by letting time go to infinity when the circuit is at rest. Once again, the inductor becomes a short circuit under these conditions, the voltage across and current through R_{eq2} are zero, and the inductor charges to the source current, $i_L(\infty) = I_N$.

The following plots illustrate the inductor current and associated voltage. Once again, the current is continuous at $t = 0$, but the voltage is not.

Complete Response: When there is a source of energy in the circuit for both $t < 0$ and $t > 0$, the response is the complete response. The following circuit illustrates a simple complete response example.

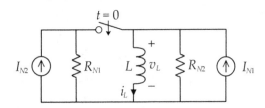

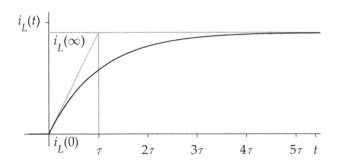

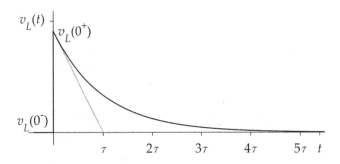

Based on the previous examples, the inductor starts at $i_L(0) = i_L(0^-) = i_L(0^+) = I_{N1}$. After the switch changes position, the inductor then charges to the final value $i_L(\infty) = I_{N1} + I_{N2}$. The time constant is determined by the equivalent resistance seen by the inductor for $t > 0$. In this case, the time constant is

$$\tau = \frac{L}{R_{eq3}}$$

where

$$R_{eq3} = R_{N1} \| R_{N2}$$

and the response is

$$i_L(t) = i_L(\infty) + \left[i_L(0) - i_L(\infty)\right]e^{-t/\tau}, \quad t \geq 0$$

which is illustrated in the following figure.

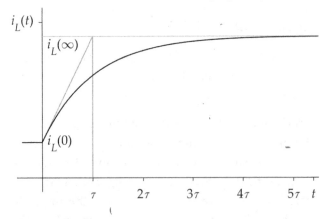

The above content regarding RL circuits was intended to illustrate the three solution types. To solve problems, it is not necessary to derive the differential equation describing the circuit. One just needs to fit the circuit to the differential equation solution.

Problem Solving Procedure

Because the complete response expression is simply the sum of the natural response and the step response, it is convenient to solve all problems starting with the complete response expression. In doing so, if the final value is zero, the solution inherently becomes the natural response, and if the initial value is zero, the solution inherently becomes the step response. In those cases where neither the initial value nor the final value is zero, the solution is the complete response. By following this approach, only one detailed procedure is needed rather than three.

Solving RC and RL Circuits

1. The complete response is given by

$$x(t) = x(\infty) + [x(0) - x(\infty)]e^{-t/\tau}, \quad t \ge 0$$

where $x(t)$ is either the capacitor voltage $v_c(t)$ or the inductor current $i_L(t)$. When $x(t)$ describes other variables that are discontinuous at $t = 0$, $x(0^+)$ is used because $x(0)$ is undefined at a discontinuity.

2. Draw the circuit for negative time $t < 0$ when the circuit is at rest and all voltages and currents are constants. The capacitor is an open circuit, $i_c(0^-) = 0$.

$$i = 0 \downarrow \quad \overset{+}{\underset{-}{\overset{\_}{C}}} \quad v = \text{constant} \Rightarrow \quad i = 0 \uparrow \quad \text{open} \atop | \quad \text{circuit}$$

The inductor is a short circuit, $v_L(0^-) = 0$.

$$\downarrow i = \text{constant} \atop L \overset{+}{\underset{-}{\gtrless}} v = 0 \Rightarrow \overset{+}{\underset{-}{|}} v = 0 \quad \text{short} \atop \text{circuit}$$

3. Find $v_c(0^-) = v_c(0^+)$ or $i_L(0^-) = i_L(0^+)$.

4. Draw the circuit for positive time $t > 0$.

5. Remove C or L from the circuit, shut OFF all sources, find the equivalent resistance R_{eq} seen looking into the terminals where C or L was located. This resistance value is what C or L sees during the transient response. This value determines the time constant.

6. $\tau = R_{eq}C$ or $\tau = L/R_{eq}$.

7. Let time go to infinity $t \to \infty$. The circuit is at rest where all voltages and currents are constants. The capacitor is an open circuit, $i_c(\infty) = 0$, and the inductor is a short circuit, $v_L(\infty) = 0$ as illustrated above.

8. Find $v_c(\infty)$ or $i_L(\infty)$.

9. Write the solution using the initial and final values plus the time constant,

$$x(t) = x(\infty) + [x(0) - x(\infty)]e^{-t/\tau}, \quad t \ge 0$$

10. Sketch the time response that fits the given solution. Label $x(0)$, and $x(\infty)$, and be sure to include the line of initial slope and mark the time axis at multiples of the time constant up to five constants.

11. If the problem requires finding other voltages or currents, solve for them given the capacitor voltage or inductor current. Be sure to note whether the other voltages or currents are discontinuous at $t = 0$. If so, $x(0) = x(0^+) \ne x(0^-)$, because $x(0)$ does not exist.

Examples

Example 1: Find the capacitor voltage $v_c(t)$ and resistor voltage $v_r(t)$ in the following circuit.

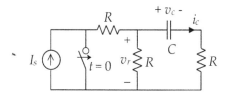

The circuit for negative time $t < 0$ is

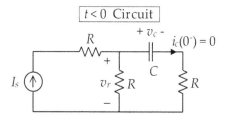

Because the circuit is at rest, the capacitor current is zero as shown. As a result, there is no voltage across the resistor on the right, $v = i_c(0^-) \cdot R = 0 \cdot R = 0$, and the source current I_s flows through the two other resistors in series. So the voltage across the capacitor is equal to the central resistor voltage v_r. Therefore, by Ohm's law the initial capacitor voltage is,

$$v_c(0^-) = v_c(0^+) = v_r(0^-) = I_s R$$

The circuit for positive time $t > 0$ is

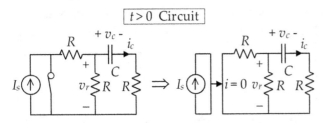

The equivalent circuit on the right shows that the current source no longer contributes current to the right side of the circuit. The switch diverts all the source current I_s directly around the current source so none can flow to the right as shown.

To find the equivalent resistance R_{eq} for the time constant, remove the capacitor and find the resistance seen looking into the terminals where the capacitor was connected. Doing so leads to the circuit below.

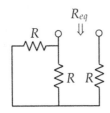

The two resistors on the left are in parallel since they form a nonessential loop. Because they have the same value, they combine to form $R \| R = R/2$. Then the equivalent resistance seen looking into the terminals is

$$R_{eq} = (R \| R) + R = \frac{R}{2} + R = \frac{3R}{2}$$

The associated time constant is

$$\tau = R_{eq} C = \frac{3R}{2} C = \frac{3}{2} RC$$

From the $t > 0$ circuit, it is clear that there is no source of energy connected to the capacitor in positive time. So, the capacitor discharges all of its energy into the equivalent resistance R_{eq}, and the final value for the capacitor voltage is

$$v_c(\infty) = 0$$

The expression for the capacitor voltage then becomes

$$v_c(t) = v_c(\infty) + \left[v_c(0) - v_c(\infty) \right] e^{-t/\tau}, \quad t \geq 0$$

$$v_c(t) = 0 + \left[v_c(0) - 0 \right] e^{-t/\tau}, \quad t \geq 0$$

$$v_c(t) = 0 + \left[I_s R \right] e^{-t/(3RC/2)}, \quad t \geq 0$$

$$v_c(t) = (I_s R) e^{-2t/(3RC)}, \quad t \geq 0$$

The following plot illustrates this solution.

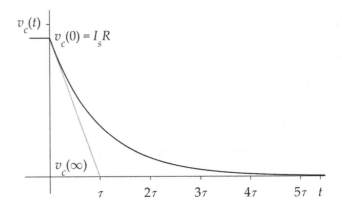

Now that the capacitor voltage is known, the resistor voltage $v_r(t)$ is easily found. The following circuit shows the $t > 0$ circuit after the two resistors on the left are combined in parallel.

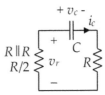

Inspection of this circuit shows that the resistor voltage $v_r(t)$ for $t > 0$ is given by voltage division between the two resistors

$$v_r(t) = \frac{R/2}{R/2 + R} v_c(t) = \frac{R/2}{3R/2} v_c(t) = \frac{v_c(t)}{3}, \quad t > 0$$

Recalling $v_r(0^-)$ from earlier, and substituting $v_c(t)$ into the above expression gives the final result

$$v_r(t) = \begin{cases} I_s R, & t < 0 \\ \dfrac{I_s R}{3} e^{-2t/(3RC)}, & t > 0 \end{cases}$$

It is important to note that this resistor voltage is discontinuous at $t = 0$ because

$$v_r(0^-) = I_s R \quad \text{and} \quad v_r(0^+) = I_s R/3$$

The following plot illustrates this response.

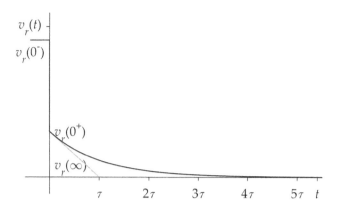

Example 2: Find the inductor current $i_L(t)$ and the voltage $v_r(t)$ in the following circuit.

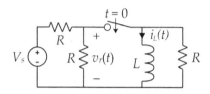

The right hand side of the circuit for negative time $t < 0$ is

Because there is no source in the circuit, the initial inductor current is zero, $i_L(0^-) = 0$, and the response is the step response.

Inspection of the left hand side of the circuit shows that $v_r(0^-)$ is given simply by the voltage division

$$v_r\left(0^-\right) = \frac{R}{R+R}V_s = \frac{V_s}{2}$$

The circuit for positive time $t > 0$ is

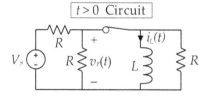

It is convenient to perform a source transformation on the voltage source in series with the resistor on the left. Doing so and combining the three resistors in parallel, *i.e.*, $R\|R\|R = R/3$, leads to the following equivalent revised circuit.

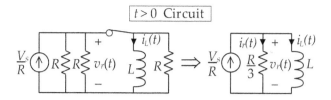

The equivalent resistance R_{eq} is the resistance as seen by the inductor with the current source shut OFF. From the equivalent circuit on the right R_{eq} is simply

$$R_{eq} = R \| R \| R = \frac{R}{3}$$

The associated time constant is then

$$\tau = \frac{L}{R_{eq}} = \frac{L}{R/3} = \frac{3L}{R}$$

The final value for the inductor current is found by letting time go to infinity, $t \to \infty$, where the circuit is at rest and the inductor is a short circuit because its voltage is zero $v_r(\infty) = v_L(\infty) = 0$. In this case, the circuit becomes

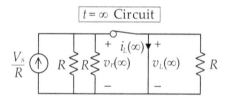

All three resistors are in parallel with the short circuit here, so the voltage across each of them is zero. By Ohm's law, the current through each of them is also zero, $i = v/R = 0/R = 0$. Therefore, all the current from the current source goes through the inductor,

$$i_L\left(\infty\right) = \frac{V_s}{R}$$

The expression for the inductor current then becomes

$$i_L\left(t\right) = i_L\left(\infty\right) + \left[i_L\left(0\right) - i_L\left(\infty\right)\right]e^{-t/\tau}, \quad t \geq 0$$

$$i_L\left(t\right) = \frac{V_s}{R} + \left[0 - \frac{V_s}{R}\right]e^{-t/(3L/R)}, \quad t \geq 0$$

$$i_L\left(t\right) = \frac{V_s}{R}\left[1 - e^{-t/(3L/R)}\right], \quad t \geq 0$$

The following figure shows a plot of this solution.

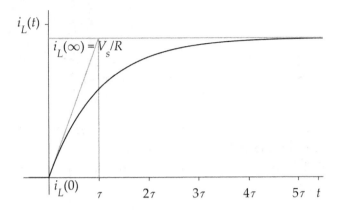

The voltage $v_r(t)$ in this circuit can be found now that the inductor current is known. The initial value of this voltage was found earlier as

$$v_r(0^-) = \frac{R}{R+R} V_s = \frac{V_s}{2}$$

To find $v_r(t)$ for $t > 0$, reconsider the simplified circuit for positive time as shown in the following figure.

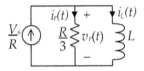

Applying KCL to the top node gives

$$i_r(t) = \frac{V_s}{R} - i_L(t)$$

and Ohm's law for the equivalent resistance gives the desired voltage

$$v_r(t) = \frac{R}{3} i_r(t)$$

Combining these two equations and substituting in the expression for the inductor current gives

$$v_r(t) = \frac{R}{3} i_r(t) = \frac{R}{3}\left(\frac{V_s}{R} - i_L(t)\right) = \frac{V_s}{3} - \frac{R}{3} i_L(t), \quad t > 0$$

which simplifies as

$$v_r(t) = \frac{V_s}{3} - \frac{R}{3} \cdot \frac{V_s}{R}\left[1 - e^{-t/(3L/R)}\right], \quad t > 0$$

$$v_r(t) = \frac{V_s}{3} - \frac{V_s}{3}\left[1 - e^{-t/(3L/R)}\right], \quad t > 0$$

$$v_r(t) = \frac{V_s}{3} - \frac{V_s}{3} + \frac{V_s}{3} e^{-t/(3L/R)}, \quad t > 0$$

$$v_r(t) = \frac{V_s}{3} e^{-t/(3L/R)}, \quad t > 0$$

Evaluating this expression at $t = 0^+$ shows that the resistor voltage jumps or is discontinuous when the switch changes state,

$$v_r(0^+) = \frac{V_s}{3} e^{-(0)/(3L/R)} = \frac{V_s}{3}$$

To summarize, the resistor voltage is

$$v_r(t) = \begin{cases} \dfrac{V_s}{2}, & t < 0 \\ \dfrac{V_s}{3} e^{-t/(3L/R)}, & t > 0 \end{cases}$$

The following plot shows the accompanying sketch of the solution.

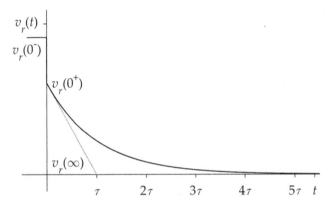

Example 3: Find the inductor current $i_L(t)$ in the following circuit. When the switch changes position in this circuit, the two sources remain connected, so this is a complete response problem.

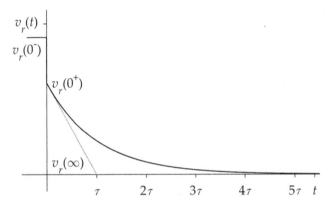

The circuit for negative time $t < 0$ is

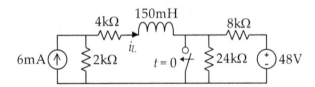

where the fact that the circuit is at rest means that $v_L(0^-) = 0$ and the inductor appears as a short circuit has been taken into account. In addition, a reference node and the two essential nodes have been labeled.

The initial inductor current $i_L(0^-)$ can be found by applying nodal analysis. Writing KCL for the two essential nodes gives

$$\text{KCL @ (1)} \qquad -6\,\text{m} + \frac{v_1}{2\,\text{k}} + \frac{v_1 - v_2}{4\,\text{k}} = 0$$

$$\text{KCL @ (2)} \qquad \frac{v_2 - v_1}{4\,\text{k}} + \frac{v_2}{24\,\text{k}} + \frac{v_2 - 48}{8\,\text{k}} = 0$$

Solving this set of equations gives the results

$$v_1 = 16\,\text{V} \qquad v_2 = 24\,\text{V}$$

Ohm's law gives the initial inductor current as

$$i_L(0^-) = i_L(0^+) = \frac{v_1 - v_2}{4\,\text{k}} = \frac{16-24}{4\,\text{k}} = \frac{-8}{4\,\text{k}} = -2\,\text{mA}$$

The circuit for positive time $t > 0$ is

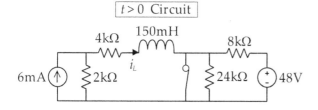

With the switch closed, the circuit elements to the right of the switch no longer have an effect because the switch places a short circuit across the circuit. Therefore, the circuit simplifies to

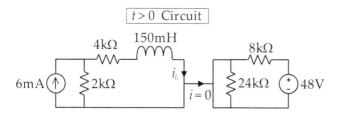

To find the equivalent resistance R_{eq} for the time constant, shut OFF the current source, remove the inductor, and find the resistance seen looking into the terminals where the inductor was connected. Doing so leads to the circuit

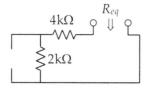

The 4 kΩ and 2 kΩ resistors are in series with the terminals, so the equivalent resistance is simply

$$R_{eq} = 4\,\text{k}\Omega + 2\,\text{k}\Omega = 6\,\text{k}\Omega$$

Then the time constant is

$$\tau = \frac{L}{R_{eq}} = \frac{150\,\text{m}}{6\,\text{k}} = 25\,\mu\text{s}$$

The final value for the inductor current is found by letting time go to infinity, $t \to \infty$, where the circuit is at rest and the inductor is a short circuit because its voltage is zero $v_L(\infty) = 0$. In this case, the circuit becomes

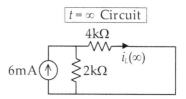

Current division provides a simple solution for the final value of the inductor current as

$$i_L(\infty) = \frac{2\,\text{k}}{2\,\text{k}+4\,\text{k}}\,6\,\text{mA} = \frac{2\,\text{k}}{6\,\text{k}}\,6\,\text{mA} = 2\,\text{mA}$$

The complete response expression for the inductor current then becomes

$$i_L(t) = i_L(\infty) + \left[i_L(0) - i_L(\infty)\right]e^{-t/\tau}, \quad t \geq 0$$

$$i_L(t) = 2\,\text{m} + \left[-2\,\text{m} - (2\,\text{m})\right]e^{-t/25\mu}, \quad t \geq 0$$

$$i_L(t) = 2 - 4\,e^{-t/25\mu} \;\text{mA}, \quad t \geq 0$$

And the corresponding plot of this response is shown in the following figure.

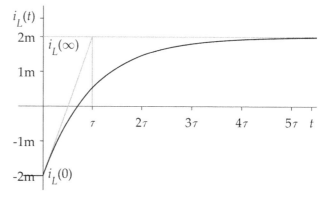

As a follow up problem, find the voltage $v_1(t)$ across the 6 mA source. The earlier solution to the $t < 0$ circuit found this voltage to be

$$v_1(0^-) = 16\,V$$

Redrawing the $t > 0$ circuit to identify node ① gives the figure on the top of the next page.

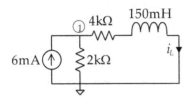

The voltage $v_1(t)$ is found by applying KCL to node ① as

$$-6\,m + \frac{v_1(t)}{2k} + i_L(t) = 0$$

Solving this equation for $v_1(t)$ gives

$$\frac{v_1(t)}{2k} = 6\,m - i_L(t)$$
$$v_1(t) = (2k)\cdot(6\,m) - (2k)\cdot i_L(t)$$
$$v_1(t) = 12 - (2k)\cdot\left(2\,m - 4\,m e^{-t/25\mu}\right)$$
$$v_1(t) = 12 - 4 + 8e^{-t/25\mu}$$
$$v_1(t) = 8 + 8e^{-t/25\mu}\ \ V,\ \ t>0$$

Though not true in general, in this particular case, $v_1(0^+) = v_1(0^-) = 16\ V$ since

$$v_1(0^+) = 8 + 8e^{-0^+/25\mu} = 8+8\cdot 1 = 16\ V$$

The following plot illustrates this solution.

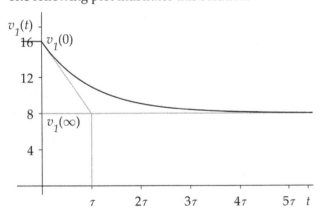

5.6 Second Order Transients

The terminal relationships for the capacitor and inductor relate the element voltage and current by differentiation. As a result, derivatives appear when writing KCL and KVL expressions for circuits containing these elements.

While a circuit may contain any number of capacitors and inductors, the fundamental behavior of a circuit having one capacitor and one inductor is vitally important. Writing the KCL or KVL equations for these circuits leads to a second order differential equation because both $i = C\,dv/dt$ and $v = L\,di/dt$ play a role in the resulting equations.

Second order differential equations were discussed in Chapter 1, Section 1.14, pages 22–30. The form of the second order differential equation is

$$\frac{d^2 x}{dt^2} + 2\alpha\frac{dx}{dt} + \omega_o^2 x = X$$

where X is zero for the natural response, and a nonzero constant for the complete response. The factor α is called the damping factor and ω_o is the resonant frequency.

The two primary and fundamental responses of second order differential equation are overdamped and underdamped. The characteristics of these two responses are shown in the following two tables. The other second order responses, critically damped and undamped, require ideal conditions that are impossible to implement in practice with real world components. So, these cases have significance from a mathematical perspective only.

Second Order Overdamped Response
$\alpha > \omega_o$
$s_1, s_2 = -\alpha \pm \sqrt{\alpha^2 - \omega_o^2}$, Real Values
$x(t) = K_1 e^{s_1 t} + K_2 e^{s_2 t} + x(\infty),\quad t\geq 0$
$\begin{bmatrix} 1 & 1 \\ s_1 & s_2 \end{bmatrix}\cdot\begin{bmatrix} K_1 \\ K_2 \end{bmatrix} = \begin{bmatrix} x(0) - x(\infty) \\ dx(0)/dt \end{bmatrix}$

When a circuit is constructed from a resistor, inductor, and capacitor, the components can be connected in series with each other or in parallel with each other as shown below. Therefore, there are two basic circuit configurations to consider using these three elements.

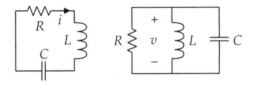

Second Order UnderDamped Response

$$\alpha < \omega_o$$

$$s_1, s_2 = -\alpha \pm j\omega_d, \quad \omega_d = \sqrt{\omega_o^2 - \alpha^2}, \text{ Complex Values}$$

$$x(t) = e^{-\alpha t}\left[B_1\cos(\omega_d t) + B_2\sin(\omega_d t)\right] + x(\infty), \quad t \geq 0$$

$$B_1 = x(0) - x(\infty), \quad B_2 = \left(dx(0)/dt + \alpha B_1\right)/\omega_d$$

or

$$x(t) = D e^{-t/\tau}\cos(\omega_d t - \phi) + x(\infty), \quad t \geq 0$$

$$\tau = 1/\alpha$$
$$D = |B_1 + jB_2| = \sqrt{B_1^2 + B_2^2}$$
$$\phi = \angle(B_1 + jB_2) = \text{atan2}\left(B_2, B_1\right)$$

Series RLC Circuits

Consider the series RLC circuit shown below. For visual simplicity, no circuitry for establishing initial conditions for the inductor current $i_L(0^-)$ and the capacitor voltage $v_c(0^-)$ is shown. Such circuitry will be included in the examples.

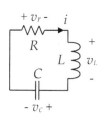

Because all three elements are in series, they share the same current i. Applying KVL to the loop formed by these three elements gives

$$v_L + v_r + v_c = 0$$
$$L\frac{di}{dt} + Ri + \frac{1}{C}\int i(\tau)d\tau = 0$$

This integro-differential equation can be solved for the current i if it is differentiated once, then simplified,

$$L\frac{d^2 i}{dt^2} + R\frac{di}{dt} + \frac{1}{C}i = 0$$
$$\frac{d^2 i}{dt^2} + \frac{R}{L}\frac{di}{dt} + \frac{1}{LC}i = 0$$

This second order differential equation matches the standard form

$$\frac{d^2 x}{dt^2} + 2\alpha\frac{dx}{dt} + \omega_o^2 x = X$$

when $i = x$, $X = 0$,

$$2\alpha = \frac{R}{L} \Rightarrow \alpha = \frac{R}{2L}$$

and

$$\omega_o^2 = \frac{1}{LC} \Rightarrow \omega_o = \frac{1}{\sqrt{LC}}$$

The solution to this differential equation depends on the relative size of α compared to ω_o.

Series Overdamped: If $\alpha > \omega_o$, the response is overdamped, giving the solution

$$i(t) = K_1 e^{s_1 t} + K_2 e^{s_2 t} + i(\infty), \quad t \geq 0$$

where $i(\infty) = 0$ because this is the natural response, and s_1 and s_2 are given by

$$s_1, s_2 = -\alpha \pm \sqrt{\alpha^2 - \omega_o^2}$$

The coefficients K_1 and K_2 depend on the initial inductor current and the initial capacitor voltage. They are found by solving the set of equations

$$\begin{bmatrix} 1 & 1 \\ s_1 & s_2 \end{bmatrix} \cdot \begin{bmatrix} K_1 \\ K_2 \end{bmatrix} = \begin{bmatrix} i(0) - i(\infty) \\ di(0)/dt \end{bmatrix}$$

Solving this set of equations requires knowledge of the right hand side. The current $i(0) = i(0^-) = i(0^+)$ is the initial inductor current. The final current $i(\infty)$ is zero because there is no source of energy in the circuit. The derivative $di(0)/dt$ requires more work. Using the terminal relationship for the inductor, this derivative is

$$v_L = L\frac{di}{dt}$$
$$\frac{v_L}{L} = \frac{di}{dt}$$

So, finding the derivative means finding the inductor voltage. This is given by the original KVL equation as

$$v_L + v_c + v_r = 0 \Rightarrow v_L = -(v_c + v_r)$$

Substituting this expression for v_L into the equation for di/dt gives

$$\frac{v_L}{L} = -\frac{(v_c + v_r)}{L} = \frac{di}{dt}$$

But the resistor voltage $v_r = iR$, so this expression becomes

$$\frac{di}{dt} = -\frac{v_c + iR}{L}$$

This equation is now in terms of the component values and the inductor current and capacitor voltage. Evaluating this at $t = 0$ gives the desired result,

$$\frac{di(0)}{dt} = -\left(\frac{v_c(0) + i(0)R}{L}\right)$$

where $v_c(0) = v_c(0^-) = v_c(0^+)$ is the initial capacitor voltage. Because the capacitor voltage and the inductor current are continuous at $t = 0$, the voltage across the inductor is also continuous.

This value for the initial current slope can be substituted into the set of equations to be solved,

$$\begin{bmatrix} 1 & 1 \\ s_1 & s_2 \end{bmatrix} \cdot \begin{bmatrix} K_1 \\ K_2 \end{bmatrix} = \begin{bmatrix} i(0) - i(\infty) \\ -\left(\dfrac{v_c(0) + i(0)R}{L}\right) \end{bmatrix}$$

Once this set of equations is solved, the final expression for the current can be found by substituting all the terms into the basic equation,

$$i(t) = K_1 e^{s_1 t} + K_2 e^{s_2 t} + i(\infty), \quad t \geq 0$$

Because s_1 and s_2 are negative real values, this response is the sum of two decaying exponential functions. The time constants associated with the exponential functions are

$$\tau_1 = \frac{-1}{s_1} = \frac{-1}{-\alpha + \sqrt{\alpha^2 - \omega_o^2}}$$

$$\tau_2 = \frac{-1}{s_2} = \frac{-1}{-\alpha - \sqrt{\alpha^2 - \omega_o^2}}$$

and the response can be rewritten as

$$i(t) = K_1 e^{-t/\tau_1} + K_2 e^{-t/\tau_2} + i(\infty), \quad t \geq 0$$

The first time constant τ_1 is larger than the second τ_2 because its denominator is smaller. Therefore, the first exponential decays more slowly than the second, and the time for the response to decay to zero is dictated by τ_1. Therefore, the overdamped response decays to $i(\infty) = 0$ in the five time constants, $t = 5\tau_1$.

For the most part, the overdamped response has no notable features. The resistor absorbs energy so quickly that the energy stored in the inductor and capacitor dissipates rapidly with little interchange of energy between the two.

In terms of the pendulum analogy, the overdamped response resembles immersing a pendulum in water, then letting the pendulum mass drop. In this case, the resistance provided by the water absorbs energy so quickly that the potential energy is largely absorbed before it is converted to kinetic energy. The pendulum mass reaches its low point and stays there with little motion around the low point.

Series Underdamped: If $\alpha < \omega_o$, the response is underdamped, giving the solution

$$i(t) = e^{-\alpha t}\left[B_1 \cos(\omega_d t) + B_2 \sin(\omega_d t)\right] + i(\infty), \quad t \geq 0$$

where $i(\infty) = 0$ because this is the natural response, and the **damped resonant frequency** ω_d is given by

$$\omega_d = \sqrt{\omega_o^2 - \alpha^2}$$

The coefficients B_1 and B_2 depend on the initial inductor current and the initial capacitor voltage. They are found by solving the equations

$$B_1 = i(0) - i(\infty)$$

$$B_2 = \left(\frac{di(0)/dt + \alpha B_1}{\omega_d}\right)$$

The current $i(0) = i(0^-) = i(0^+)$ is the initial inductor current. The final current $i(\infty)$ is zero because there is no source of energy in the circuit. The derivative $di(0)/dt$ remains unchanged from that derived for the overdamped case,

$$\frac{di(0)}{dt} = -\left(\frac{v_c(0) + i(0)R}{L}\right)$$

So, this value can be substituted into the expression for B_2.

This response can also be expressed in the alternative form

$$i(t) = D e^{-t/\tau} \cos(\omega_d t - \phi), \quad t \geq 0$$

where

$$\tau = 1/\alpha$$

$$D = |B_1 + jB_2| = \sqrt{B_1^2 + B_2^2}$$

$$\phi = \angle(B_1 + jB_2) = \text{atan2}(B_2, B_1)$$

When the natural response is written in this form, it is possible to express the energy stored in the inductor as

$$w_L = \frac{1}{2}Li^2$$

$$w_L(t) = \frac{1}{2}L\left(De^{-t/\tau}\cos(\omega_d t - \phi)\right)^2, \quad t \geq 0$$

$$w_L(t) = \frac{1}{2}LD^2 e^{-2t/\tau}\cos^2(\omega_d t - \phi), \quad t \geq 0$$

This expression is too complex to gain any analytic insight. However, it is useful for plotting the energy stored in the inductor as a function of time.

To describe the energy stored in the capacitor, it is necessary to find the capacitor voltage. This can be done two ways. First, the KVL relationship provides one expression,

$$v_L + v_c + v_r = 0 \Rightarrow v_c = -(v_L + v_r)$$

where the terms on the right hand side are easily written in terms of the solved current i as

$$v_c = -(v_L + v_r) = -\left(L\frac{di}{dt} + Ri\right)$$

Alternatively, the capacitor voltage is related to the inductor current through integration,

$$v_c(t) = \frac{1}{C}\int_0^t i(\tau)d\tau + v_c(0)$$

Finding the capacitor voltage through either of these expressions is not easy. Symbolic algebra software helps a great deal. After a great deal of symbolic manipulation, the capacitor voltage can be written as

$$v_c(t) = -DM_s e^{-t/\tau}\cos(\omega_d t - \phi + \beta), \quad t \geq 0$$

where

$$M_s = \sqrt{\frac{L}{C}}$$

$$\beta = \text{atan}(\omega_d \tau)$$

When written in this form, it is possible to express the energy stored in the capacitor as

$$w_c(t) = \frac{1}{2}Cv_c^2(t)$$

$$w_c(t) = \frac{1}{2}C\left(-DM_s e^{-t/\tau}\cos(\omega_d t - \phi + \beta)\right)^2, \quad t \geq 0$$

$$w_c(t) = \frac{1}{2}C(DM_s)^2 e^{-2t/\tau}\cos^2(\omega_d t - \phi + \beta), \quad t \geq 0$$

Once again, this expression is useful for plotting purposes. The only significant analytic insight is the phase shift β between the inductor current and capacitor voltage. This phase shift makes the peaks in the energy expressions occur out of phase with each other. As a result, the energy moves back and forth between the inductor and capacitor, just as the energy in the pendulum moves back and forth between potential and kinetic energy as the pendulum swings from side to side.

Given the energy stored in the inductor and the capacitor, it is possible to find the energy dissipated in or absorbed by the resistor. Starting with the initial energy stored in the circuit,

$$w(0) = w_L(0) + w_c(0)$$

the energy dissipated in the resistor is equal to the net amount not stored in either the inductor or capacitor over time,

$$w_r(t) = w(0) - w_L(t) - w_c(t)$$

A plot of the energy in all three elements visually demonstrates the movement of energy within the circuit.

Parallel RLC Circuits

Consider the following parallel RLC circuit. For visual simplicity, no circuitry for establishing initial conditions for the inductor current $i_L(0^-)$ and the capacitor voltage $v_c(0^-)$ is shown. Such circuitry will be included in the examples.

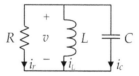

Because all three elements are in parallel, they share the same voltage v. Applying KCL to the upper node gives

$$i_c + i_r + i_L = 0$$

$$C\frac{dv}{dt} + \frac{v}{R} + \frac{1}{L}\int v(\tau)d\tau = 0$$

This integro-differential equation can be solved for the voltage v if it is differentiated once, then simplified as

$$C\frac{d^2v}{dt^2} + \frac{1}{R}\frac{dv}{dt} + \frac{1}{L}v = 0$$

$$\frac{d^2v}{dt^2} + \frac{1}{RC}\frac{dv}{dt} + \frac{1}{LC}v = 0$$

This second order differential equation matches the standard form

$$\frac{d^2x}{dt^2} + 2\alpha\frac{dx}{dt} + \omega_o^2 x = X$$

when $v = x$, $X = 0$,

$$2\alpha = \frac{1}{RC} \Rightarrow \alpha = \frac{1}{2RC}$$

and

$$\omega_o^2 = \frac{1}{LC} \Rightarrow \omega_o = \frac{1}{\sqrt{LC}}$$

The expression for α here differs from that for the series RLC circuit, but the value for ω_o remains unchanged.

The solution to this differential equation depends on the relative size of α compared to ω_o.

Parallel Overdamped: If $\alpha > \omega_o$, the response is overdamped, giving the solution

$$v(t) = K_1 e^{s_1 t} + K_2 e^{s_2 t} + v(\infty), \quad t \geq 0$$

where $v(\infty) = 0$ because this is the natural response, and s_1 and s_2 are given by

$$s_1, s_2 = -\alpha \pm \sqrt{\alpha^2 - \omega_o^2}$$

The coefficients K_1 and K_2 depend on the initial conditions on the inductor current and the capacitor voltage, and are found by solving the set of equations

$$\begin{bmatrix} 1 & 1 \\ s_1 & s_2 \end{bmatrix} \cdot \begin{bmatrix} K_1 \\ K_2 \end{bmatrix} = \begin{bmatrix} v(0) - v(\infty) \\ dv(0)/dt \end{bmatrix}$$

Solving this set of equations requires knowledge of the right hand side. The voltage $v(0) = v(0^-) = v(0^+)$ is the initial capacitor voltage. The final voltage $v(\infty)$ is zero because there is no source of energy in the circuit. The derivative $dv(0)/dt$ requires more work. Using the terminal relationship for the capacitor, this derivative is

$$i_c = C\frac{dv}{dt}$$

$$\frac{i_c}{C} = \frac{dv}{dt}$$

So, finding the derivative means finding the capacitor current. This is given by the original KCL equation as

$$i_r + i_L + i_c = 0 \Rightarrow i_c = -(i_r + i_L)$$

Substituting this expression for i_c into the equation for dv/dt gives

$$\frac{i_c}{C} = -\frac{(i_r + i_L)}{C} = \frac{dv}{dt}$$

But the resistor current is $i_r = v/R$, so this expression becomes

$$\frac{dv}{dt} = -\frac{v/R + i_L}{C}$$

This equation is now in terms of the component values and the inductor current and capacitor voltage. Evaluating this at $t = 0$ gives the desired result,

$$\frac{dv(0)}{dt} = -\left(\frac{v(0)/R + i_L(0)}{C}\right)$$

$$\frac{dv(0)}{dt} = -\left(\frac{v(0) + i_L(0)R}{RC}\right)$$

where $i_L(0) = i_L(0^-) = i_L(0^+)$ is the initial inductor current. Because the capacitor voltage and the inductor current are continuous at $t = 0$, the current through the capacitor is also.

This value for the initial voltage slope can be substituted into the set of equations to be solved,

$$\begin{bmatrix} 1 & 1 \\ s_1 & s_2 \end{bmatrix} \cdot \begin{bmatrix} K_1 \\ K_2 \end{bmatrix} = \begin{bmatrix} v(0) - v(\infty) \\ -\left(\dfrac{v(0) + i_L(0)R}{RC}\right) \end{bmatrix}$$

Once this set of equations is solved, the final expression for the voltage can be found by substituting all the terms into the basic equation,

$$v(t) = K_1 e^{s_1 t} + K_2 e^{s_2 t} + v(\infty), \quad t \geq 0$$

Because s_1 and s_2 are negative real values, this response is the sum of two decaying exponentials. The time constants associated with the two exponentials are

$$\tau_1 = \frac{-1}{s_1} = \frac{-1}{-\alpha + \sqrt{\alpha^2 - \omega_o^2}}$$

$$\tau_2 = \frac{-1}{s_2} = \frac{-1}{-\alpha - \sqrt{\alpha^2 - \omega_o^2}}$$

and the response can be rewritten as

$$v(t) = K_1 e^{-t/\tau_1} + K_2 e^{-t/\tau_2} + v(\infty), \quad t \geq 0$$

The first time constant τ_1 is larger than the second τ_2 because its denominator is smaller. Therefore, the first exponential decays more slowly than the second, and the overdamped response decays to $v(\infty) = 0$ in the five time constants, $t = 5\tau_1$.

For the most part, the overdamped response has no notable features. The resistor absorbs energy so quickly that the energy stored in the inductor and capacitor dissipates rapidly with little interchange of energy between the two.

In terms of the pendulum analogy, the overdamped response resembles immersing a pendulum in water, then letting the pendulum mass drop. In this case, the resistance provided by the water absorbs energy so quickly that the potential energy is largely absorbed before it is converted to kinetic energy. The pendulum mass reaches its low point and stays there with little motion around the low point.

Parallel Underdamped: If $\alpha < \omega_o$, the response is underdamped, giving the solution

$$v(t) = e^{-\alpha t}\Big[B_1 \cos(\omega_d t) + B_2 \sin(\omega_d t)\Big] + v(\infty), \quad t \geq 0$$

where $v(\infty) = 0$ because there is no energy source in the circuit, and the **damped resonant frequency** ω_d is given by

$$\omega_d = \sqrt{\omega_o^2 - \alpha^2}$$

The coefficients B_1 and B_2 depend on the initial conditions on the inductor current and the capacitor voltage, and are found by solving the equations

$$B_1 = v(0) - v(\infty)$$

$$B_2 = \left(\frac{dv(0)/dt + \alpha B_1}{\omega_d}\right)$$

The voltage $v(0) = v(0^-) = v(0^+)$ is the initial capacitor voltage. The derivative $dv(0)/dt$ remains unchanged from that derived for the overdamped case,

$$\frac{dv(0)}{dt} = -\left(\frac{v(0) + i_L(0)R}{RC}\right)$$

The natural response can also be expressed in the alternative form

$$v(t) = D e^{-t/\tau}\cos(\omega_d t - \phi), \quad t \geq 0$$

where

$$\tau = 1/\alpha$$

$$D = |B_1 + jB_2| = \sqrt{B_1^2 + B_2^2}$$

$$\phi = \angle(B_1 + jB_2) = \text{atan2}\big(B_2, B_1\big)$$

When written in this form, it is possible to express the energy stored in the capacitor as

$$w_c = \frac{1}{2}C v^2$$

$$w_c(t) = \frac{1}{2}C\Big(D e^{-t/\tau}\cos(\omega_d t - \phi)\Big)^2, \quad t \geq 0$$

$$w_c(t) = \frac{1}{2}C D^2 e^{-2t/\tau}\cos^2(\omega_d t - \phi), \quad t \geq 0$$

This expression is too complex to gain any analytic insight. However, it is useful for plotting the energy stored in the inductor as a function of time.

To describe the energy stored in the inductor, it is necessary to find the inductor current. This can be done two ways. First, the KCL relationship provides one expression,

$$i_L + i_c + i_r = 0 \implies i_L = -(i_c + i_r)$$

where the terms on the right hand side are easily written in terms of the solved voltage v as

$$i_L = -(i_c + i_r) = -\left(C\frac{dv}{dt} + \frac{v}{R}\right)$$

Alternatively, the inductor current is related to the voltage through integration,

$$i_L(t) = \frac{1}{L}\int_0^t v(\tau)d\tau + i_L(0)$$

Finding the inductor current through either of these expressions is not fun. Symbolic algebra software helps a great deal. After a great deal of symbolic manipulation, the inductor current can be written as

$$i_L(t) = -D M_p e^{-t/\tau}\cos(\omega_d t - \phi + \beta), \quad t \geq 0$$

where

$$M_p = \sqrt{\frac{C}{L}}$$

$$\beta = \operatorname{atan}(\omega_d \tau)$$

When written in this form, it is possible to express the energy stored in the inductor as

$$w_L(t) = \frac{1}{2} L i_L^2(t)$$

$$w_L(t) = \frac{1}{2} L \left(-D M_p e^{-t/\tau} \cos(\omega_d t - \phi + \beta) \right)^2, \quad t \geq 0$$

$$w_L(t) = \frac{1}{2} L (D M_p)^2 e^{-2t/\tau} \cos^2(\omega_d t - \phi + \beta), \quad t \geq 0$$

Once again, this expression is useful for plotting purposes. The only significant analytic insight is the phase shift β between the inductor current and capacitor voltage. This phase shift makes the peaks in the energy expressions occur out of phase with each other. As a result, the energy moves back and forth between the inductor and capacitor, just as the energy in the pendulum moves back and forth between potential and kinetic energy as the pendulum swings from side to side.

Given the energy stored in the inductor and the capacitor, it is possible to find the energy dissipated in or absorbed by the resistor. Starting with the initial energy stored in the circuit,

$$w(0) = w_L(0) + w_c(0)$$

the energy dissipated in the resistor is equal to the net amount not stored in either the inductor or capacitor over time,

$$w_r(t) = w(0) - w_L(t) - w_c(t)$$

A plot of the energy in all three elements visually demonstrates the movement of energy within the circuit.

Problem Solving Procedure

Solving simple RLC circuits is generally more involved than solving the RC and RL circuits considered earlier. RLC circuits can appear in series or in parallel. Series RLC circuits are solved for the inductor current i that all elements share, and the damping factor is related to the inductance, $\alpha = R/(2L)$. Parallel RLC circuits are solved for the capacitor voltage v that all elements share, and the damping factor is related to the capacitance, $\alpha = 1/(2RC)$.

In addition, circuit responses can be either overdamped or underdamped. The overdamped response is characterized by two decaying exponents that mimic the responses found for RC and RL circuits. On the other hand, the underdamped response is characterized by a decaying sinusoidal response, commonly called "ringing."

The procedure for solving both series and parallel RLC circuits is as follows.

Solving RLC Circuits
1. Identify whether the RLC circuit is in series or parallel form by studying the circuit for positive time $t > 0$ and shutting OFF all sources.
2. Draw the circuit for negative time $t < 0$ when the circuit is at rest and all voltages and currents are constants. When at rest, the capacitor is an open circuit, $i = 0$ $v = \text{constant}$ $\Rightarrow$ $i = 0$ open circuit   And the inductor is a short circuit, $i = \text{constant}$, $v = 0$ $\Rightarrow$ $v = 0$ short circuit
3. Determine the initial conditions by finding the capacitor voltage $v_c(0^-)$ and the inductor current $i_L(0^-)$.
4. Draw the circuit for positive time $t > 0$
5. If a source remains in the circuit, find the final value of the current $i(\infty)$ for the series circuit or the final value of the voltage $v(\infty)$ for the parallel circuit. The circuit is at rest at $t = \infty$, so the capacitor is an open circuit and the inductor is a short circuit once again.
6. Compute the damping factor α and the resonant frequency ω_o,   Series: $\alpha = \dfrac{R}{2L}$ Parallel: $\alpha = \dfrac{1}{2RC}$ $\omega_o = \dfrac{1}{\sqrt{LC}}$

7. Determine if the circuit is overdamped or underdamped,

$$\text{Overdamped:} \quad \alpha > \omega_o$$
$$\text{Underdamped:} \quad \alpha < \omega_o$$

8. The overdamped solution for $t > 0$ is

$$\text{Series:} \quad i(t) = K_1 e^{s_1 t} + K_2 e^{s_2 t} + i(\infty), \quad t \geq 0$$

$$\text{Parallel:} \quad v(t) = K_1 e^{s_1 t} + K_2 e^{s_2 t} + v(\infty), \quad t \geq 0$$

where s_1 and s_2 are

$$s_1, s_2 = -\alpha \pm \sqrt{\alpha^2 - \omega_o^2}$$

and where the coefficients K_1 and K_2 are given by the solution to the set of equations

$$\text{Series:} \quad \begin{bmatrix} 1 & 1 \\ s_1 & s_2 \end{bmatrix} \cdot \begin{bmatrix} K_1 \\ K_2 \end{bmatrix} = \begin{bmatrix} i(0) - i(\infty) \\ -\left(\dfrac{v_c(0) + i(0)R}{L}\right) \end{bmatrix}$$

$$\text{Parallel:} \quad \begin{bmatrix} 1 & 1 \\ s_1 & s_2 \end{bmatrix} \cdot \begin{bmatrix} K_1 \\ K_2 \end{bmatrix} = \begin{bmatrix} v(0) - v(\infty) \\ -\left(\dfrac{v(0) + i_L(0)R}{RC}\right) \end{bmatrix}$$

9. The underdamped solution for $t > 0$ is

$$\text{Series:} \quad i(t) = e^{-\alpha t}\left[B_1 \cos(\omega_d t) + B_2 \sin(\omega_d t)\right] + i(\infty)$$

$$\text{Parallel:} \quad v(t) = e^{-\alpha t}\left[B_1 \cos(\omega_d t) + B_2 \sin(\omega_d t)\right] + v(\infty)$$

where

$$\omega_d = \sqrt{\omega_o^2 - \alpha^2}$$

and where the coefficients B_1 and B_2 are given by

$$\text{Series:} \quad B_1 = i(0) - i(\infty) \qquad B_2 = \left(\dfrac{di(0)/dt + \alpha B_1}{\omega_d}\right)$$

in which

$$\frac{di(0)}{dt} = -\left(\frac{v_c(0) + i(0)R}{L}\right)$$

and

$$\text{Parallel:} \quad B_1 = v(0) - v(\infty) \qquad B_2 = \left(\dfrac{dv(0)/dt + \alpha B_1}{\omega_d}\right)$$

in which

$$\frac{dv(0)}{dt} = -\left(\frac{v(0) + i_L(0)R}{RC}\right)$$

10. If the problem requires finding other voltages or currents, solve for them given the primary solution given above. Be sure to note whether the other voltages or currents are discontinuous at $t = 0$. In particular, expressions for the capacitor voltage in the series case and the inductor current for the parallel case were derived earlier. For the underdamped case, plots of the energy stored in the inductor and capacitor and the energy dissipated in or absorbed by the resistor provide valuable insight.

Examples

Example 1: Consider the following series RLC circuit where $V_s = 12$ V, $C = 62.5$ µF, $L = 0.1$ H, and $R = 100$ Ω.

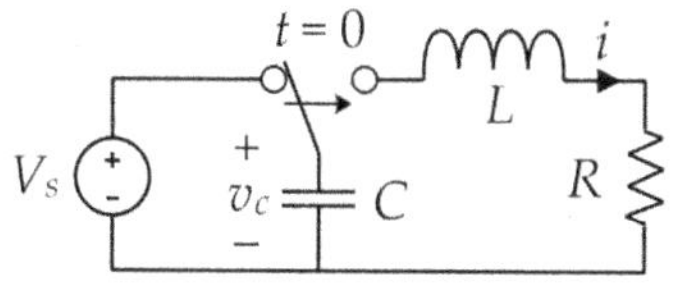

This is a series RLC circuit because the circuit contains one resistor, one inductor, and one capacitor connected in series for $t > 0$. The voltage source appears solely to establish an initial capacitor voltage.

The circuit for negative time is as shown above where the inductor and resistor are unconnected. The initial capacitor voltage is provided by the voltage source so $v_c(0^-) = V_s = 12$ V. The initial inductor current is $i_L(0^-) = 0$.

For positive time, the voltage source is disconnected, leaving a series RLC circuit. Therefore, $i(\infty) = 0$.

The damping factor and resonant frequency of this circuit are

$$\alpha = \frac{R}{2L} = \frac{100}{2 \cdot (0.1)} = 500$$

$$\omega_o = \frac{1}{\sqrt{LC}} = \frac{1}{\sqrt{(0.1)(6.25\text{e-}5)}} = 400$$

Since $\alpha > \omega_o$, this is an overdamped RLC circuit, and the values for s_1 and s_2 are

$$s_1, s_2 = -\alpha \pm \sqrt{\alpha^2 - \omega_0^2}$$

$$s_1, s_2 = -500 \pm \sqrt{500^2 - 400^2}$$

$$s_1, s_2 = -500 \pm \sqrt{300^2}$$

$$s_1, s_2 = -500 \pm 300$$

$$s_1 = -500 + 300 = -200$$

$$s_2 = -500 - 300 = -800$$

The time constants associated with these values are

$$\tau_1 = \frac{-1}{s_1} = \frac{-1}{-200} = 5\,\text{ms}$$

$$\tau_2 = \frac{-1}{s_2} = \frac{-1}{-800} = 1.25\,\text{ms}$$

The coefficients K_1 and K_2 are given by

$$\begin{bmatrix} 1 & 1 \\ s_1 & s_2 \end{bmatrix} \cdot \begin{bmatrix} K_1 \\ K_2 \end{bmatrix} = \begin{bmatrix} i(0) - i(\infty) \\ -\left(\dfrac{v_c(0) + i(0)R}{L} \right) \end{bmatrix}$$

$$\begin{bmatrix} 1 & 1 \\ -200 & -800 \end{bmatrix} \cdot \begin{bmatrix} K_1 \\ K_2 \end{bmatrix} = \begin{bmatrix} 0-0 \\ -\left(\dfrac{12+(0)100}{0.1} \right) \end{bmatrix} = \begin{bmatrix} 0 \\ -120 \end{bmatrix}$$

The solution of this set of equations yields

$$\begin{bmatrix} K_1 \\ K_2 \end{bmatrix} = \begin{bmatrix} -0.2 \\ 0.2 \end{bmatrix}$$

The final expression for the current is then

$$i(t) = K_1 e^{-s_1 t} + K_2 e^{-s_2 t} + i(\infty), \quad t \geq 0$$

$$i(t) = K_1 e^{-t/\tau_1} + K_2 e^{-t/\tau_2} + i(\infty), \quad t \geq 0$$

$$i(t) = -0.2\,e^{-t/(5\text{m})} + 0.2\,e^{-t/(1.25\text{m})}\,\text{A}, \quad t \geq 0$$

The larger of the two time constants is $\tau_1 = 5$ ms, so it takes $5\tau_1 = 25$ ms for this response to go to zero. A sketch of this response appears in the following figure. The individual solution components due to each time constant are shown as is their sum. The time axis has units equal to multiples of the larger time constant, $\tau_1 = 5$ ms. The solution component due to the faster time constant, $\tau_2 = 1.25$ ms, decays four times faster than τ_1 as expected.

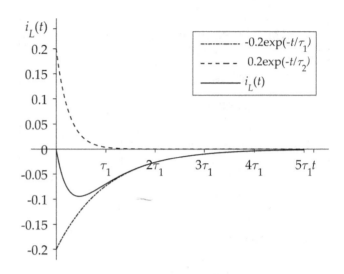

Example 2: Consider the following RLC circuit where $V_s = 12$ V, $R_s = 120\ \Omega$, $C = 5\ \mu\text{F}$, $L = 0.2$ H, and $R = 284\ \Omega$.

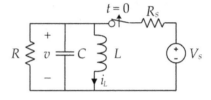

This is a parallel RLC circuit because the circuit contains one resistor, one inductor, and one capacitor connected in parallel for $t > 0$. The voltage source V_s and resistor R_s appear solely to establish an initial inductor current.

The circuit for negative time is as shown above. Since the circuit is at rest, the inductor acts as a short circuit, so the voltage v is zero. Therefore the initial capacitor voltage is zero $v(0^-) = 0$, and the initial inductor current is given by Ohm's law as

$$i_L(0^-) = i_L(0^+) = \frac{V_s}{R_s} = \frac{12}{120} = 0.1\,\text{A} = 100\ \text{mA}$$

For positive time, the voltage source V_s and resistor R_s are disconnected, leaving just a parallel RLC circuit. Therefore, $v(\infty) = 0$ since there is no longer a source of energy in the circuit.

The damping factor and resonant frequency of this circuit are

$$\alpha = \frac{1}{2RC} = \frac{1}{2(284)(5\text{e-}6)} = 352$$

$$\omega_0 = \frac{1}{\sqrt{LC}} = \frac{1}{\sqrt{(0.2)(5\text{e-}6)}} = 1000$$

Since $\alpha < \omega_o$, this is an underdamped RLC circuit, and the value for the damped resonant frequency is

$$\omega_d = \sqrt{\omega_o^2 - \alpha^2}$$
$$\omega_d = \sqrt{1000^2 - 352^2} = 936$$

The unknown coefficients in the solution are

$$B_1 = v(0) - v(\infty) = 0 - 0 = 0$$

$$B_2 = \frac{dv(0)/dt + \alpha B_1}{\omega_d} = \frac{dv(0)/dt + \alpha \cdot (0)}{\omega_d} = \frac{1}{\omega_d}\frac{dv(0)}{dt}$$

where

$$\frac{dv(0)}{dt} = -\left(\frac{v(0) + i_L(0)R}{RC}\right)$$

$$\frac{dv(0)}{dt} = -\left(\frac{0 + (0.1)(284)}{(284)(5\mu)}\right) = -\frac{0.1}{5\mu} = -20\,\text{kV/s}$$

So B_2 is

$$B_2 = \frac{1}{\omega_d}\frac{dv(0)}{dt} = \frac{1}{936}\cdot(-20\,\text{k}) = -21.4$$

The voltage across the parallel RLC circuit is then

$$v(t) = e^{-\alpha t}\left[B_1\cos(\omega_d t) + B_2\sin(\omega_d t)\right] + v(\infty),\quad t\geq 0$$
$$v(t) = e^{-352t}\left[0\cos(936t) - 21.4\sin(936t)\right] + 0,\quad t\geq 0$$
$$v(t) = -21.4\,e^{-352t}\sin(936t)\;\text{V},\quad t\geq 0$$

This can be written in the alternative form as

$$v(t) = D\,e^{-t/\tau}\cos(\omega_d t - \phi),\quad t\geq 0$$

where

$$\tau = 1/\alpha = 1/352 = 2.84\;\text{ms}$$
$$D = |B_1 + jB_2| = |0 - j21.4| = 21.4\;\text{V}$$
$$\phi = \angle(B_1 + jB_2) = \angle(0 - j21.4) = -90\,°$$

that leads to

$$v(t) = 21.4\,e^{-t/(2.84\,\text{ms})}\cos(936t + 90°)\;\text{V},\quad t\geq 0$$

This form makes it possible to describe the inductor current as

$$i_L(t) = -DM_p\,e^{-t/\tau}\cos(\omega_d t - \phi + \beta)\;\text{A},\quad t\geq 0$$

where

$$M_p = \sqrt{(C/L)} = \sqrt{(5\text{e-}6)/(0.2)} = 5\text{m}$$

$$\beta = \text{atan}(\omega_d\tau) = \text{atan}(936\cdot 2.84\,\text{m}) = 69.4°$$

giving

$$i_L(t) = -(21.4)(5\text{m})e^{-t/(2.84\,\text{m})}\cos(936t + 90° + 69.4°)$$
$$i_L(t) = -107\,e^{-t/(2.84\,\text{m})}\cos(936t + 159.4°)\;\text{mA},\quad t\geq 0$$

Given the voltage across the circuit, the energy stored in the capacitor is

$$w_c(t) = (1/2)Cv^2(t),\quad t\geq 0$$

the energy stored in the inductor is

$$w_L(t) = (1/2)Li_L^2(t),\quad t\geq 0$$

and the energy dissipated in the resistor is

$$w_r(t) = w(0) - w_L(t) - w_c(t)$$

These results can be plotted to illustrate the response of this underdamped circuit.

The voltage $v(t)$ across the parallel circuit is shown below. As illustrated in Chapter 1, the upper and lower envelopes that describe the decaying amplitude are also shown. The voltage starts at zero volts as required by the initial conditions and decays in five time constants.

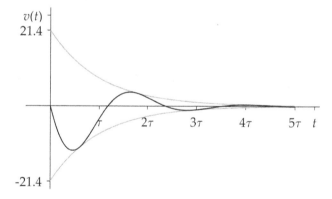

The following inductor current plot demonstrates that the inductor current starts at its initial condition of 0.1 A and decays to zero in five time constants within the same upper and lower envelopes as the voltage.

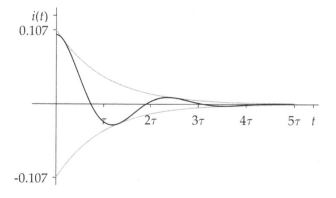

Given the capacitor voltage $v(t)$ and the inductor current $i_L(t)$, the energy stored in the capacitor and inductor as well as the energy dissipated in the resistor can be computed using the expressions developed in this chapter. Doing so leads to the final plot shown below.

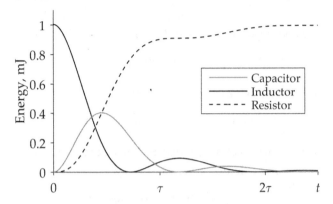

The energy stored in the capacitor starts at zero because the capacitor's initial voltage is zero. The energy stored in the inductor starts at a maximum because the inductor current has its peak value 0.1 A at $t = 0$. As the energy stored in the inductor leaves the inductor after $t = 0$, some of it is stored in the capacitor and the rest is dissipated in the resistor. As the resistor dissipates more and more energy, the energy available for the inductor and for the capacitor to store diminishes as they pass energy back and forth between them.

Because energy is proportional to the square of voltage or current, the effective time constant is $\tau/2$ and the energy decays at a rate twice as fast as the voltage and current.

Because power is equal to the derivative of energy, $p = dw/dt$, and because power in a resistor is always positive, the slope of the energy dissipated in the resistor is always positive as demonstrated in the plot.

5.7 Summary

Capacitors

$$+ \quad \downarrow i = C\frac{dv}{dt}$$
$$v \quad \frac{}{=} C$$
$$-$$

$$i = 0 \downarrow \quad + \qquad i = 0 \uparrow \quad \text{open}$$
$$C \frac{}{=} \; v = \text{constant} \Rightarrow \quad | \quad \text{circuit}$$
$$-$$

v is always continuous, e.g., $v(0^-) = v(0) = v(0^+)$
i is often discontinuous, e.g., $i(0^-) \neq i(0^+)$

$dv/dt = i/C$, a capacitor tries
to keep its voltage from changing.

Energy: $w_C = \dfrac{1}{2}Cv^2$

Typical values: $1 \text{ nF} \leq C \leq 1 \text{ mF}$

Inductors

$$i \downarrow \quad +$$
$$L \gtrless \quad v = L\frac{di}{dt}$$
$$-$$

$$\downarrow i = \text{constant}$$
$$L \gtrless \; \begin{matrix} + \\ v = 0 \\ - \end{matrix} \Rightarrow \quad \begin{matrix} + \\ v = 0 \\ - \end{matrix} \quad \begin{matrix} \text{short} \\ \text{circuit} \end{matrix}$$

i is always continuous, e.g., $i(0^-) = i(0) = i(0^+)$
v is often discontinuous, e.g., $v(0^-) \neq v(0^+)$

$di/dt = v/L$, an inductor tries
to keep its current from changing.

Energy: $w_L = \dfrac{1}{2}Li^2$

Typical values: $1 \text{ nH} \leq L \leq 10 \text{ H}$

Solving RC and RL Circuits

1. The complete response is given by

$$x(t) = x(\infty) + [x(0) - x(\infty)]e^{-t/\tau}, \quad t \geq 0$$

where $x(t)$ is either the capacitor voltage $v_c(t)$ or the inductor current $i_L(t)$. When $x(t)$ describes other variables that are discontinuous at $t = 0$; $x(0^+)$ is used because $x(0)$ is undefined at a discontinuity.

2. Draw the circuit for negative time $t < 0$ when the circuit is at rest and all voltages and currents are constants. The capacitor is an open circuit, $i_c(0^-) = 0$.

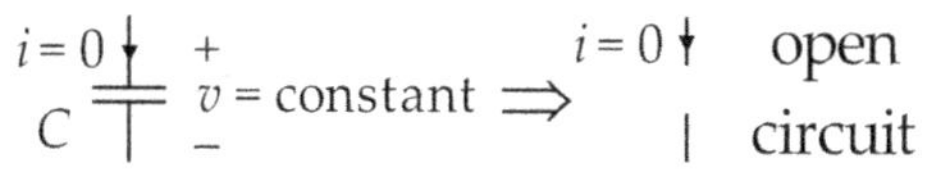

The inductor is a short circuit, $v_L(0^-) = 0$.

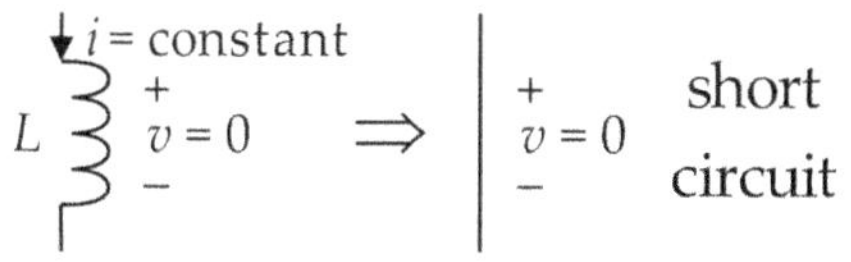

3. Find $v_c(0^-) = v_c(0^+)$ or $i_L(0^-) = i_L(0^+)$.

4. Draw circuit for positive time $t > 0$.

5. Remove C or L from the circuit, shut OFF all sources, find the equivalent resistance R_{eq} seen looking into the terminals where C or L was located. This resistance value is what C or L sees during the transient response. This value determines the time constant.

6. $\tau = R_{eq}C$ or $\tau = L/R_{eq}$.

7. Let time go to infinity $t \to \infty$. The circuit is at rest again where all voltages and currents are constants. The capacitor is an open circuit, $i_c(\infty) = 0$, and the inductor is a short circuit, $v_L(\infty) = 0$, as shown above.

8. Find $v_c(\infty)$ or $i_L(\infty)$.

9. Write the solution using the initial and final values plus the time constant,

$$x(t) = x(\infty) + [x(0) - x(\infty)]e^{-t/\tau}, \quad t \geq 0$$

10. Sketch the time response that fits the given solution. Label $x(0)$, and $x(\infty)$, and be sure to include the line of initial slope and mark the time axis at multiples of the time constant up to five constants.

11. If the problem requires finding other voltages or currents, solve for them given the capacitor voltage or inductor current. Be sure to note whether the other voltages or currents are discontinuous at $t = 0$. If so, $x(0) = x(0^+) \neq x(0^-)$, because $x(0)$ does not exist.

Solving RLC Circuits

1. Identify whether the RLC circuit is in series or parallel form by studying the circuit for positive time $t > 0$ and shutting OFF all sources.

2. Draw the circuit for negative time $t < 0$ when the circuit is at rest and all voltages and currents are constants. When at rest, the capacitor is an open circuit,

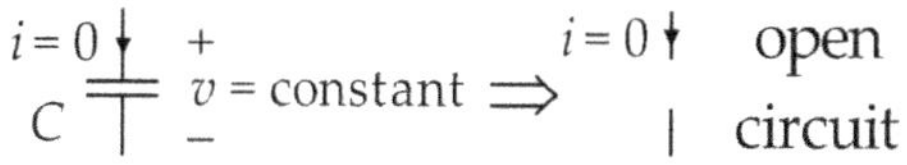

And the inductor is a short circuit,

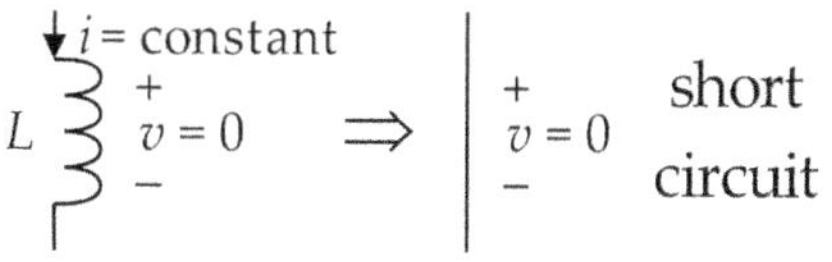

3. Determine the initial conditions by finding the capacitor voltage $v_c(0^-)$ and the inductor current $i_L(0^-)$.

4. Draw the circuit for positive time $t > 0$

5. If a source remains in the circuit, find the final value of the current $i(\infty)$ for the series circuit or the final value of the voltage $v(\infty)$ for the parallel circuit. The circuit is at rest at $t = \infty$, so the capacitor is an open circuit and the inductor is a short circuit once again.

6. Compute the damping factor α and the resonant frequency ω_o,

Series: $\alpha = \dfrac{R}{2L}$ Parallel: $\alpha = \dfrac{1}{2RC}$

$$\omega_0 = \dfrac{1}{\sqrt{LC}}$$

7. Determine if the circuit is overdamped or under-damped,

Overdamped: $\alpha > \omega_0$

Underdamped: $\alpha < \omega_0$

8. The overdamped solution for $t > 0$ is

Series: $i(t) = K_1 e^{s_1 t} + K_2 e^{s_2 t} + i(\infty), \quad t \geq 0$

Parallel: $v(t) = K_1 e^{s_1 t} + K_2 e^{s_2 t} + v(\infty), \quad t \geq 0$

where s_1 and s_2 are

$$s_1, s_2 = -\alpha \pm \sqrt{\alpha^2 - \omega_0^2}$$

and where the coefficients K_1 and K_2 are given by the solution to the set of equations

Series: $\begin{bmatrix} 1 & 1 \\ s_1 & s_2 \end{bmatrix} \begin{bmatrix} K_1 \\ K_2 \end{bmatrix} = \begin{bmatrix} i(0) - i(\infty) \\ -\left(\dfrac{v_c(0) + i(0)R}{L} \right) \end{bmatrix}$

Parallel: $\begin{bmatrix} 1 & 1 \\ s_1 & s_2 \end{bmatrix} \begin{bmatrix} K_1 \\ K_2 \end{bmatrix} = \begin{bmatrix} v(0) - v(\infty) \\ -\left(\dfrac{v(0) + i_L(0)R}{RC} \right) \end{bmatrix}$

9. The underdamped solution for $t > 0$ is

Series: $i(t) = e^{-\alpha t}\left[B_1 \cos(\omega_d t) + B_2 \sin(\omega_d t) \right] + i(\infty)$

Parallel: $v(t) = e^{-\alpha t}\left[B_1 \cos(\omega_d t) + B_2 \sin(\omega_d t) \right] + v(\infty)$

where

$$\omega_d = \sqrt{\omega_0^2 - \alpha^2}$$

and where the coefficients B_1 and B_2 are given by

Series: $B_1 = i(0) - i(\infty) \quad B_2 = \left(\dfrac{di(0)/dt + \alpha B_1}{\omega_d} \right)$

in which

$$\dfrac{di(0)}{dt} = -\left(\dfrac{v_c(0) + i(0)R}{L} \right)$$

and

Parallel: $B_1 = v(0) - v(\infty) \quad B_2 = \left(\dfrac{dv(0)/dt + \alpha B_1}{\omega_d} \right)$

in which

$$\dfrac{dv(0)}{dt} = -\left(\dfrac{v(0) + i_L(0)R}{RC} \right)$$

10. If the problem requires finding other voltages or currents, solve for them given the primary solution found above. Be sure to note if the other voltages or currents are discontinuous at $t = 0$. In particular, expressions for the capacitor voltage in the series case and the inductor current for the parallel case appear earlier. For the underdamped case, plots of the energy stored in the inductor and capacitor and the energy dissipated or absorbed by the resistor provide valuable insight.

Second Order Underdamped Response
$\alpha < \omega_0$
$s_1, s_2 = -\alpha \pm j\omega_d, \quad \omega_d = \sqrt{\omega_0^2 - \alpha^2}$, Complex Values
$x(t) = e^{-\alpha t}\left[B_1 \cos(\omega_d t) + B_2 \sin(\omega_d t) \right] + x(\infty), \quad t \geq 0$
$B_1 = x(0) - x(\infty), \quad B_2 = \left(dx(0)/dt + \alpha B_1 \right)/\omega_d$
Alternate Form:
$x(t) = D e^{-t/\tau} \cos(\omega_d t - \phi) + x(\infty), \quad t \geq 0$
$\tau = 1/\alpha$ $D = \left\| B_1 + jB_2 \right\| = \sqrt{B_1^2 + B_2^2}$ $\phi = \angle(B_1 + jB_2) = \text{atan2}\left(B_2, B_1 \right)$

5.8 Problems

5.1 Given the circuit below where the capacitor voltage and current are

$$v_c(t) = 60e^{-500t} \text{ V} \qquad t \geq 0$$

$$i_c(t) = -30e^{-500t} \text{ mA} \quad t > 0$$

find τ, R, C, $w_c(0^+)$.

5.2 Find and sketch $v_c(t)$ in the circuit below given $v_c(0^-) = 0$.

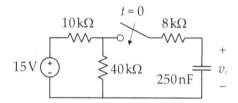

5.3 Find and sketch $v_c(t)$ in the circuit below if: (a) the switch closes at $t = 0$, (b) the switch opens at $t = 0$.

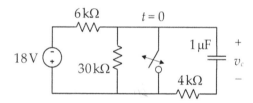

5.4 Find and sketch $v_c(t)$ in the circuit below if: (a) the switch closes at $t = 0$, (b) the switch opens at $t = 0$.

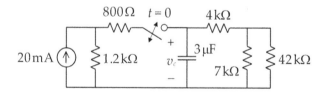

5.5 Find and sketch $v_c(t)$ in the circuit below if: (a) the switch moves to the left at $t = 0$, (b) the switch moves to the right at $t = 0$.

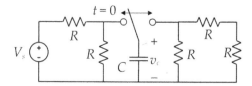

5.6 Find and sketch $v_c(t)$ in the circuit below if: (a) the switch closes at $t = 0$, (b) the switch opens at $t = 0$.

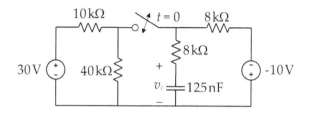

5.7 Given the circuit below where the inductor current and voltage are

$$i_L(t) = 24e^{-800t} \text{ mA} \qquad t \geq 0$$

$$v_L(t) = -28.8e^{-800t} \text{ V} \quad t > 0$$

find τ, R, L, $w_L(0^+)$.

5.8 Find and sketch $i_L(t)$ in the circuit below if: (a) the switch closes at $t = 0$, (b) the switch opens at $t = 0$.

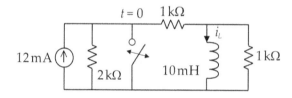

5.9 Find and sketch $i_L(t)$ in the circuit below if: (a) the switch closes at $t = 0$, (b) the switch opens at $t = 0$.

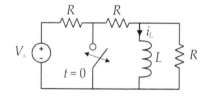

5.10 Find and sketch $i_L(t)$ in the circuit below if: (a) the switch closes at $t = 0$, (b) the switch opens at $t = 0$.

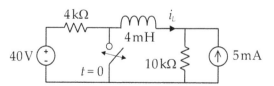

5.11 Find and sketch $i_L(t)$ in the following circuit. Using the solution for $i_L(t)$ and Ohm's law, find and sketch $v_{sw}(t)$ for $t > 0$. The resistor R_{sw} models the resistance of the air between the contacts of the switch when it is opened. If $R_{sw} = 10 \text{ M}\Omega$, $V_s = 10 \text{ V}$, and

$R = 100\ \Omega$, what are $v_{sw}(0^-)$ and $v_{sw}(0^+)$? Based on the value of $v_{sw}(0^+)$ what would you expect to your eyes to observe at the switch contacts when the switch is opened?

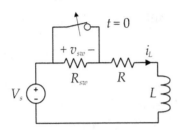

5.12 Find and sketch $i_L(t)$ in the circuit below if: (a) the switch closes at $t = 0$, (b) the switch opens at $t = 0$. Using the solution for $i_L(t)$ and Ohm's law, find and sketch $v_{cc}(t)$ for $t > 0$. If $V_s = 5\ V$, and $R = 1\ k\Omega$, find $i_L(0^-)$, $i_L(0^+)$, $v_{cc}(0^-)$ and $v_{cc}(0^+)$.

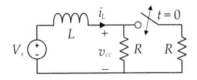

5.13 The discontinuity, i.e., jump, in $v_{cc}(t)$ found in problem 5.12 can be eliminated by using the fundamental fact that the voltage across a capacitor cannot jump as shown in the circuit below. (a) If the switch in the circuit below closes at $t = 0$, find $i_L(0^-)$, $i_L(0^+)$, $i_c(0^-)$, $i_c(0^+)$, $v_{cc}(0^-)$, $v_{cc}(0^+)$. (b) If the switch in the circuit below opens at $t = 0$, find $i_L(0^-)$, $i_L(0^+)$, $i_c(0^-)$, $i_c(0^+)$, $v_{cc}(0^-)$, $v_{cc}(0^+)$. (c) If $V_s = 5\ V$, and $R = 1\ k\Omega$, Compare these results to those found in problem 5.12.

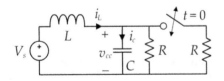

5.14 Find $i(t)$ in the circuit below.

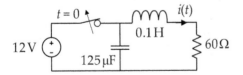

5.15 Find $i(t)$ and $v_c(t)$ in the following circuit. If you can, create plots of $i(t)$ and $v_c(t)$. In addition, find and create plots of $w_L(t)$, $w_c(t)$, and $w_r(t)$ on a single axes.

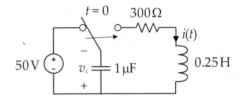

5.16 Find $v(t)$ in the circuit below.

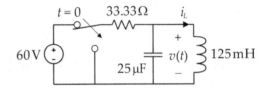

5.17 Find $v(t)$ and $i_L(t)$ in the circuit below. If you can, create plots of $v(t)$ and $i_L(t)$. In addition, find and create plots of $w_L(t)$, $w_c(t)$, and $w_r(t)$ on a single axes.

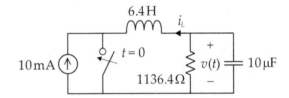

6 AC Analysis

This chapter studies the analysis of circuits that are excited by sinusoidal voltages and currents. Solving circuits excited in this way is called AC analysis where AC stands for alternating current. When voltages and currents follow a sinusoidal form, their polarity or sign changes every 180 degrees. So they alternate in polarity, direction, or sign periodically. Thus the reason for calling this AC analysis. It is also called sinusoidal steady state analysis because the circuit is in steady state operation and there are no switches as appeared in transient circuits.

6.1 Why Sinusoids?

Out of all the infinite number of shapes a voltage or current could have, why consider the sinusoidal form? Why not some other shape? What makes the sinusoidal shape so special?

The answers to these questions are pretty simple. First, the sinusoidal form appears in nature. If you make a plot of the deviation in the length of daylight every day throughout a year, that plot will have a sinusoidal shape. If you measure the tides anywhere and plot tide height versus time, that plot will have a sinusoidal shape. The sinusoidal shape and the exponential shape are two fundamental shapes in nature. In fact, these two shapes are closely related to each other through the Euler identity,

$$e^{j\theta} = \cos(\theta) + j\sin(\theta)$$

What makes the sinusoidal shape special is that the derivative of a sinusoid is another sinusoid, *e.g.*,

$$\frac{d}{d\theta}\sin(\theta) = \cos(\theta)$$

$$\frac{d}{d\theta}\cos(\theta) = -\sin(\theta)$$

Differentiation produces a phase shift, but does not alter the basic shape. The result remains sinusoidal. The only other shape that has this feature is the exponential that also routinely appears in nature. The derivative of an exponential is another exponential.

It should not be surprising that electricity is generated and distributed in sinusoidal form. What appears at a wall outlet is a sinusoidal voltage.

Sinusoidal voltages and currents have the form

$$y(t) = F_m \cos(\omega t + \theta)$$

where F_m is the amplitude or magnitude, ω is the frequency in rad/s and θ is the phase in degrees. The derivative of this expression was found in Chapter 1 as

$$\frac{dy}{dt} = \frac{d}{dt}\Big(F_m \cos(\omega t + \theta)\Big)$$

$$\frac{dy}{dt} = -\omega F_m \sin(\omega t + \theta)$$

$$\frac{dy}{dt} = \omega F_m \cos(\omega t + \theta + 90°)$$

Differentiation changed the amplitude and shifted the phase, but the frequency ω remains unchanged. The $+90°$ phase shift shows that the derivative dy/dt leads the original function by $90°$.

Using the above results, when a sinusoidal voltage appears across a capacitor, the current is sinusoidal,

$$i(t) = C\frac{dv}{dt}$$

$$i(t) = C\frac{d}{dt}\Big(V_m \cos(\omega t + \theta)\Big)$$

$$i(t) = \omega C V_m \cos(\omega t + \theta + 90°)$$

This phenomenon also applies to the inductor current,

$$v(t) = L\frac{di}{dt}$$

$$v(t) = L\frac{d}{dt}\Big(I_m \cos(\omega t + \theta)\Big)$$

$$v(t) = \omega L I_m \cos(\omega t + \theta + 90°)$$

So when a circuit is excited by sinusoidal sources, all the voltages and currents in the circuit are also sinusoidal at the same frequency. They just have different amplitudes and phases at different places due to phase and amplitude shifts created by the differentiation that relates voltages and currents in capacitors and inductors.

This is the way things are in nature as well. Tide amplitudes vary at different places around the world and the times high tide appear vary at different places around the world. This time difference is a phase shift in the sinusoidal shape of the tide movement variation.

6.2 Sinusoidal Circuit Excitation

When a circuit contains sinusoidal sources, all the voltages and currents in the circuit are sinusoidal at the same frequency as the sources. Even though the source values are changing every instant, KCL, KVL, $v = iR$, $i = C\,dv/dt$, and $v = L\,di/dt$ still hold. The fundamental principles that flow must add up and pressure must add up must hold at every instant.

Consider the following circuit where the voltage source is some function of time.

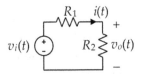

Voltage division gives the output voltage $v_o(t)$ as

$$v_o(t) = \frac{R_2}{R_1 + R_2}\, v_i(t)$$

No matter what $v_i(t)$ is, the output follows along instantaneously as directed by voltage division. If $v_i(t)$ is sinusoidal, so is $v_o(t)$.

Next, consider the following circuit where the R_2 has been replaced by a capacitor C.

Voltage division is no longer applicable. When $v_i(t)$ is sinusoidal, then $i(t)$ and $v_o(t)$ are also sinusoidal. It isn't clear how to solve this circuit. If $v_i(t)$ has the form

$$v_i(t) = V_i \cos(\omega t + \theta_i)$$

then $v_o(t)$ will have the form

$$v_o(t) = V_o \cos(\omega t + \theta_o)$$

The amplitude V_o and phase θ_o of the output voltage $v_o(t)$ are determined by the amplitude V_i and phase θ_i of the source $v_i(t)$. The relationship between these two voltages is given by applying KVL

$$v_i(t) = v_o(t) + R\,i(t)$$

$$v_i(t) = v_o(t) + R\,C\frac{dv_o}{dt}$$

This is the differential equation describing the circuit. From here it is not clear how to proceed to find the expression for $v_o(t)$. Trying to do so in a brute force fashion gets cumbersome quickly. For circuits having more components, identifying the amplitude and phase of each sinusoidal voltage and current in the circuit and then trying to find their values make this a nearly impossible problem to tackle in a brute force way.

Fortunately, there is a very simple way to solve all problems having sinusoidal sources. All it requires is the use of complex number addition and subtraction. Complex algebra becomes the tool for solving AC circuits. There are no complex voltages and currents in a real circuit. If there were, how would you measure $\sqrt{-1}$ in the laboratory? **Complex algebra is simply a mathematical tool that changes a complicated problem into an easy one.** Because of this, electrical and computer engineers use complex numbers all the time.

6.3 The Phasor Transform

The **phasor transform** was illustrated in Chapter 1. It relates the amplitude and phase of two sinusoids to the amplitude and phase of their sum. That is,

$$F \cos(\theta + \phi) = A\cos(\theta + \phi_a) + B\cos(\theta + \phi_b)$$

where A, B, φ_a, and φ_b are known, F and φ are given by the complex sum,

$$F \angle \phi = A\angle \phi_a + B\angle \phi_b$$

This says, simply create complex numbers in polar form from the individual amplitudes and phases, add them together, and the resulting complex number in polar form gives you the correct amplitude and phase for the desired result. This is much simpler than dragging out a bunch of trigonometric identities and applying them in the correct order at the correct time. Trying that in the working world would quickly lead to unemployment.

To demonstrate use of the phasor transform, consider the following circuit node having three currents entering the node and one leaving the node.

KCL gives the obvious result that the sum of the currents entering the node is equal to the current leaving the node.

Let this node be in a circuit excited by a sinusoidal source, and let the currents entering the node be

$$i_1(t) = 12\cos(\omega t + 30°)\ \text{mA}$$
$$i_2(t) = 9\cos(\omega t - 10°)\ \text{mA}$$
$$i_3(t) = 25\cos(\omega t + 135°)\ \text{mA}$$

Letting ωt take the place of θ in the phasor transform expression and applying it to the sinusoids above results in the complex number sum of

$$F\angle\phi = (12\angle 30°) + (9\angle -10°) + (25\angle 135°)$$
$$F\angle\phi = 22.2\angle 85.9°$$

which leads to $i_4(t)$ as

$$i_4(t) = 22.2\cos(\omega t + 85.9°)\ \text{mA}$$

That is all there is to it. Let your calculator do the complex algebra.

The phasor transform only works if the frequency ω of all terms is the same. If any of the frequencies are different, the phasor transform fails. Sinusoids at different frequencies do not simplify when added together. If they did, what frequency would the result have? Your choice?

To summarize, the phasor transform identifies a relationship between a sinusoid

$$f(t) = F_m\cos(\omega t + \theta)$$

and the complex number in polar form

$$\underline{F} = F_m\angle\theta$$

The complex number $\underline{F}$ is called the **phasor** associated with the above sinusoid or the phasor representation of the sinusoid. **Phasor variables are underlined to distinguish them from DC values and amplitudes of sinusoids.** Complex algebra with the

phasor solves equivalent algebra with the sinusoid. This relationship is often written succinctly as

$$f(t) = F_m\cos(\omega t + \theta) \quad\Leftrightarrow\quad \underline{F} = F_m\angle\theta$$

The sinusoidal function $f(t)$ is a function of time, so it is said to be in the **time domain**. On the other hand, the phasor $\underline{F}$ is a complex number and not a function of time, so it can't be in the time domain. It is said to be in the **phasor domain** or **frequency domain**.

The phasor transformation is a powerful tool for solving AC circuits.

Phasor Transform
$f(t) = F_m\cos(\omega t + \theta) \Leftrightarrow \underline{F} = F_m\angle\theta$
Time Domain: $f(t) = F_m\cos(\omega t + \theta)$
Phasor or Frequency Domain: $\underline{F} = F_m\angle\theta$

6.4 Phasor Circuits

Rather than write differential equations describing a circuit, and then applying the phasor transform, it is much more convenient to draw an equivalent **phasor circuit** where phasor voltages and currents exist. To do so requires writing the circuit element characteristics $v = iR$, $i = C\,dv/dt$, and $v = L\,di/dt$ in terms of their phasor transforms.

Resistor: If the current flowing through a resistor R and its phasor representation are

$$i(t) = I_m\cos(\omega t + \theta) \quad\Leftrightarrow\quad \underline{I} = I_m\angle\theta$$

then by Ohm's law the voltage is

$$v(t) = R\cdot i(t)$$
$$v(t) = R\cdot I_m\cos(\omega t + \theta)$$

The phasor transform of this expression is

$$\underbrace{v(t)}_{\underline{V}} = R\cdot \underbrace{I_m\cos(\omega t + \theta)}_{\underline{I}}$$
$$\underline{V} = R\cdot \underline{I}$$

So the resistor is characterized by

$$v(t) = R\,i(t) \quad\Leftrightarrow\quad \underline{V} = R\,\underline{I}$$

In other words, Ohm's law is unchanged when dealing with phasors.

Inductor: If the current flowing through an inductor L and its phasor representation are

$$i(t) = I_m\cos(\omega t + \theta) \quad\Leftrightarrow\quad \underline{I} = I_m\angle\theta$$

then the voltage across the inductor is

$$v(t) = L\frac{di}{dt} = \omega L I_m \cos(\omega t + \theta + 90°)$$

where the derivative result was shown earlier in this chapter and derived in Chapter 1. The phasor transform of this voltage is

$$\underline{V} = (\omega L I_m)\angle(\theta + 90°)$$

This can be written in terms of the phasor current $\underline{I}$, by noting how complex numbers multiply when expressed in polar form, namely that the magnitudes multiply, and the phases add. For example,

$$M\angle(\theta + \phi) = (M\angle\theta)\cdot(1\angle\phi)$$

Using this relationship, the phasor relationship for the inductor becomes

$$\underline{V} = (\omega L I_m)\angle(\theta + 90°)$$
$$\underline{V} = \omega L\cdot(I_m\angle\theta)\cdot(1\angle90°)$$
$$\underline{V} = (1\angle90°)\omega L\underline{I}$$
$$\underline{V} = j\omega L\underline{I}$$

where the last form recognizes that $1\angle90° = 0 + j1 = j$.

Therefore the inductor is characterized by

$$v(t) = L\frac{di}{dt} \quad\Leftrightarrow\quad \underline{V} = j\omega L\underline{I}$$

The phasor form is an Ohm's law like form. The product of the phasor current and $j\omega L$ gives the phasor voltage. The term $j\omega L$ must have units of ohms, but it clearly is not a resistance since this is an imaginary value.

Capacitor: If the voltage across a capacitor C and its phasor representation are

$$v(t) = V_m\cos(\omega t+\theta) \quad\Leftrightarrow\quad \underline{V} = V_m\angle\theta$$

then the current through the capacitor is

$$i(t) = C\frac{dv}{dt} = \omega C V_m \cos(\omega t + \theta + 90°)$$

where the derivative result was shown earlier in this chapter and derived in Chapter 1. The phasor transform of this current is

$$\underline{I} = (\omega C V_m)\angle(\theta + 90°)$$

This can be written in terms of the phasor voltage $\underline{V}$, by noting how complex numbers multiply when expressed in polar form, namely that the magnitudes multiply, and the phases add. For example,

$$M\angle(\theta + \phi) = (M\angle\theta)\cdot(1\angle\phi)$$

Using this relationship, the phasor relationship for the capacitor becomes

$$\underline{I} = (\omega C V_m)\angle(\theta + 90°)$$
$$\underline{I} = \omega C\cdot(V_m\angle\theta)\cdot(1\angle90°)$$
$$\underline{I} = (1\angle90°)\omega C\underline{V}$$
$$\underline{I} = j\omega C\underline{V}$$

where the last form recognizes that $1\angle90° = 0 + j1 = j$.

Therefore the capacitor is characterized by

$$i(t) = C\frac{dv}{dt} \quad\Leftrightarrow\quad \underline{I} = j\omega C\underline{V}$$

This phasor form is easily rewritten in terms of the voltage as

$$\underline{V} = \frac{\underline{I}}{j\omega C} = j\frac{\underline{I}}{j^2\omega C} = j\frac{\underline{I}}{(-1)\omega C} = -j\frac{1}{\omega C}\underline{I}$$

This last phasor form is an Ohm's law like form. The product of the phasor current and $-j1/(\omega C)$ gives the phasor voltage. The term $-j1/(\omega C)$ must have units of ohms, but it clearly is not a resistance since this is an imaginary value.

Impedance: The phasor relationships for all three passive components have the Ohm's law form

$$\underline{V} = Z\cdot\underline{I}$$

where

$$Z = R \qquad \text{for the resistor,}$$
$$Z = j\omega L \qquad \text{for the inductor,}$$
$$Z = -j\frac{1}{\omega C} \qquad \text{for the capacitor}$$

where Z has units of ohms (Ω). Because this appears so frequently, Z is called **impedance** (*i.e.*, to "impede" is to "resist").

The beauty of this result is that resistors, capacitors, and inductors all obey Ohm's law in a phasor circuit. All the tools and techniques used for DC circuits apply again. As a result, all circuits are easily solved as shown in the diagram at the top of the next page.

Starting with a time domain circuit in the upper left, applying the phasor transform leads to the phasor equivalent circuit in the lower left. This circuit is then solved using known techniques, which leads to phasor solutions $\underline{F} = F_m\angle\theta$ for whatever voltages and

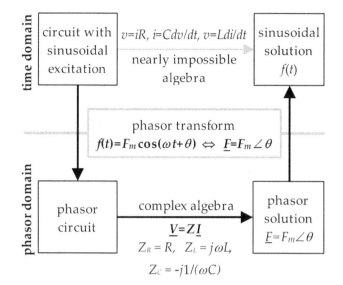

currents are desired in the lower right. These phasor values are then converted back to their time domain sinusoidal forms to give the desired solutions in the upper right.

The solution path through the diagram is counterclockwise down from the upper left, across to the right, then back up. The path left to right across the top from the *circuit with sinusoidal excitation* to *sinusoidal solution f(t)* is never taken because of its difficulty. Engineers don't waste their time trying.

All the circuit analysis tools developed for DC circuits work here as well. Resistors in series become impedances in series; resistors in parallel becomes impedances in parallel; voltage division, current division, source transformations, superposition, and nodal analysis all work. The only difference is that the algebra involves complex numbers.

6.5 Solving Phasor Circuits

To demonstrate the usefulness of using phasors, consider the following examples.

Example 1: Consider finding the output voltage $v_o(t)$ in the following circuit

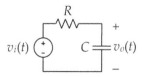

where the component values are

$$R = 1\,k\Omega \quad C = 1\,\mu F$$
$$v_i(t) = 12\cos(1000t) \ V$$

This is the circuit in the upper left of the phasor solution diagram. To convert it to the phasor circuit in the lower left of the diagram, the components are converted to their phasor equivalents

$$R \Rightarrow R = 1\,k\Omega$$
$$C \Rightarrow Z_c = -j\frac{1}{\omega C} = -j\frac{1}{10^3 \cdot 10^{-6}} = -j1\,k\Omega$$
$$v_i(t) \Rightarrow \underline{V}_i = 12\angle 0° \ V$$

and the phasor circuit is drawn with these component values as shown below.

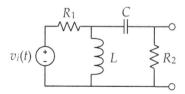

This circuit contains sources and components that have units of ohms. So all the tools that worked for DC circuits containing sources and resistors work here as well. The only difference is that the algebra involves complex values.

The output voltage $\underline{V}_o$ is given by voltage division,

$$\underline{V}_o = \frac{Z_c}{R + Z_c}\,\underline{V}_i$$
$$\underline{V}_o = \frac{-j1k}{1k - j1k}12\angle 0°$$
$$\underline{V}_o = (0.7071\angle -45°)\cdot 12\angle 0°$$
$$\underline{V}_o = 8.49\angle -45° \ V$$

This is the phasor solution in the lower right corner of the diagram. The time domain solution is simply

$$v_o(t) = 8.49\cos(1000t - 45°) \ V$$

That completes this problem.

Example 2: Find the Thévenin equivalent of the following circuit at the terminals shown

where the component values are

$$R_1 = 1\,\text{k}\Omega \quad R_2 = 2\,\text{k}\Omega$$

$$C = 25\,\text{nF} \quad L = 300\,\text{mH}$$

$$v_i(t) = 20\cos\left(10^4 t + 30°\right)\ \text{V}$$

This is the time domain circuit. The phasor circuit is described by the phasor equivalents of the given components

$$R_1 \Rightarrow R_1 = 1\ \text{k}\Omega$$

$$R_2 \Rightarrow R_2 = 2\ \text{k}\Omega$$

$$C \Rightarrow Z_c = -j\frac{1}{\omega C} = -j\frac{1}{10^4 \cdot (25 \cdot 10^{-9})} = -j4\ \text{k}\Omega$$

$$L \Rightarrow Z_L = j\omega L = 10^4 \cdot (0.3) = j3\ \text{k}\Omega$$

$$v_i(t) \Rightarrow V_i = 20\angle 30°\ \text{V}$$

These impedances and the source phasor value lead to the following phasor circuit.

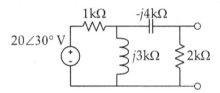

There are two approaches that can be followed to find the Thévenin equivalent. First, a sequence of source transformations could be done until the circuit appears in the form of the Thévenin equivalent. Second, the circuit can be solved for the open circuit voltage and impedance (not resistance!) seen looking into the terminals with the source shut off. Consider the first approach here and consider the second approach in the next example.

Perform a source transformation between the voltage source and the 1 kΩ resistor as shown in the following circuit.

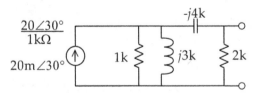

Combine the 1 kΩ resistor and j3 kΩ inductive impedance in parallel to get

$$1\,\text{k}\Omega \| j3\,\text{k}\Omega = \frac{1\text{k} \cdot j3\text{k}}{1\text{k} + j3\text{k}} = 900 + j300\,\Omega = 948.7 \angle 18.43°$$

It is usually more convenient to use rectangular form for impedances and polar form for voltages and cur-

rents. In this case, both forms were given. The rectangular form is exact. The polar form was given with four significant digits accuracy for the magnitude and 0.01 ° accuracy for the angle so that the final result is accurate to three significant digits and 0.1 ° respectively.

After combining these two impedances, another source transformation is possible as shown in the following circuit.

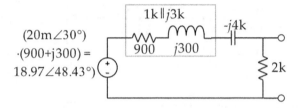

As is common in complex algebra, values seldom work out to be exact values as one solves a circuit. It is vitally important to maintain four significant digits accuracy for magnitudes and 0.01 ° accuracy for angles so that final results have sufficient accuracy. It is even better if greater precision intermediate values are kept in calculator memory while solving a problem.

There are three impedances in series with the voltage source in the above circuit that combine as $900 + j300 - j4000 = 900 - j3700$. The revised circuit is shown below.

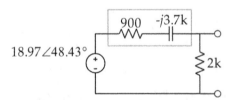

As shown below, yet another source transformation is possible between the voltage source and the series combined impedance.

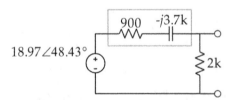

Now the 900 − j3700 impedance is in parallel with the final 2 kΩ resistor and can be combined to get

$$(900 - j3700) \| 2000 = 1620 \angle -24.42° = 1475 - j669.7$$

The revised circuit is shown below.

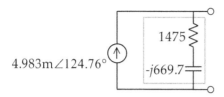

This is the Norton equivalent circuit. One final source transformation gives the following phasor Thévenin equivalent circuit where the source value is

$$(4.983\,\text{m}\angle 124.76°)\cdot(1475 - j\,669.7) = 8.072\angle 100.34°\,\text{V}$$

The resulting phasor Thévenin circuit shown below is composed of the source $\underline{V}_{TH} = 8.072\angle 100.34°$ in series with the impedance $Z_{TH} = 1475 - j669.7\,\Omega$.

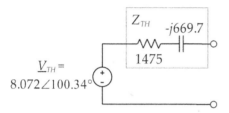

Since the original circuit was given in the time domain, the last step is to use the phasor transform and convert this circuit back to the time domain. The time domain component values are

$$\underline{V}_{TH} = 8.07\angle 100.3° \Rightarrow v_{TH}(t) = 8.07\cos\left(10^4 t + 100.3°\right)\,V$$

$$R = 1475\,\Omega \Rightarrow 1475\,\Omega$$

$$-j\,669.7 = -j\frac{1}{\omega C} \Rightarrow C = \frac{1}{10^4\cdot 669.7} = 149\,\text{nF}$$

The final time domain circuit is shown in the following figure. For simplicity, the expression for $v_{TH}(t)$ was not included in the figure.

Example 3: Find the Thévenin equivalent of the circuit from the preceding example by finding the open circuit voltage and the impedance seen looking into the terminals. The component values and given circuit are repeated as follows.

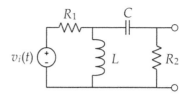

$$R_1 = 1\,\text{k}\Omega \qquad R_2 = 2\,\text{k}\Omega$$
$$C = 25\,\text{nF} \qquad L = 300\,\text{mH}$$
$$v_i(t) = 20\cos\left(10^4 t + 30°\right)\text{V}$$

The phasor circuit is described by the phasor equivalents of the given components

$$R_1 \Rightarrow R_1 = 1\,\text{k}\Omega$$
$$R_2 \Rightarrow R_2 = 2\,\text{k}\Omega$$
$$C \Rightarrow Z_c = -j\frac{1}{\omega C} = -j\frac{1}{10\text{k}\cdot(25\text{n})} = -j\,4\,\text{k}\Omega$$
$$L \Rightarrow Z_L = j\omega L = j\,10\text{k}\cdot(0.3) = j\,3\,\text{k}\Omega$$
$$v_i(t) \Rightarrow \underline{V}_i = 20\angle 30°\ \text{V}$$

Using these impedances and source phasor value leads to the following phasor circuit.

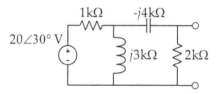

Finding the open circuit voltage $\underline{V}_{oc}$ is easily accomplished by using nodal analysis using the labeling shown in the circuit shown below.

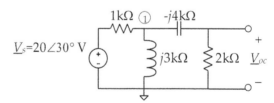

Once $\underline{V}_1$ is known, $\underline{V}_{oc}$ can be computed using voltage division. Writing the KCL equation for node ① gives

$$\frac{\underline{V}_1 - \underline{V}_s}{1\text{k}} + \frac{\underline{V}_1}{j\,3\text{k}} + \frac{\underline{V}_1}{2\text{k} - j\,4\text{k}} = 0$$

which simplifies to

$$\underline{V}_1\left(\frac{1}{1\text{k}} + \frac{1}{j\,3\text{k}} + \frac{1}{2\text{k} - j\,4\text{k}}\right) = \frac{\underline{V}_s}{1\text{k}}$$

multiplying through by 1k, and solving for $\underline{V}_1$ gives

$$V_1\left(1 + \frac{1}{j3} + \frac{1}{2 - j4}\right) = 20\angle 30°$$

$$V_1 = \frac{20\angle 30°}{1 + \dfrac{1}{j3} + \dfrac{1}{2 - j4}} = 18.05\angle 36.91° \text{ V}$$

Voltage division gives the open circuit and Thévenin voltage as

$$V_{TH} = V_{oc} = \frac{2k}{2k - j4k}V_1 = 8.072\angle 100.34° \text{ V}$$

This agrees with the solution given in the previous example.

The Thévenin impedance Z_{TH} (not resistance!) is equal to the equivalent impedance seen looking into the terminals with the source set to zero as shown in the following circuit.

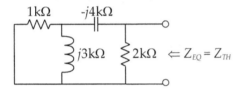

This circuit is simplified by starting at the left and working toward the terminals where the solution is desired. The sequence of steps is shown next. First, the 1 kΩ and $j3$ kΩ impedances are in parallel:

1k‖j3k
900+j300

-j4k

2k ⇐ $Z_{EQ} = Z_{TH}$

Rather than show the individual elements composing the parallel equivalent, a generic circuit element block was used above for simplicity. Next, the $900 + j300$ is in series with the $-j4k$:

900+j300 - j4000
900 - j3700

2k ⇐ $Z_{EQ} = Z_{TH}$

Finally, the remaining impedances are in parallel, so the Thévenin impedance is simply

$$Z_{EQ} = Z_{TH} = (900 - j3700)\|2000 = 1475 - j669.7\,\Omega$$

Again, this value matches that found in Example 2.

Example 4: Find the voltage $v_o(t)$ in the circuit below

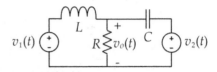

where the component values are given by

$$L = 1\text{ H} \quad C = 125\text{ nF} \quad R = 2\text{ k}\Omega$$
$$v_1(t) = 10\cos(2000\,t + 45°)\text{ V}$$
$$v_2(t) = 10\cos(4000\,t - 30°)\text{ V}$$

> **In this example, the two sources are at different frequencies.** The impedances of the inductor $Z_L = j\omega L$ and the capacitor $Z_c = -j1/(\omega C)$ have different values for each source. So how are these values computed with both sources operating? **The answer is to use superposition.** Find the contribution to $v_o(t)$ from each source acting alone, then sum the results. The impedances of the inductor and capacitor then change when the source frequency changes.

First, set the right source to zero and solve the phasor circuit as shown below.

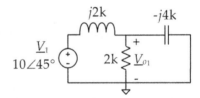

where the phasor equivalents at $\omega = 2000$ are

$$L \Rightarrow Z_L = j\omega L = j2\text{ k}\cdot(1) = j2\text{ k}\Omega$$
$$R \Rightarrow R = 2\text{ k}\Omega$$
$$C \Rightarrow Z_c = -j\frac{1}{\omega C} = -j\frac{1}{2\text{k}\cdot 125\text{ n}} = -j4\text{ k}\Omega$$
$$v_1(t) \Rightarrow V_1 = 10\angle 45°\text{ V}$$

This circuit is easily solved by applying nodal analysis since there is only one essential node and its voltage is the value sought. Applying KCL to the top essential node gives

$$\frac{V_{o1} - 10\angle 45°}{j2k} + \frac{V_{o1}}{2k} + \frac{V_{o1}}{-j4k} = 0$$

Simplifying this equation gives

$$V_{o1}\left(\frac{1}{j2\,k}+\frac{1}{2\,k}-\frac{1}{j4\,k}\right)=\frac{10\angle45°}{j2\,k}$$

which gives the phasor and time domain solutions

$$V_{o1}=8.94\angle-18.4°\ \text{V}$$
$$v_{o1}(t)=8.94\cos(2000t-18.4°)\ \text{V}$$

Next, set the left source to zero and solve the phasor circuit as shown below.

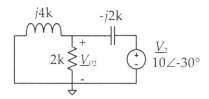

where the phasor equivalents at $\omega=4000$ are

$$L \Rightarrow Z_L=j\omega L=j4\,k\cdot(1)=j4\ k\Omega$$
$$R \Rightarrow R=2\ k\Omega$$
$$C \Rightarrow Z_c=-j\frac{1}{\omega C}=-j\frac{1}{4\,k\cdot125\,n}=-j2\ k\Omega$$
$$v_2(t) \Rightarrow V_2=10\angle-30°\ \text{V}$$

Following the same procedure as before, solve this circuit using nodal analysis by applying KCL to the top essential node as

$$\frac{V_{o2}-10\angle-30°}{-j2\,k}+\frac{V_{o2}}{2\,k}+\frac{V_{o2}}{j4\,k}=0$$

Simplifying this equation gives

$$V_{o2}\left(\frac{1}{-j2\,k}+\frac{1}{2\,k}+\frac{1}{j4\,k}\right)=\frac{10\angle30°}{-j2\,k}$$

which gives the phasor and time domain solutions

$$V_{o2}=8.94\angle93.4°\ \text{V}$$
$$v_{o2}(t)=8.94\cos(4000t+93.4°)\ \text{V}$$

The final solution is the sum of the partial solutions,

$$v_o(t)=v_{o1}(t)+v_{o2}(t)$$
$$v_o(t)=8.94\cos(2000t-18.4°)+8.94\cos(4000t+93.4°)\,\text{V}$$

It is vitally important to note that the two voltages sum in the time domain, not the phasor domain. The sum of the phasor solutions

$$V_o \neq V_{o1}+V_{o2}$$

has no physical meaning. The two partial results are phasor values at different frequencies, i.e., $\omega=2000$ and $\omega=4000$ respectively. When these are added,

what would the frequency of the result be? **Phasors at different frequencies do NOT add.**

Phasor Analysis Guidelines
1. Follow the phasor analysis diagram.
2. Use underlined uppercase letters for phasor voltages and currents, e.g., V and I. If they are not underlined, they are DC values.
3. Express phasor voltages and currents in polar form. The magnitude and phase are equal to the magnitude and phase of a sinusoidal voltage or current. Rectangular form has no meaning.
4. Use the capital letter Z for impedances. These are NOT phasors, so do NOT underline them.
5. Express impedances in rectangular form where the real part is a resistance and the imaginary part is related to either an inductance or capacitance.
6. Resistors are not complex values, so don't use the R for impedances. For example, $R \neq 12+j312$, but it is an impedance, $Z=12+j312\ \Omega$.
7. Don't mix time domain and phasor domain expressions. There are no complex numbers in the time domain, and there are no time functions in the phasor domain. For example, $v(t)\neq20\angle30°$, $L\neq j435$.
8. The impedance of a capacitor is always negative, $Z_c=-j1/(\omega C)$. The impedance of an inductor is always positive, $Z_L=j\omega L$.
9. Phasors at different frequencies do not add. Superposition is required when sources at different frequencies exist in a circuit.

6.6 Terminology

In addition to impedance Z, there are a number of other related terms that commonly appear in practice.

When combining impedances in series or parallel, the result always has the form

$$Z = R \pm jX$$

where R is the real part or the resistive part. The term X is called the **reactance**, so $\pm jX$ is the imaginary part or reactive part. For example, $Z=12+j312$ is composed of a resistance of $R=12\ \Omega$ and a reactance of $X=312\ \Omega$. Similarly, $Z=12-j312$ is composed of a resistance of $R=12\ \Omega$ and a reactance of $X=312\ \Omega$.

The impedance of an inductor is $Z_L = j\omega L$, so its reactance X_L is

$$Z_L = jX_L \qquad X_L = \omega L$$

The impedance of a capacitor is $Z_c = -j1/(\omega C)$, so its reactance X_c is

$$Z_c = -jX_c \qquad X_c = \frac{1}{\omega C}$$

Earlier, the inverse of resistance was defined as conductance, $G = 1/R$, which has units of siemens (S). Using this as guidance, the inverse of impedance is **admittance** (i.e., to "admit" is to "conduct"),

$$Y = \frac{1}{Z} = G + jB$$

where the real part is a conductance G and the imaginary part is called the **susceptance** B. It should be clear that if $Z = R + jX$, then $Y \neq 1/R + 1/(jX)$. Complex algebra does not work that way.

Using these terms, the impedance and admittance of an inductor and capacitor are

$$Z_L = j\omega L \qquad Y_L = \frac{1}{Z_L} = -j\frac{1}{\omega L}$$

$$Z_c = -j\frac{1}{\omega C} \qquad Y_c = \frac{1}{Z_c} = j\omega C$$

Example: In the circuit below the resistance R and inductive reactance X_L are known. Find the capacitive reactance X_c such that the equivalent impedance Z_{eq} has no imaginary component. That is, $Z_{eq} = R_{eq} + j0$.

Applying the basic expression for impedances in parallel, Z_{eq} can be expressed as

$$\frac{1}{Z_{eq}} = \frac{1}{-jX_c} + \frac{1}{R + jX_L}$$

The left hand side can be written as

$$\frac{1}{Z_{eq}} = \frac{1}{R_{eq} + j0} = \frac{1}{R_{eq}}$$

so the impedances in parallel expression becomes

$$\frac{1}{R_{eq}} = \frac{1}{-jX_c} + \frac{1}{R + jX_L}$$

Since the left hand side has no reactive part, the goal is to find X_c so that the right hand side has no reactive part. This requires eliminating complex values from the denominator of both terms on the right hand side,

$$\frac{1}{R_{eq}} = \frac{1}{-jX_c}\left(\frac{j}{j}\right) + \frac{1}{R+jX_L}\left(\frac{R-jX_L}{R-jX_L}\right)$$

$$\frac{1}{R_{eq}} = \frac{j}{-(j^2)X_c} + \frac{R-jX_L}{R^2+X_L^2}$$

$$\frac{1}{R_{eq}} = j\frac{1}{X_c} + \frac{R}{R^2+X_L^2} - \frac{jX_L}{R^2+X_L^2}$$

Now separate and group the real and imaginary parts of the right hand side,

$$\frac{1}{R_{eq}} = \frac{R}{R^2+X_L^2} + j\left(\frac{1}{X_c} - \frac{X_L}{R^2+X_L^2}\right)$$

Setting the imaginary part to zero gives the result,

$$\left(\frac{1}{X_c} - \frac{X_L}{R^2+X_L^2}\right) = 0$$

$$\frac{1}{X_c} = \frac{X_L}{R^2+X_L^2}$$

$$X_c = \frac{R^2+X_L^2}{X_L}$$

When this is true, $Z_{eq} = R_{eq} + j0$, where

$$R_{eq} = \frac{R^2+X_L^2}{R}$$

Interestingly, these two results show that $R_{eq} > R$ and $X_c > X_L$. The resulting equivalence is shown in the following circuit.

$$X_c = \frac{R^2+X_L^2}{X_L} \qquad R_{eq} = \frac{R^2+X_L^2}{R}$$

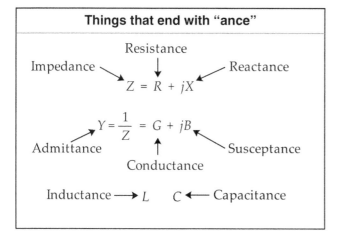

Things that end with "ance"

$$Z = R + jX$$

Impedance, Resistance, Reactance

$$Y = \frac{1}{Z} = G + jB$$

Admittance, Conductance, Susceptance

Inductance $\longrightarrow L \quad C \longleftarrow$ Capacitance

6.7 Transformers

Transformers are the single biggest reason why electrical power is generated and distributed in sinusoidal form. Transformers are to electricity what a mechanical transmission or gearbox is to rotational motion.

A mechanical transmission or gearbox changes the input speed and torque to some other speed and torque at its output. Since the product of torque and speed is power, when the speed increases, the torque decreases and vice versa. This is what the transmission in an automobile does.

Electrical transformers perform the same function. Since power is the product of voltage and current, a transformer changes an input voltage and current into some other voltage and current at its output. When voltage increases, current decreases and vice versa. This is what common power transformers on utility poles do in providing power to dwellings. They decrease the voltage level so that it is safe to use. In North America, household voltage is 120 V, whereas the voltage on the utility lines on the other side of the transformer is typically sixty times greater or 7200 V.

The reason for transformers is simple. When voltage increases, current decreases. When the voltage goes up by a factor of sixty from 120 V to 7200 V, the current goes down by a factor of sixty. Therefore, the cross sectional area of the wire can be sixty times smaller on the side having smaller current as well.

So, the higher the voltage, the lower the current; the lower the current, the smaller the wire; the smaller the wire, the cheaper the cost of stringing wire from utility pole to utility pole. So moving massive amounts of power over long distances is cheaper at higher voltages. Transformers do not work with DC currents, so that is why AC power is generated, distributed, and consumed.

To fully understand transformers (and inductors for that matter), it would be necessary to study magnetic fields and magnetic circuits in much greater depth than is possible in a course covering electric circuits. Therefore, the best that can be done here is to summarize fundamental relationships. If this is not satisfactory, a great deal of information can be found in other more specialized texts and online.

Transformers are simply two inductors where the magnetic field created by one coil not only passes through the coil generating the magnetic field, but also passes through or links a second coil. The following figure shows a representative sketch where the two coils are wrapped on a magnetic core. The coils for the two inductors are typically wound tightly together so that ideally all the magnetic field created by one coil passes through or links the second coil and vice versa.

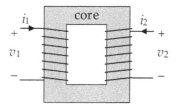

For an inductor formed by a single coil, the flux linkage $\lambda = Li$ describes the total magnetic flux passing through or linking all N turns making up a coil. When this flux linkage changes with time, a voltage is induced across the coil, *i.e.*,

$$v = \frac{d\lambda}{dt} = \frac{d}{dt}Li = L\frac{di}{dt}$$

This is the standard inductor terminal relationship derived earlier.

In a transformer, the magnetic flux linking the first coil has two components, one from the first coil itself, λ_1, and the other due to magnetic flux created by current in the second coil passing through the first, λ_{12}. That is,

$$\lambda = \lambda_1 + \lambda_{12}$$

where $\lambda_1 = L_1 i_1$ and $\lambda_{12} = \pm M i_2$ and the sign on M is determined by the direction of the current in the second coil relative to the voltage labeled on the first. The sign on the $\lambda_1 = L_1 i_1$ term is given by the passive sign convention.

In this case, the voltage induced across the first coil is

$$v_1 = \frac{d\lambda}{dt} = \frac{d}{dt}\left(\lambda_1 + \lambda_{12}\right) = L_1 \frac{di_1}{dt} \pm M \frac{di_2}{dt}$$

The first term above is the common inductance relationship and the second term is the voltage induced in the first coil due to current flowing in the second coil.

The above voltage expression makes sense only if the units on M are henries (H) just as they are for the inductance L, because the product of henries and amperes per second is volts, $V = H \cdot A/s$.

When two coils interact in this way, L is called **self inductance** and M is called **mutual inductance**. The self inductance is due to the magnetic field produced in a coil by itself, and the mutual inductance is due to the mutual interaction between two coils.

Following the same procedure used above for the second coil, gives the voltage induced across the second coil as

$$v_2 = \frac{d\lambda}{dt} = \frac{d}{dt}\left(\lambda_2 + \lambda_{21}\right)$$

$$v_2 = L_2 \frac{di_2}{dt} \pm M \frac{di_1}{dt}$$

where $\lambda_{21} = \pm M i_1$ and M has the same value for this coil because the magnetic field created by the two coils share the same physical space.

The mutual inductance M cannot have any arbitrary value. With a great deal of analysis, it can be shown that M is limited to the range

$$0 \leq M \leq \sqrt{L_1 L_2}$$

If two inductors are completely separated from each other, their respective magnetic fields do not interact, so $M = 0$. In this case, there are just two everyday inductors acting alone. However, under ideal conditions when the two coils are tightly intertwined, M will be equal to its maximum value.

Because of this limited range, it is sometimes convenient to express the mutual inductance as some fraction of its maximum value. That is, M can be written as

$$M = k\sqrt{L_1 L_2}$$

where the k has the range

$$0 \leq k \leq 1$$

When expressed in this way, k is called the **coupling coefficient**.

The Linear Transformer

The two relationships for the voltages induced in each coil are summarized as

$$v_1 = L_1 \frac{di_1}{dt} \pm M \frac{di_2}{dt}$$

$$v_2 = L_2 \frac{di_2}{dt} \pm M \frac{di_1}{dt}$$

These two equations define what is called the linear transformer. The schematic symbol for the linear transformer is shown below.

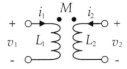

The two individual inductors are labeled according to the passive sign convention with current entering the node labeled positive. The mutual inductance M is simply labeled near the two inductors. The two dots are used to provide a visual indication of the sign on the mutual voltage terms $\pm M di/dt$.

The **dot convention** rule is as follows. The mutual voltage is positive, i.e., $+M di/dt$, at the dotted terminal on one side, if the current is entering the dotted terminal on the other side. Otherwise, it is negative, i.e., $-M di/dt$.

For the above circuit, the current is entering the dotted terminals on both sides so the mutual voltage is positive at the dotted terminals on both sides. In this case, the linear transformer equations become

$$v_1 = L_1 \frac{di_1}{dt} + M \frac{di_2}{dt}$$

$$v_2 = L_2 \frac{di_2}{dt} + M \frac{di_1}{dt}$$

At this point it is possible to play all sorts of labeling games where the passive sign convention may or may not hold on either or both sides, and where the dots move around randomly. Then, the game is to figure out how to write the linear transformer equations. The sign on each of the four terms can be either '+' or '−'. As a result, there are a total of 24 sign labeling possibilities here. The simplest way to avoid this problem is to label or relabel the transformer as shown in the preceding diagram and use the '+' for all four terms. This follows the basic idea of always labeling the voltage and current for circuit elements so they obey the passive sign convention.

For example, consider the linear transformer shown below.

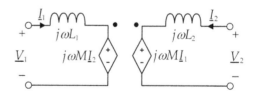

The inductor L_1 is labeled according to the passive sign convention, so its contribution to v_1 is $+L_1 di_1/dt$. The inductor L_2 is not labeled according to the passive sign convention, so its contribution to v_2 is negative, $-L_2 di_2/dt$.

Current is leaving the dotted terminal on L_2, so the voltage induced in L_1 is negative at the dotted terminal, which disagrees with the polarity assigned to v_1, so this term subtracts from v_1, i.e., $-M di_2/dt$. Current is entering the dotted terminal on L_1, so the voltage induced in L_2 is positive at the dotted terminal, which agrees with the polarity assigned to v_2, so this term adds to v_2, i.e., $+M di_1/dt$.

Therefore, the linear transformer equations for the above example are

$$v_1 = L_1 \frac{di_1}{dt} - M \frac{di_2}{dt}$$

$$v_2 = -L_2 \frac{di_2}{dt} + M \frac{di_1}{dt}$$

Now there are only 22 other possibilities to consider that are not all that important either.

The fact that a varying current in one coil produces a voltage in another coil is what allows a transformer to transform voltages and currents. That currents must be changing, i.e., $di/dt \neq 0$, for voltages to be induced means that transformers do not transform anything when currents are constant, i.e., for DC currents. That is why electrical power is generated and distributed in AC sinusoidal form.

The linear transformer equations are seldom used as presented. Transformers are inherently used for transforming AC voltages and currents. So, the phasor equivalent of the transformer equations is very important. The inductor relationship provides guidance for determining the phasor equivalent,

$$v = L \frac{di}{dt} \quad \Leftrightarrow \quad V = j\omega L I$$

Differentiation in the time domain effectively becomes multiplication by $j\omega$ in the phasor domain. Using this as guidance, the phasor domain equations for the linear transformer become

$$v_1 = L_1 \frac{di_1}{dt} + M \frac{di_2}{dt} \quad \Leftrightarrow \quad V_1 = j\omega L_1 I_1 + j\omega M I_2$$

$$v_2 = L_2 \frac{di_2}{dt} + M \frac{di_1}{dt} \quad \Leftrightarrow \quad V_2 = j\omega L_2 I_2 + j\omega M I_1$$

The last term in each of these equations is a voltage produced in one place due to a current flowing in another place. This action describes a current controlled voltage source. As a result, the phasor equations describe the circuit below that contains two dependent sources. Writing KVL equations for each side of the transformer leads to the above phasor equations for the linear transformer.

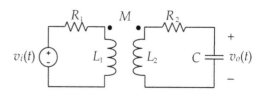

Example: Find $v_o(t)$ in the following circuit having the component values

$$R_1 = 120 \ \Omega \quad R_2 = 2.5 \ \text{k}\Omega \quad C = 200 \ \text{nF}$$
$$L_1 = 80 \ \text{mH} \quad L_2 = 1.28 \ \text{H} \quad M = 160 \ \text{mH}$$
$$v_i(t) = 20 \cos(2000 \, t) \ \text{V}$$

The voltages and currents associated with the linear transformer have not been specified, so make it easy by labeling them so that all terms in the transformer equations are positive as shown below.

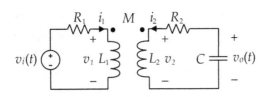

Next compute the phasor equivalents of all components as shown below, and draw the phasor circuit using the phasor model for the transformer.

$$R_1 \Rightarrow R_1 = 120 \ \Omega$$

$$R_2 \Rightarrow R_2 = 2.5 \ k\Omega$$

$$L_1 \Rightarrow j\omega L_1 = j(2\,k)(80\,m) = j160 \ \Omega$$

$$L_2 \Rightarrow j\omega L_2 = j(2\,k)(1.28) = j2.56 \ k\Omega$$

$$M \Rightarrow j\omega M = j(2\,k)(160\,m) = j320 \ \Omega$$

$$C \Rightarrow -j\frac{1}{\omega C} = -j\frac{1}{(2k)(200\,n)} = -j2.5 \ k\Omega$$

$$v_i(t) \Rightarrow V_i = 20\angle 0° \ V$$

Finding $v_o(t)$ is now simply a matter of solving the phasor circuit for V_o, and then writing down the equivalent time domain expression. There are no essential nodes in this circuit, so it is not clear how to solve it using nodal analysis. However, KVL can be written for the two loops.

Starting in the lower left hand corner of each loop and proceeding clockwise gives

$$20\angle 0° - 120\,I_1 - j160\,I_1 - j320\,I_2 = 0$$

$$j320\,I_1 + j2.5\,k\,I_2 + 2.5\,k\,I_2 + (-j2.5\,k)\,I_2 = 0$$

These are two equations in the two unknown currents. The equations can be put in matrix form giving

$$\begin{bmatrix} 120+j160 & j320 \\ j320 & 2.5k+j2.5\,k-j2.5\,k \end{bmatrix} \cdot \begin{bmatrix} I_1 \\ I_2 \end{bmatrix} = \begin{bmatrix} 20\angle 0° \\ 0 \end{bmatrix}$$

The solution to this set of equations is

$$\begin{bmatrix} I_1 \\ I_2 \end{bmatrix} = \begin{bmatrix} 88.12\,m \angle -44.83° \\ 11.28\,m \angle -134.83° \end{bmatrix}$$

Because the passive sign convention is false for the capacitor, Ohm's law for phasors then gives the output voltage as $V_o = (-1) \cdot Z_c I_2$,

$$V_o = -\left(-j2.5\,k\right)I_2 = (j2.5\,k)\cdot(11.28\,m\angle -134.83°)$$

$$V_o = 28.2\angle 135.2° \ V$$

The corresponding time domain solution is

$$v_o(t) = 28.2\cos(2000\,t + 135.2°) \ V$$

Interestingly, the amplitude of the voltage across the capacitor is greater than that of the source $v_i(t)$ supplying the circuit. Computing $v_2(t)$ shows that its amplitude is equal to 39.9 V. Because the voltage $v_2(t)$ is greater than the source, this is called a **step up transformer** since it steps up the voltage. If the opposite had occurred, and the voltage went down, this would be a **step down transformer**.

The linear transformer finds application in the processing of information, but not in the processing of power. It also finds application in analyzing noise and interference in cabling and conductor paths on PC boards.

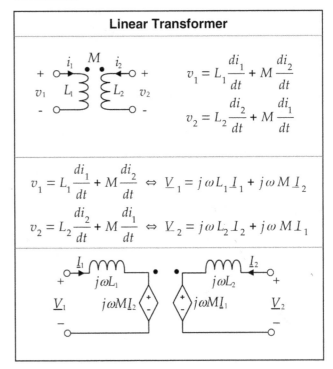

The Ideal Transformer

The ideal transformer is the idealized model for a power transformer, like those used in the transmission and distribution of electrical power.

The ideal transformer is a simple model for a transformer when the two coils are each composed of many turns and they are wound around ferromagnetic material that maximizes both the magnetic field produced and the flux linking the two coils. When this occurs, the differential equations relating the voltages and currents disappear and the transformer is described by simple algebra as shown in the figure below.

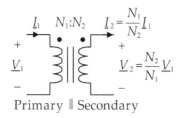

Primary ∥ Secondary

The transformer symbol has changed to reflect the fact that this is an ideal transformer and not a linear transformer. The variables N_1 and N_2 are the number of turns in the respective coils. The voltages and currents scale by the ratio of these turns. The voltages and currents are related by algebra. Surprisingly, the inductances of the two coils disappears. The reasons for these dramatic changes requires an understanding of magnetic fields and ferromagnetic materials, which are beyond the scope of this material.

In the ideal transformer, the voltage is greater on the side having the greater number of turns and the opposite is true for the current. The current is greater on the side with the lesser number of turns. The product relationship $\underline{V}_1\underline{I}_1 = \underline{V}_2\underline{I}_2$ holds because the transformer is just two tightly coupled inductors. It cannot generate power. So, if the voltage goes up, the current must go down and vise versa. **By convention the side power is applied to is called the *primary* and the side connected to the load is called the *secondary*.**

The model of a real power transformer, such as those used in the transmission and distribution of electrical power, starts with the ideal model above, and then adds components to model inherent non-ideal characteristics. This modeling is often a topic in more specialized courses.

Ideal Transformer

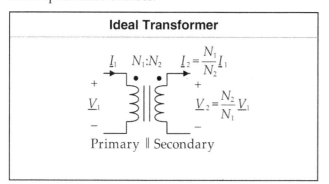

Primary ∥ Secondary

Example: In the following ideal transformer circuit, find the transformer voltages $\underline{V}_1$ and $\underline{V}_2$ and currents $\underline{I}_1$ and $\underline{I}_2$ when the load resistor R_2 takes on the values **(a)** $R_2 = \infty$, **(b)** $R_2 = 0$, and **(c)** $R_2 = R_1$.

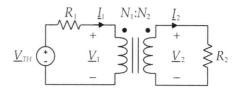

(a) When $R_2 = \infty$, the circuit becomes

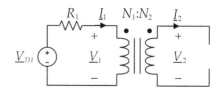

The secondary current is zero, $\underline{I}_2 = 0$, because there is no place for current to flow. The primary current is then also equal to zero because

$$\underline{I}_1 = \frac{N_2}{N_1}\cdot\underline{I}_2 = \frac{N_2}{N_1}\cdot 0 = 0$$

Because the primary current is zero, the voltage across resistor R_1 is zero by Ohm's law, $0\cdot R_1 = 0$. Therefore, by KVL, $\underline{V}_1 = \underline{V}_{TH}$. The transformer relationship then gives the secondary voltage as

$$\underline{V}_2 = \frac{N_2}{N_1}\cdot\underline{V}_1 = \frac{N_2}{N_1}\cdot\underline{V}_{TH}$$

The source voltage gets scaled by the turns ratio N_2/N_1 to give the secondary voltage. If $N_2 > N_1$, the voltage is stepped up, otherwise it is stepped down.

(b) When $R_2 = 0$, the circuit becomes

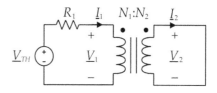

Now the secondary voltage is zero due to the short circuit. So the transformer relationship gives the primary voltage as

$$\underline{V}_1 = \frac{N_1}{N_2}\cdot\underline{V}_2 = \frac{N_1}{N_2}\cdot 0 = 0$$

The voltage across the primary is zero. Then the primary current is

$$I_1 = \frac{V_{TH} - V_1}{R_1} = \frac{V_{TH} - 0}{R_1} = \frac{V_{TH}}{R_1}$$

Using the transformer relationship, the secondary current is

$$I_2 = \frac{N_1}{N_2} I_1 = \frac{N_1}{N_2} \frac{V_{TH}}{R_1}$$

If $N_2 > N_1$, the current is stepped down. If $N_2 < N_1$, the current is stepped up.

(c) When $R_2 = R_1$, the circuit becomes

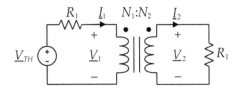

This circuit is solved by writing equations for the primary and secondary sides of the transformer. The secondary is described by Ohm's law

$$V_2 = R_1 I_2$$

and the primary is described by applying KVL

$$V_{TH} = V_1 + I_1 R_1$$

This gives two equations in the four unknowns V_1, I_1, V_2, and V_2. The remaining two equations are the ideal transformer relationships

$$V_2 = a V_1$$

$$I_2 = \frac{1}{a} I_1$$

where a is called the **turns ratio**

$$a = \frac{N_2}{N_1} = \text{turns ratio}$$

These equations can be solved by appropriately substituting equations into each other, or by solving the four equations in four unknowns. Since this problem does not have numerical values, it is easiest to solve it by appropriate substitutions.

Start by substituting the transformer relationships into the Ohm's law expression and solving for the equivalent impedance looking into the primary, $Z_{eq} = V_1/I_1$,

$$\left. \begin{array}{r} V_2 = R_1 I_2 \\ a V_1 = R_1 \left(\frac{1}{a} I_1 \right) \end{array} \right\}$$

$$Z_{eq} = \frac{V_1}{I_1} = \frac{R_1}{a^2}$$

Given this impedance (a resistance in this example), the transformer and secondary can be replaced by Z_{eq} as shown in the following circuit.

This circuit is easily solved. V_1 is given by voltage division,

$$V_1 = \frac{Z_{eq}}{R_1 + Z_{eq}} V_{TH}$$

$$V_1 = \frac{\dfrac{R_1}{a^2}}{R_1 + \dfrac{R_1}{a^2}} V_{TH}$$

$$V_1 = \frac{\dfrac{R_1}{a^2}}{R_1 + \dfrac{R_1}{a^2}} \cdot \left(\frac{\dfrac{a^2}{R_1}}{\dfrac{a^2}{R_1}} \right) V_{TH}$$

$$V_1 = \frac{1}{a^2 + 1} V_{TH}$$

And the current I_1 is given by Ohm's law

$$I_1 = \frac{V_{TH}}{R_1 + Z_{eq}} = \frac{V_{TH}}{R_1 + R_1/a^2} = \frac{V_{TH}}{R_1} \frac{a^2}{1 + a^2}$$

Using the transformer equations, the secondary voltage V_2 and current I_2 are found as

$$V_2 = a V_1 \qquad I_2 = \frac{I_1}{a}$$

6.8 Average Power

Since AC electrical power is generated, transmitted, distributed, and consumed throughout the world, it is important to study power. In particular, it is important to study power when voltages and currents are sinusoidal.

Consider the following very simple circuit.

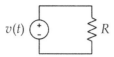

Let the voltage source be described by the sinusoid

$$v(t) = V_m \cos(\omega t)$$

which is plotted in the following figure where the period is $T = 2\pi/\omega$.

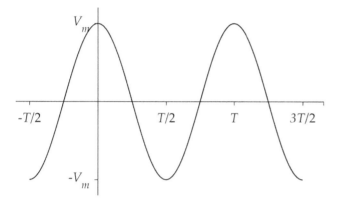

Being sinusoidal, the voltage crosses through zero twice each period. At those instants of time, there is no current flowing through the resistor R and no power being absorbed by it.

The power absorbed by the resistor is given by

$$p(t) = \frac{v^2(t)}{R} = \frac{V_m^2 \cos^2(\omega t)}{R}$$

This is the instantaneous power because it clearly changes every instant in time. A plot of the instantaneous power is shown in the following figure.

Comparing the instantaneous power plot to the voltage plot, the power is indeed zero when the voltage is zero. In addition, the power is never negative, as it must be, since a resistor only absorbs power. The frequency of the power is double that of the voltage.

More insight is gained if the power expression is simplified as

$$p(t) = \frac{V_m^2}{R} \cos^2(\omega t) = \frac{V_m^2}{2R} + \frac{V_m^2}{2R} \cos(2\omega t)$$

where the identity

$$\cos^2(\omega t) = \frac{1}{2} + \frac{1}{2} \cos(2\omega t)$$

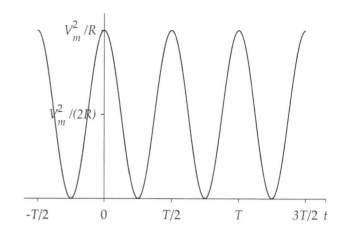

is used to write the result as the sum of two terms, one being a constant equal to one half the peak instantaneous value and the other being a sinusoidal term at twice the frequency of the voltage.

If the voltage source was the voltage available at a wall outlet and the resistor was the heating element in a toaster, then $p(t)$ describes the instantaneous power in watts being absorbed by the toaster heating element. At the instants when $p(t) = 0$, the heating element is not creating any heat. But yet, if you observe the heating element in a toaster, it doesn't go black or go cold at those instants. Similarly, it does not glow more brightly at the peaks in $p(t)$ either. The heating element glows at a constant brightness. What matters to bread in the toaster being toasted is what is happening on average. The peaks and valleys in $p(t)$ don't matter, rather it is what happens on average that matters.

While the importance of the average is easily understood in terms of a toaster, the importance of average power applies in essentially all uses of electrical power. For this reason, **average power is fundamentally important, and instantaneous power has little significance.**

Average Power: There are two ways to find the average power P. The first is to simply look at the above instantaneous power plot and expression. The average value is simply the constant term in the expression. It is equal to one half the peak value.

The other approach is to use calculus as demonstrated in Chapter 1. The average of a periodic function is given by the expression

$$P = \frac{1}{T} \int_0^T p(t)\, dt$$

and the average value of the square of a sinusoid is

$$\frac{1}{T}\int_0^T \cos^2(\omega t)\,dt = \frac{1}{2}$$

Applying this to $p(t)$ and following the derivation presented in Chapter 1 gives

$$P=\frac{1}{T}\int_0^T \frac{v^2(t)}{R}\,dt=\frac{1}{T}\int_0^T \frac{V_m^2\cos^2(\omega t)}{R}\,dt=\frac{V_m^2}{R}\cdot\left(\frac{1}{2}\right)=\frac{V_m^2}{2R}$$

The average value is one half of the peak value.

Effective and RMS Values: This is not good. Average power P for AC sinusoidal voltages has a factor of two in the denominator that does not appear when a DC voltage V_{DC} is applied across a resistor, i.e.,

$$\begin{array}{ccc} \text{DC} & \text{versus} & \text{AC} \\ P=\dfrac{V_{DC}^2}{R} & \text{versus} & P=\dfrac{V_m^2}{2R} \end{array}$$

To eliminate the factor of two in the AC voltage case, the standard practice is to define a new voltage, called the **effective value or RMS value** as

$$V_{eff}=V_{rms}=\frac{V_m}{\sqrt{2}}$$

Using this new variable, the average power P in a resistor when the voltage is sinusoidal is

$$P=\frac{V_m^2}{2R}=\frac{V_m^2}{(\sqrt{2})^2 R}=\left(\frac{V_m}{\sqrt{2}}\right)^2\frac{1}{R}=\frac{V_{eff}^2}{R}=\frac{V_{rms}^2}{R}$$

The subscript "eff" or effective is used because it identifies the effective DC value that a sinusoid has in terms of power absorbed in a resistor.

The subscript "rms" is used because of the mathematical process for computing it. The average power expression can be written as

$$\frac{V_m^2}{2R}=\frac{V_{rms}^2}{R}=\frac{1}{T}\int_0^T \frac{v^2(t)}{R}\,dt$$

Multiplying through by R and solving for V_{rms} gives

$$V_{rms}^2=\frac{1}{T}\int_0^T v^2(t)\,dt$$

$$V_{rms}=\sqrt{\frac{1}{T}\int_0^T v^2(t)\,dt}$$

The right hand side expression is the square **R**oot of the **M**ean of the **S**quare of the voltage. This leads to

use of the acronym RMS when the corresponding subscript "rms" is used. While use of the term *effective* is more descriptive, RMS appears much more frequently even though most people do not know what it stands for or what it means.

In North America, the standard voltage at wall outlets is 120 volts RMS, which is written as 120 Vrms. So if a toaster plugged into a 120 Vrms wall outlet makes toast in 3 minutes, the toaster would also make toast in the same 3 minutes if it were plugged into a 120 V DC source. **120 Vrms has the same effect as 120 V DC.**

The peak value or amplitude of a 120 Vrms sinusoid is

$$V_m=\sqrt{2}V_{rms}=\sqrt{2}\cdot120=170\text{ V}$$

When dealing with power, the peak value of a sinusoid has little utility. As a result, everyone uses the RMS value. The following two statements are equivalent, but the second is used almost exclusively.

$$v(t)=V_m\cos(\omega t+\theta)\text{ V}$$
$$v(t)=V_{rms}\cos(\omega t+\theta)\text{ Vrms}$$

The first expresses the voltage in terms of its peak value or amplitude V_m, and the second identifies the voltage in terms of its RMS value V_{rms}. **As shown, when expressed in terms of RMS values, the units are denoted Vrms, rather than the standard units V for the amplitude.**

For a standard wall outlet in the USA the following are equivalent statements.

$$v(t)=170\cos(\omega t+\theta)\text{ V}$$
$$v(t)=120\cos(\omega t+\theta)\text{ Vrms}$$

While this derivation focused on voltage, it could have just as easily expressed the instantaneous power in a resistor as $p(t)=i^2(t)R$. In this case, the effective or RMS value of the current would be

$$I_{eff}=I_{rms}=\frac{I_m}{\sqrt{2}}$$

and current can be written as

$$i(t)=I_m\cos(\omega t+\theta)\text{ A}$$
$$i(t)=I_{rms}\cos(\omega t+\theta)\text{ Arms}$$

where Arms expresses the RMS value and the standard unit A expresses the amplitude.

So if you look at a toaster and its specifications are 120 Vrms and 8 Arms, then the average power absorbed by the toaster is $P = 120 \cdot 8 = 960$ W. If these specifications were given as the equivalent amplitudes of 170 V and 11.3 A respectively, the average power absorbed by the toaster would be computed as $P = (170 \cdot 11.3)/2 = 960$ W, where the division by 2 is required. By using RMS values to begin with, the factor of two can be forgotten. It is contained in the definition of RMS values. That is the reason why it is standard practice to express AC voltages in terms of their RMS values when dealing with power.

Because the peak values V_m and I_m are not as descriptive as the effective or RMS values V_{rms} and I_{rms} when dealing with power, the RMS values are used exclusively in power applications. A mixture of terms is avoided so that mistakes are minimized.

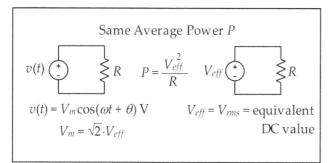

Same Average Power P

$P = \dfrac{V_{eff}^2}{R}$

$v(t) = V_m \cos(\omega t + \theta)$ V $V_{eff} = V_{rms}$ = equivalent
$V_m = \sqrt{2} \cdot V_{eff}$ DC value

Average Power in a Resistor

$P = \dfrac{V_m^2}{2R} = \dfrac{V_{rms}^2}{R}$	V_{rms} and I_{rms} are NOT phasors.
$P = \dfrac{I_m^2}{2}R = I_{rms}^2 R$	They are the RMS magnitudes of a
$P = \dfrac{V_m I_m}{2} = V_{rms} I_{rms}$	phasor voltage $\underline{V}$ and a current $\underline{I}$.

Effective and RMS Values

$$v(t) = V_m \cos(\omega t + \theta) \ \text{V}$$
$$v(t) = V_{rms} \cos(\omega t + \theta) \ \text{Vrms}$$

$$i(t) = I_m \cos(\omega t + \theta) \ \text{A}$$
$$i(t) = I_{rms} \cos(\omega t + \theta) \ \text{Arms}$$

$$V_{rms} = \frac{V_m}{\sqrt{2}} \qquad I_{rms} = \frac{I_m}{\sqrt{2}}$$

6.9 Complex Power

Engineers who work in the electric utility industry deal with power extensively. It is the fundamental product that they generate, transmit, and distribute for consumption. For this reason, power computations play a key role in their work. Over time, special terminology has been created to maximize productivity. This section introduces some of the important terms and concepts involved. More detailed knowledge requires dedicated study in the area of power systems.

The introduction of effective or RMS values makes the computation of average power in a resistor very simple. The resulting expressions for circuits containing AC sources are identical to those for DC sources.

It is worthwhile to consider instantaneous and average power for inductors and capacitors as well. For these components their impedance can be written as

$$Z = j\omega L = +jX$$

for the inductor and

$$Z = -j\frac{1}{\omega C} = -jX$$

for the capacitor. Therefore, the impedance can be written as $Z = \pm jX$.

If the current flowing through $\pm jX$ is

$$i(t) = I_m \cos(\omega t + \theta) \ \text{A}$$

the current as a phasor is

$$\underline{I} = I_m \angle \theta \ \text{A}$$

The resulting voltage across the impedance is

$$\underline{V} = Z\underline{I}$$
$$\underline{V} = \pm jX\underline{I}$$
$$\underline{V} = (X \angle \pm 90°) \cdot (I_m \angle \theta)$$
$$\underline{V} = XI_m \angle (\theta \pm 90°) \ \text{V}$$

which in the time domain is

$$v(t) = X I_m \cos(\omega t + \theta \pm 90°) \text{ V}$$

Given the time domain expressions for the current and voltage, the instantaneous power is

$$p(t) = v(t) \cdot i(t)$$
$$p(t) = X I_m \cos(\omega t + \theta \pm 90°) \cdot I_m \cos(\omega t + \theta)$$
$$p(t) = X I_m^2 \cos(\omega t + \theta \pm 90°) \cos(\omega t + \theta)$$
$$p(t) = \mp X \frac{I_m^2}{2} \sin(2\omega t + 2\theta)$$
$$p(t) = \mp X I_{rms}^2 \sin(2\omega t + 2\theta)$$

where

$$I_{rms} = \frac{I_m}{\sqrt{2}}$$

and the basic trigonometric identity

$$\cos(\alpha) \cos(\alpha \pm 90°) = \mp \frac{1}{2} \sin(2\alpha)$$

have been used to describe the final result.

A ±90 degree phase shift occurs between the voltage and current with inductors and capacitors. This phase shift changes the instantaneous power expression a great deal. The instantaneous power here does not contain a constant term like it did for the resistor. Here it has a sinusoidal term only and the average value of a sinusoid is zero as derived in Chapter 1. That is,

$$P = \frac{1}{T} \int_0^T p(t) \, dt = \frac{1}{T} \int_0^T \left(\mp X I_{rms}^2 \sin(2\omega t + 2\theta) \right) dt$$
$$P = \frac{\mp X I_{rms}^2}{T} \int_0^T \left(\sin(2\omega t + 2\theta) \right) dt$$
$$P = \frac{\mp X I_{rms}^2}{T} \cdot (0)$$
$$P = 0 \text{ W}$$

Therefore, the average power P in an inductor or capacitor is zero. This agrees with intuition since inductors and capacitors store energy and give it back, but they do not convert it to heat as a resistor does. They simply charge and discharge.

> **The average power P in an inductor L or in a capacitor C is zero!**

Consider the scenario where an inductor or capacitor is connected to a voltage source having an amplitude of $V_{rms} = 120$ Vrms and the associated current

amplitude is $I_{rms} = 8$ Arms. Taking the product of these gives

$$V_{rms} I_{rms} = 120 \cdot 8 = 960$$

The units on this result are *apparently* watts because this is the product of volts and amperes. So 960 is apparently the power in the inductor or capacitor? But yet the average power P must be zero for these elements, so this cannot be average power. It must be something. This product is called the **apparent power** and it is denoted using the notation

$$|S| = V_{rms} I_{rms}$$

To keep this from being confused with average power P that has units of watts, volt-amperes (VA) are the units given to this product. Therefore, if someone says 960 volt-amperes, you know they are talking about apparent power $|S|$. Whereas, if someone says 960 watts, you know they are talking about average power P.

In the case of a toaster having a resistive heating element where $V_{rms} = 120$ Vrms and the associated current amplitude is $I_{rms} = 8$ Arms, the apparent power and the average power are both equal to 960. For resistors the apparent power and average power are the same, but for inductors and capacitors, they are not. Inductors and capacitors have zero average power, $P = 0$.

The trouble with apparent power is that it ignores the phase relationship between the voltage and current. For a resistor, the voltage and current are in phase because the voltage is simply a scaled replica of the current by Ohm's law,

$$\underline{V} = R \underline{I}$$

and the apparent power $|S|$ and average power P are the same.

However, for the inductor and capacitor, there is a ±90° phase shift between the voltage and current as shown earlier in the instantaneous power derivation,

$$\underline{V} = \pm j X \underline{I} = (X \angle \pm 90°) \underline{I}$$

This ±90° phase shift is the reason why the average power is zero.

To organize these concepts, engineers have found it useful to define a new quantity called **complex power** that is defined by

$$S = \underline{V} \, \underline{I}^*$$

where the asterisk * denotes the complex conjugate, e.g., $(2 + j3)^* = (2 - j3)$ or $(5\angle 10°)^* = (5\angle -10°)$. The variable S is not underlined because it is not a phasor representing a voltage or current. However, the complex power S is generally a complex number having a real and imaginary part when expressed in rectangular form,

$$S = \underline{V} \, \underline{I}^* = P + jQ$$

and having a magnitude and phase when expressed in polar form,

$$S = \underline{V} \, \underline{I}^* = |S| \angle \theta_z$$

where $|S|$ is the apparent power so the complex power S also has units of volt-amperes (VA). These complex power relationships are shown on the complex plane as shown in the following figure.

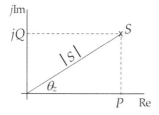

The usefulness of complex power is best shown by example. Once again consider a resistor. If the current is

$$\underline{I} = I_{rms} \angle \theta \text{ Arms}$$

the voltage is

$$\underline{V} = R \underline{I} = R I_{rms} \angle \theta \text{ Vrms}$$

then the complex power is

$$S = \underline{V} \, \underline{I}^* = (R I_{rms} \angle \theta) \cdot (I_{rms} \angle -\theta) = I_{rms}^2 R$$

This result has a real part only that is equal to the average power absorbed in a resistor. Writing this in rectangular form

$$S = I_{rms}^2 R = I_{rms}^2 R + j0 = P + j0$$

shows that the real part of the complex power is equal the average power P absorbed in the resistor and that the imaginary part is equal to zero, $jQ = j0$.

Writing this result in polar form

$$S = I_{rms}^2 R = I_{rms}^2 R \angle 0° = |S| \angle 0°$$

shows that the result is equal to the apparent power $|S|$. For the earlier toaster example, $P = |S| = 960$, so the apparent power and average power are equal.

Next consider the general reactance, $Z = \pm jX$. If the current is

$$\underline{I} = I_{rms} \angle \theta \text{ Arms}$$

then the associated voltage is

$$\underline{V} = \pm jX \underline{I}$$
$$\underline{V} = (X \angle \pm 90°) \cdot (I_{rms} \angle \theta)$$
$$\underline{V} = X I_{rms} \angle (\theta \pm 90°) \text{ Vrms}$$

and the complex power is

$$S = \underline{V} \, \underline{I}^*$$
$$S = (X I_{rms} \angle \theta \pm 90°) \cdot (I_{rms} \angle -\theta)$$
$$S = X I_{rms}^2 \angle \pm 90°$$

Writing this result in the polar form gives

$$S = X I_{rms}^2 \angle \pm 90° = |S| \angle \pm 90°$$

So the apparent power is $|S| = X I_{rms}^2$ and the angle is $\theta_z = \pm 90°$. This angle is called the **power factor angle**.

Writing the result in rectangular form gives

$$S = X I_{rms}^2 \angle \pm 90° = 0 \pm j X I_{rms}^2 = 0 \pm jQ$$

which shows that the real part P is zero. Therefore, the average power P in a reactance $\pm jX$ is zero as expected. The result has an imaginary part Q only. This part has no physical meaning since inductors and capacitors do not absorb power, but its natural units are watts. Rather than discard this term, it is given the name **reactive power. To distinguish it from the other terms, it is given the units of volt-amperes-reactive (VAR).**

Complex power components and terminology are summarized in the following table.

For a given phasor voltage and current, complex power provides the average power P in its real part. It also identifies a reactive power Q in its imaginary part. The magnitude of the complex power gives the apparent power.

In the diagram, simple geometry gives the real part P as

$$P = |S| \cos(\theta_z)$$

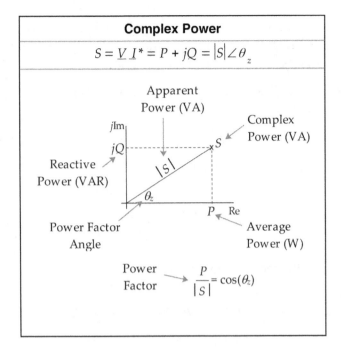

Complex Power

$$S = \underline{V}\,\underline{I}^* = P + jQ = |S| \angle \theta_z$$

Apparent Power (VA)

Complex Power (VA)

Reactive Power (VAR)

Power Factor Angle

Average Power (W)

Power Factor $\longrightarrow \dfrac{P}{|S|} = \cos(\theta_z)$

This relationship shows that the average power P is a fraction of the apparent power $|S|$ since $|\cos(\theta_z)| \leq 1$ always holds. This fraction,

$$pf = \frac{P}{|S|} = \cos(\theta_z)$$

is called the **power factor**. It describes the fractional amount of the apparent power that is the average power. Because the angle θ_z determines the power factor, it is called the **power factor angle** and is often written as θ_{pf}.

Because conservation of energy must hold, the sum of the average powers in all components in a circuit is zero. This is also true for reactive power. The sum of the reactive powers in all components in a circuit is zero as well. **Since the total average power and total reactive power in a circuit is zero, the total complex power is also zero. Conservation of both power and reactive power holds.**

Complex power is most often computed when the voltage and current are associated with an impedance

$$Z = R \pm jX = |Z| \angle \theta_z$$

In this case, if the current is

$$\underline{I} = I_{rms} \angle \theta \ \text{Arms}$$

the associated voltage in polar form is given by

$$\begin{aligned}
\underline{V} &= Z\,\underline{I} \\
\underline{V} &= \left(|Z| \angle \theta_z\right) \cdot \left(I_{rms} \angle \theta\right) \\
\underline{V} &= |Z| I_{rms} \angle (\theta + \theta_z)
\end{aligned}$$

then the complex power is

$$\begin{aligned}
S &= \underline{V}\,\underline{I}^* \\
S &= \left[|Z| I_{rms} \angle (\theta + \theta_z)\right] \cdot \left(I_{rms} \angle -\theta\right) \\
S &= |Z| I_{rms}^2 \angle \theta_z = |S| \angle \theta_z
\end{aligned}$$

The apparent power is $|S| = |Z| I_{rms}^2$ and the power factor angle θ_{pf} is equal to the angle of the impedance θ_z.

If the voltage is computed using the impedance in rectangular form as

$$\underline{V} = (R \pm jX)\underline{I}$$

then the complex power becomes

$$\begin{aligned}
S &= \underline{V}\,\underline{I}^* = \left[(R \pm jX)\underline{I}\right] \cdot \underline{I}^* \\
S &= (R \pm jX)\left(I_{rms} \angle \theta\right) \cdot \left(I_{rms} \angle -\theta\right) \\
S &= (R \pm jX)I_{rms}^2 \\
S &= R I_{rms}^2 \pm jX I_{rms}^2 = P \pm jQ
\end{aligned}$$

The average power is the same as it was for the earlier resistor only case,

$$P = I_{rms}^2 R$$

and the reactive power is the same as it was for the earlier reactance only case,

$$Q = \pm I_{rms}^2 X$$

So, the complex power does exactly what is needed. It computes and separates the average power from the reactive power for a general impedance.

Given these expressions, the power factor can be written in several forms as

$$pf = \frac{P}{|S|} = \cos(\theta_z) = \frac{I_{rms}^2 R}{I_{rms}^2 |Z|} = \frac{R}{|Z|}$$

Because cosine is an even function, $\cos(\alpha) = \cos(-\alpha)$, the power factor does not depend on the sign of θ_z. As a result, it is common to call the power factor a **lagging power factor** when θ_z is positive, *i.e.*, when the impedance is inductive, $Z = R + jX$. And the power factor is a **leading power factor** when θ_z is negative, *i.e.*, when the impedance is capacitive, $Z = R - jX$.

The above complex power content is the starting point for the work performed by engineers who work in the electric utility industry. To those interested, there is much more to learn. Finding additional material online or in a book is a good start. The best option is to take a course in power systems.

Complex Power for $Z = R \pm jX$	
Impedance	$Z = R \pm jX = \|Z\| \angle \theta_z$ Ω
Current	$\underline{I} = I_{rms} \angle \theta_i$ Arms
Voltage	$\underline{V} = V_{rms} \angle \theta_v = Z\underline{I}$ Vrms
Complex Power	$S = \underline{V} \cdot \underline{I}^*$
Complex Power	$S = P + jQ = R I_{rms}^2 \pm jX I_{rms}^2$ VA
Complex Power	$S = \|Z\| I_{rms}^2 \angle \theta_z = \|S\| \angle \theta_z$ VA
Apparent Power	$\|S\| = V_{rms} I_{rms} = I_{rms}^2 \|Z\|$ VA
Average Power	$P = I_{rms}^2 R$ W
Reactive Power	$Q = I_{rms}^2 X$ VAR
Power Factor	$pf = \dfrac{P}{\|S\|} = \dfrac{R}{\|Z\|} = \cos(\theta_z)$

Example 1: Find the complex power in each of the elements in the following phasor circuit. Show that the total complex power S_{tot} in the circuit is zero.

First use current division to find the two currents,

$$\underline{I}_1 = \frac{300 + j400}{300 + j400 - j200} 2\angle 30° = 2.774 \angle 49.44° \text{ Arms}$$

$$\underline{I}_2 = \frac{-j200}{300 + j400 - j200} 2\angle 30° = 1.109 \angle -93.69° \text{ Arms}$$

Rather than find the voltage across each of the elements so that complex power can be computed from its basic equation $S = \underline{V} \cdot \underline{I}^*$, it is much easier to use the previous results where complex power is related to current and impedance $Z = R \pm jX$,

$$S = R I_{rms}^2 \pm jX I_{rms}^2$$

The complex power in the capacitor having impedance $Z = 0 - j200$ Ω is

$$S_c = (0) \cdot I_{rms}^2 - j200 I_{rms}^2$$
$$S_c = 0 - j200 \cdot (2.774)^2$$
$$S_c = 0 - j1538 \text{ VA}$$

The complex power in the inductor having impedance $Z = 0 + j400$ Ω is

$$S_L = (0) \cdot I_{rms}^2 + j400 I_{rms}^2$$
$$S_L = 0 + j400 \cdot (1.109)^2$$
$$S_L = 0 + j492 \text{ VA}$$

The complex power in the resistor having impedance $Z = 300 + j0$ Ω is

$$S_R = (300) \cdot I_{rms}^2 + j(0) \cdot I_{rms}^2$$
$$S_R = (300) \cdot (1.109)^2 + j0$$
$$S_R = 369 + j0 \text{ VA}$$

To find the complex power in the source, the voltage across it $\underline{V}_s$ must be found. A simple way to find this voltage is to recognize that it is equal to the voltage across the capacitor,

$$\underline{V}_s = (\underline{I}_1) \cdot (-j200)$$
$$\underline{V}_s = (2.774 \angle 49.44°) \cdot (-j200) = 554.8 \angle -40.56° \text{ Vrms}$$

The passive sign convention is not met for the voltage source since the current is shown coming out of the side labeled positive (+). Therefore, the complex power must include a negative sign (–),

$$S_I = -\underline{V}_s \cdot \underline{I}_s^*$$
$$S_I = -(554.8 \angle -40.56°) \cdot (2 \angle -30°)$$
$$S_I = 1110 \angle -70.56° = -369 + j1046 \text{ VA}$$

Adding all of the complex powers gives

$$S_{tot} = S_c + S_L + S_R + S_I$$
$$S_{tot} = -j1538 + j492 + 369 + (-369 + j1046) = 0$$

which shows that the total or net complex power is zero.

Example 2: In the following circuit, find (a) the power factor of the load and (b) the efficiency η with which power is delivered to the load by computing the ratio of the average power absorbed in the load to the magnitude of that generated by the source.

The power factor is simply the cosine of the angle of the impedance,

$$pf = \cos(\theta_z)$$

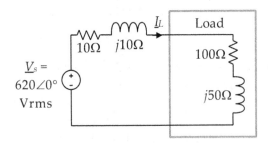

Writing the impedance in polar form gives

$$Z = 100 + j50 = 111.8\angle 26.57°$$

so the power factor is

$$pf = \cos(\theta_z) = \cos(26.57°) = 0.894$$

Since $\theta_z > 0$ and the load is inductive, this is a lagging power factor.

Once the current I_L is known, the ratio of powers can be found. Ohm's law gives the load current as

$$I_L = \frac{620\angle 0°}{10 + j10 + 100 + j50}$$

$$I_L = \frac{620}{110 + j60} = 4.948\angle -28.61° \text{ Arms}$$

The average power in the load is equal to the average power in the 100 Ω load resistor since the load inductance has zero average power. The average power in the load is then

$$P_L = |I_L|^2 \cdot R_L = 4.948^2 \cdot 100 = 2448 \text{ W}$$

The average power generated by the source can be found in two ways. First, the complex power in the source can be found. Then, the real part of its complex power gives its average power. Alternatively, knowing that conservation of energy holds, the average power generated by the source is equal to the sum of the average power absorbed by the 10 Ω and the 100 Ω resistors. Following this second approach, the average power generated by the source is

$$P_s = -(4.948^2)\cdot(10 + 100) = -2693 \text{ W}$$

This power is negative because the source generates power. The efficiency is then

$$\eta = \frac{P_L}{|P_s|} = \frac{2448}{2693} = 90.9\%$$

Therefore 90.9% of the power generated gets to the load.

Example 3: Reconsider the circuit in Example 2 above and place a capacitor across the load and choose its reactance so that the power factor of the load with the capacitor in place is equal to one. This is called the unity power factor solution. Then compute the efficiency again.

The revised circuit is shown below.

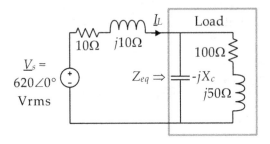

Setting the power factor equal to one gives

$$pf = \cos(\theta_z) = 1$$

The solution of this equation is $\theta_z = 0$, which means that the equivalent impedance seen looking into the revised load is

$$Z_{eq} = |Z_{eq}|\angle\theta_z = |Z_{eq}|\angle 0° = R_{eq} + j0$$

Finding the capacitive reactance value X_c that makes the equivalent impedance have a zero imaginary part was solved in an earlier example in this chapter. That solution was found earlier as

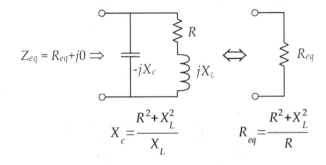

$$Z_{eq} = R_{eq} + j0 \Rightarrow \qquad\Leftrightarrow$$

$$X_c = \frac{R^2 + X_L^2}{X_L} \qquad R_{eq} = \frac{R^2 + X_L^2}{R}$$

Using this result, the capacitive reactance value is

$$X_c = \frac{R^2 + X_L^2}{X_L} = \frac{100^2 + 50^2}{50} = 250 \ \Omega$$

and the associated equivalent resistance is

$$R_{eq} = \frac{R^2 + X_L^2}{R} = \frac{100^2 + 50^2}{100} = 125 \ \Omega$$

The resulting equivalent circuit is shown below.

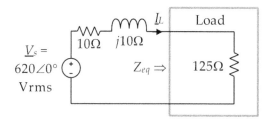

The current flowing through the load is now

$$I_L = \frac{620\angle 0°}{10+j10+125} = \frac{620}{135+j10} = 4.580\angle -4.23° \text{ Arms}$$

and the average power absorbed by the load is

$$P_L = \left|I_L\right|^2 \cdot R_L = 4.580^2 \cdot 125 = 2622 \text{ W}$$

The average power generated by the source is

$$P_s = -\left(4.580^2\right)\cdot(10+125) = -2832 \text{ W}$$

Therefore, the efficiency of the unity power factor load is

$$\eta = \frac{P_L}{\left|P_s\right|} = \frac{2622}{2832} = 92.6\%$$

So the efficiency with which power is delivered to the load has increased by making the load appear to be purely resistive.

Because efficiency is a primary consideration in the implementation of power systems, this practice of placing capacitors across power lines to maximize the power factor is routinely done. If you pay attention, you will notice capacitors placed across power lines on utility poles at various locations.

6.10 Residential Power

The material in this section generally applies to residential power in North America and countries that follow the same guidelines.

The typical residence in North America is supplied from a transformer that steps down 7200 Vrms to two 120 Vrms voltages in series as shown in the following figure.

The reason for this stacked configuration is that it makes 120 + 120 = 240 Vrms available for appliances that consume large amounts of power, such as electric stoves, electric water heaters, and central air conditioners.

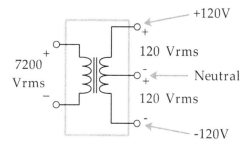

Since the average power in a resistive load is

$$P = V_{rms} I_{rms}$$

the current required for a given power is inversely proportional to the voltage, *i.e.,*

$$I_{rms} = \frac{P}{V_{rms}}$$

Therefore, by supplying 240 Vrms to appliances that consume a lot of power, the current required drops in half compared to what would be needed if the appliance was supplied by 120 Vrms. The lower current allows the cross-sectional area of the wire to drop in half, which reduces its cost.

In reality, this is the reason why transformers are used throughout the electric utility industry. For example, if a residence consumes 100 Arms at 120 Vrms, that current drops by a factor of 60 to 100/60 = 1.67 Arms on the other side of the transformer where the voltage is a factor of 60 times greater, 120·60 = 7200 Vrms. **When the voltage goes up by a factor of N, the current and corresponding wire cross-sectional area drop by a factor of N. This very fact is the primary reason why power is generated, distributed, and consumed in the form of AC sinusoids.**

At the circuit breaker panel the +120 V, neutral, and −120 V leads get split into multiple paths as shown in the following diagram.

The two "hot" wires go to multiple circuit breakers that distribute power to groups of outlets and light fixtures. The neutral wire is typically connected to the earth either through a connection to a long stake in the ground outside the dwelling, or to a municipal water main entrance inside the dwelling.

The presence of a third "ground" wire, usually uninsulated, that goes to all outlets and light fixtures is not shown above. Inside the circuit breaker panel, all ground wires are connected to the neutral near the

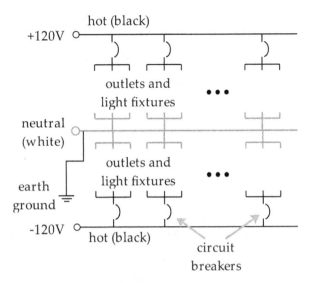

earth ground connection. The purpose of this third wire is for safety. Inside an appliance, this ground is connected to the chassis, such as the metal cabinet of a refrigerator, washing machine, or microwave oven. If the hot wire becomes disconnected or breaks within the appliance and touches the chassis, the connection back to neutral through the ground wire provides a short circuit that trips the circuit breaker. The refrigerator, washing machine, or microwave stops working, but the metal chassis is not electrified when you touch it.

Many appliances do not use the third ground wire. Many of them either do not have a metal chassis, or they are double-insulated internally, meaning they have two layers of insulation everywhere. If one insulation layer fails, the other remains in place. Vacuum cleaners and AC powered power tools are typically double-insulated.

The two hot wires, the neutral, and a separate ground wire are supplied to appliances that require 240 Vrms. Again, the ground wire is connected to the chassis for safety purposes. For example, the ground wire is connected to the frame of an electric stove.

The reasons for connecting the neutral to the earth through the earth ground are numerous and sometimes subtle. One obvious reason for grounding to the earth is to provide a path for lightning to travel if it strikes a power line or dwelling. Another reason is that it provides a conductive path so that hundreds or thousands of volts of static electricity do not build up. While the presence of earth ground is primarily for safety reasons, it is not a panacea. Just as there are rare fatalities caused by air bags in an automobile,

there are rare fatalities caused by earth ground as well. You can find a great deal of both informed and ill-informed information regarding the use of earth ground online.

6.11 Three Phase Power

Electrical power is universally generated and distributed in the form of three interconnected voltage sources. This is also how very large consumers of electricity such as large commercial and industrial facilities are supplied electrical power. The study of power systems focuses on three phase power systems and in the study of power flow in an interconnected system where there are many generating plants and many power consumers. More recently, the impact of renewable energy sources such as windmills and photovoltaics on power system operation has become important.

The study of three phase power can easily consume several semesters' worth of courses. The purpose of this section is simply to introduce some of the basic features of three phase power systems.

The most common three phase connection is shown in the following figure where the term "three phase" derives from the fact that the three sources are out of phase with each other by 120°.

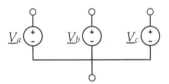

That is, the sources have the form

$$\underline{V}_a = V_{rms}\angle 0° \text{ Vrms}$$
$$\underline{V}_b = V_{rms}\angle 120° \text{ Vrms}$$
$$\underline{V}_c = V_{rms}\angle -120° \text{ Vrms}$$

In the standard terminology of power systems, this is called a balanced, negative sequence, Y-connected source. It is balanced because each of the sources has the same amplitude and they are equally out of phase with each other. It is called a negative sequence because phases (b) and (c) are labeled as shown. If the phase (b) and (c) labeling are swapped, it is called a positive sequence. It is called a Y-connection because it somewhat resembles an uppercase letter Y when drawn as shown below.

Because the phases of the three sources are equally spaced around a circle, the sources are almost universally drawn to match their relative phases as shown in the circuit below.

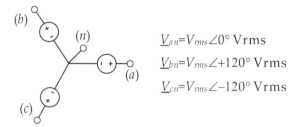

$$\underline{V}_{an} = V_{rms} \angle 0° \text{ Vrms}$$
$$\underline{V}_{bn} = V_{rms} \angle +120° \text{ Vrms}$$
$$\underline{V}_{cn} = V_{rms} \angle -120° \text{ Vrms}$$

Here nodal analysis labeling is used with double subscripts to uniquely identify voltages and their polarities. For example, $\underline{V}_{bn}$ is the voltage between phase (b) and the neutral (n). The positive node appears first in the subscript followed second by the negative node. These voltages measured with respect to the neutral are called **phase voltages**. Interestingly, when balanced, the sum of the phase voltages is equal to zero,

$$\underline{V}_{an} + \underline{V}_{bn} + \underline{V}_{cn} = V_{rms}\angle 0° + V_{rms}\angle 120° + V_{rms}\angle -120°$$
$$\underline{V}_{an} + \underline{V}_{bn} + \underline{V}_{cn} = V_{rms}\cdot\left(1\angle 0° + 1\angle 120° + 1\angle -120°\right)$$
$$\underline{V}_{an} + \underline{V}_{bn} + \underline{V}_{cn} = V_{rms}\cdot(0) = 0$$

Voltages can also be measured from phase node to phase node. These are called **line voltages** as labeled in the circuit below.

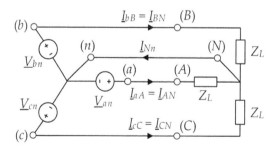

For example, KVL gives voltage from node (b) to node (a) as

$$\underline{V}_{bn} + \underline{V}_{ab} - \underline{V}_{an} = 0$$
$$\underline{V}_{ab} = \underline{V}_{an} - \underline{V}_{bn}$$
$$\underline{V}_{ab} = V_{rms}\angle 0° - V_{rms}\angle 120°$$
$$\underline{V}_{ab} = V_{rms}\cdot\left(1\angle 0° - 1\angle 120°\right)$$
$$\underline{V}_{ab} = V_{rms}\cdot\left(\sqrt{3}\angle -30°\right)$$
$$\underline{V}_{ab} = \sqrt{3}V_{rms}\angle -30°$$

Applying KVL gives the other line voltages as

$$\underline{V}_{bc} = \sqrt{3}V_{rms}\angle 90°$$
$$\underline{V}_{ca} = \sqrt{3}V_{rms}\angle -150°$$

The line voltages have amplitudes that are $\sqrt{3}$ times larger than the phase voltages and the three line voltages are also out of phase with each other by 120°.

Given the line voltages above, the Y-connection can be redrawn in an equivalent Δ-connection as shown in the following circuit.

$$\underline{V}_{ab} = \sqrt{3}V_{rms}\angle -30° \text{ Vrms}$$
$$\underline{V}_{bc} = \sqrt{3}V_{rms}\angle +90° \text{ Vrms}$$
$$\underline{V}_{ca} = \sqrt{3}V_{rms}\angle -150° \text{ Vrms}$$

This connection is valid because applying KVL around the loop leads to zero volts as required by KVL,

$$\underline{V}_{ab} + \underline{V}_{bc} + \underline{V}_{ca} = \sqrt{3}V_{rms}\cdot\left(1\angle -30° + 1\angle 90° + 1\angle -150°\right)$$
$$\underline{V}_{ab} + \underline{V}_{bc} + \underline{V}_{ca} = \sqrt{3}V_{rms}\cdot(0) = 0$$

The line voltages are equal for the Y-connection and Δ-connection, so the two configurations are equivalent. The only strange thing is that there is no neutral node (n) in the Δ-connection.

The simplest three phase circuit has a balanced Y-connected load connected to a balanced Y-connected source as shown in the following figure.

Here the load uses uppercase letters for its node labeling. The diagram also shows how currents are labeled. The first subscript on a current variable is the node from where the current is leaving from, and the second subscript is the node to where the current is entering. For example, $\underline{I}_{AN}$ is the **phase current** flowing from node (A) to node (N). The equivalent **line**

current $\underline{I}_{aA}$ is the current flowing from node (a) to node (A).

Applying KCL to the neutral node (N) gives

$$\underline{I}_{Nn} = \underline{I}_{AN} + \underline{I}_{BN} + \underline{I}_{CN}$$

The current in the neutral wire $\underline{I}_{Nn}$ serves as a common return path for the current flowing through each phase. That is, the contribution from each phase to this neutral current can be found independently. For example the current $\underline{I}_{AN}$ is given by Ohm's law as

$$\underline{I}_{AN} = \frac{\underline{V}_{an}}{Z_L}$$

since the voltage $\underline{V}_{an}$ appears directly across its associated load.

Using this fact, the neutral current $\underline{I}_{Nn}$ can be computed as

$$\underline{I}_{Nn} = \underline{I}_{AN} + \underline{I}_{BN} + \underline{I}_{CN}$$

$$\underline{I}_{Nn} = \frac{\underline{V}_{an}}{Z_L} + \frac{\underline{V}_{bn}}{Z_L} + \frac{\underline{V}_{cn}}{Z_L}$$

$$\underline{I}_{Nn} = \frac{1}{Z_L}\cdot\left(V_{rms}\angle 0° + V_{rms}\angle 120° + V_{rms}\angle -120°\right)$$

$$\underline{I}_{Nn} = \frac{V_{rms}}{Z_L}\cdot\left(1\angle 0° + 1\angle 120° + 1\angle -120°\right)$$

$$\underline{I}_{Nn} = \frac{V_{rms}}{Z_L}\cdot(0) = 0$$

There is no current flowing in the neutral wire. At first this may seem amazing, but the fact that the three phase voltages add to zero as shown earlier makes this happen.

Because there is no current flowing in the neutral wire, it can be removed without changing the circuit solution in any way, as shown in the following figure.

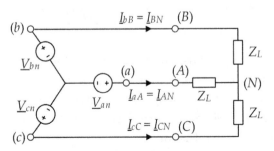

With the neutral wire removed, the Δ-connected equivalent to the Y-connected source can be substi-

tuted as shown in the following circuit without changing the solution in any way.

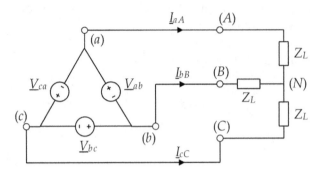

Since the three phase source can appear in either Y-connected or Δ-connected form, it makes sense that the load can as well. That is, the Y-connected load has the equivalent Δ-connected form shown in the following circuit.

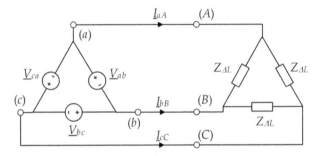

To have the same currents flowing from the three phase source, the load impedances must be different in the Δ-connected load than those of the Y-connected load. The relationship between the two loads is

$$Z_{\Delta L} = 3Z_L$$

This derivation is easily found online. This relationship has numerous names, including the Y-Δ transformation, the wye-delta transformation, and the T-π transformation.

Of course all of the above equivalences only exist when both the three phase source and the load are balanced. When either is unbalanced, there will be current flowing in the neutral wire. However, the amount of current will be proportional to the degree of imbalance. Small imbalances will lead to small neutral currents.

Since three phase sources can be connected in either the Y or Δ configuration, and loads can also be connected in either configuration, there are four possible balanced circuit combinations:

Source	Load
Y	Y
Y	Δ
Δ	Δ
Δ	Y

In addition, three phase sources can exist in either positive or negative sequence form. And then there is always the case of unbalanced operation for any of these possible combinations. This level of detail is considered in power systems courses, but it is beyond the scope of this introductory treatment.

Example: Consider the following negative sequence, balanced three phase circuit where V_{rms} = 120 Vrms and Z_L = 12 + $j4$ Ω. Find (a) $\underline{V}_{ab}$, (b) $\underline{V}_{ca}$, (c) $\underline{I}_{bB}$, (d) the total average power absorbed by the load, and (e) the total complex power generated by the sources.

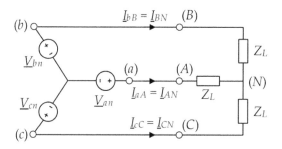

Given V_{rms}, the three sources are

$$\underline{V}_{an} = 120\angle 0° \text{ Vrms}$$
$$\underline{V}_{bn} = 120\angle 120° \text{ Vrms}$$
$$\underline{V}_{cn} = 120\angle -120° \text{ Vrms}$$

Even though the neutral wire is not shown, the circuit can be solved as if it were there since the circuit is balanced.

The voltage $\underline{V}_{ab}$ is found by applying KVL to the loop formed by $\underline{V}_{an}$, $\underline{V}_{bn}$, and $\underline{V}_{ab}$,

$$\underline{V}_{bn} + \underline{V}_{ab} - \underline{V}_{an} = 0$$
$$\underline{V}_{ab} = \underline{V}_{an} - \underline{V}_{bn}$$
$$\underline{V}_{ab} = 120\angle 0° - 120\angle 120°$$
$$\underline{V}_{ab} = 208\angle -30° \text{ Vrms}$$

This agrees with the earlier analytic result

$$\underline{V}_{ab} = \sqrt{3} V_{rms}\angle -30° \text{Vrms}$$
$$\underline{V}_{ab} = \sqrt{3}\cdot 120\angle -30° \text{Vrms}$$
$$\underline{V}_{ab} = 208\angle -30° \text{Vrms}$$

The voltage $\underline{V}_{ca}$ is found by applying KVL to the loop formed by $\underline{V}_{cn}$, $\underline{V}_{an}$, and $\underline{V}_{ca}$,

$$\underline{V}_{an} + \underline{V}_{ca} - \underline{V}_{cn} = 0$$
$$\underline{V}_{ca} = \underline{V}_{cn} - \underline{V}_{an}$$
$$\underline{V}_{ca} = 120\angle -120° - 120\angle 0°$$
$$\underline{V}_{ca} = 208\angle -150° \text{ Vrms}$$

The current $\underline{I}_{bB}$ is found by applying Ohm's law,

$$\underline{I}_{bB} = \frac{V_{bn}}{Z_L} = \frac{120\angle 120°}{12 + j4} = 9.49\angle 101.6° \text{ Arms}$$

The total average power absorbed by the load is the sum of that absorbed in each of the individual loads. So the total power absorbed is equal to three times that of any individual load.

Since $\underline{I}_{bB}$ is known, the average power absorbed in the Z_L = 12 + $j4$ Ω impedance it flows through is

$$P_{BN} = I_{rms}^2 R = 9.487^2 \cdot 12 = 1080 \text{ W}$$

Therefore the total power is

$$P = 3 P_{BN} = 3\cdot 1080 = 3240 \text{ W}$$

Finally, the total complex power absorbed by the sources is the sum of that from each source. Therefore, the total complex power is three times that from any individual source.

The complex power in the source $\underline{V}_{bn}$ is

$$S_{bn} = -\underline{V}_{bn}\underline{I}_{bB}^*$$
$$S_{bn} = -(120\angle 120°)\cdot(9.487\angle 101.6°)^*$$
$$S_{bn} = 1138\angle 161.6° \text{ VA}$$

The negative sign out front of this equation is due to the fact that the passive sign convention is not met for the way the voltages and currents are labeled for the sources.

The total complex power is then

$$S = 3 S_{bn} = 3\cdot 1138\angle 161.6°$$
$$S = 3 S_{bn} = 3415\angle 161.6° \text{ VA}$$
$$S = -3240 - j1080 \text{ VA}$$

The real part here is equal to the negative of the total average power absorbed in the load, which is what it must be for the net average power to be zero.

6.12 Summary

Phasor Transform
$f(t) = F_m \cos(\omega t + \theta) \Leftrightarrow \underline{F} = F_m \angle \theta$
Time Domain: $f(t) = F_m \cos(\omega t + \theta)$
Phasor Domain: $\underline{F} = F_m \angle \theta$
Phasors at different frequencies do NOT add. Apply superposition at each frequency that appears.

Phasor Analysis Guidelines
1. Follow the phasor analysis diagram.
2. Use underlined capital letters for phasor voltages and currents, e.g., $\underline{V}$ and $\underline{I}$. If they are not underlined, they are DC values.
3. Express phasor voltages and currents in polar form. The magnitude and phase are equal to the magnitude and phase of a sinusoidal voltage or current. Rectangular form has no meaning.
4. Use the capital letter Z for impedances. These are NOT phasors, so do NOT underline them.
5. Express impedances in rectangular form where the real part is a resistance and the imaginary part is related to either an inductor or capacitor.
6. Resistors do not have complex values, so don't use the R for impedances. For example, $R \neq 12 + j312$, but $Z = 12 + j312 \ \Omega$.
7. Don't mix time domain and phasor domain expressions. There are no complex numbers in the time domain, and there are no time functions in the phasor domain. For example, $v(t) \neq 20\angle30°$, $L \neq j435$.
8. The impedance of a capacitor is always negative, $Z_c = -j1/(\omega C)$. The impedance of an inductor is always positive, $Z_L = j\omega L$.
9. Phasors at different frequencies do not add. Superposition is required when sources at different frequencies exist in a circuit.

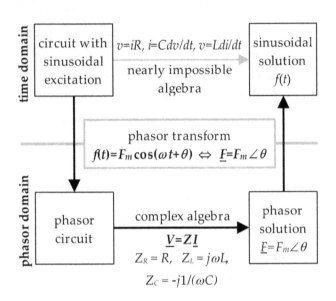

Things that end with "ance"

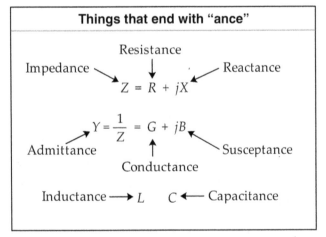

Linear Transformer

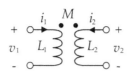

$$v_1 = L_1 \frac{di_1}{dt} + M \frac{di_2}{dt}$$

$$v_2 = L_2 \frac{di_2}{dt} + M \frac{di_1}{dt}$$

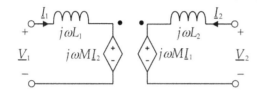

$$v_1 = L_1 \frac{di_1}{dt} + M \frac{di_2}{dt} \Leftrightarrow \underline{V}_1 = j\omega L_1 \underline{I}_1 + j\omega M \underline{I}_2$$

$$v_2 = L_2 \frac{di_2}{dt} + M \frac{di_1}{dt} \Leftrightarrow \underline{V}_2 = j\omega L_2 \underline{I}_2 + j\omega M \underline{I}_1$$

Ideal Transformer

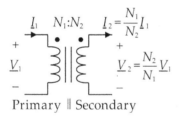

Primary ‖ Secondary

Same Average Power P

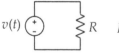 $P = \dfrac{V_{eff}^2}{R}$

$v(t) = V_m \cos(\omega t + \theta)$ V $\qquad V_{eff} = V_{rms}$ = equivalent
$V_m = \sqrt{2} \cdot V_{eff}$ $\qquad\qquad$ DC value

Effective and RMS Values

$$v(t) = V_m \cos(\omega t + \theta) \text{ V}$$
$$v(t) = V_{rms} \cos(\omega t + \theta) \text{ Vrms}$$

$$i(t) = I_m \cos(\omega t + \theta) \text{ A}$$
$$i(t) = I_{rms} \cos(\omega t + \theta) \text{ Arms}$$

$$V_{rms} = \frac{V_m}{\sqrt{2}} \qquad I_{rms} = \frac{I_m}{\sqrt{2}}$$

Average Power in a Resistor

$$P = \frac{V_m^2}{2R} = \frac{V_{rms}^2}{R}$$

$$P = \frac{I_m^2}{2}R = I_{rms}^2 R$$

$$P = \frac{V_m I_m}{2} = V_{rms} I_{rms}$$

V_{rms} and I_{rms} are NOT phasors.

They are the RMS magnitudes of a phasor voltage $\underline{V}$ and a current $\underline{I}$.

Explaining RMS

The RMS value of an AC voltage or current is equal to the value of a DC voltage or current that produces the same power.
For example, a toaster will make toast in the same amount of time if it uses 120 volts RMS or if it uses 120 volts DC.

Complex Power
$S = \underline{V}\,\underline{I}^* = P + jQ = \lvert S \rvert \angle \theta_z$

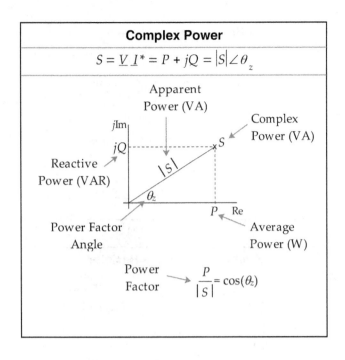

$$\text{Power Factor} \longrightarrow \frac{P}{\lvert S \rvert} = \cos(\theta_z)$$

Complex Power for $Z = R \pm jX$	
Impedance	$Z = R \pm jX = \lvert Z \rvert \angle \theta_z \ \Omega$
Current	$\underline{I} = I_{rms} \angle \theta \ \text{Arms}$
Voltage	$\underline{V} = Z\,\underline{I} \ \text{Vrms}$
Complex Power	$S = \underline{V} \cdot \underline{I}^*$
Complex Power	$S = P + jQ = R\,I_{rms}^2 \pm jX\,I_{rms}^2 \ \text{VA}$
Complex Power	$S = \lvert Z \rvert I_{rms}^2 \angle \theta_z = \lvert S \rvert \angle \theta_z \ \text{VA}$
Apparent Power	$\lvert S \rvert = V_{rms}\,I_{rms} = I_{rms}^2\,\lvert Z \rvert \ \text{VA}$
Average Power	$P = I_{rms}^2\,R \ \text{W}$
Reactive Power	$Q = I_{rms}^2\,X \ \text{VAR}$
Power Factor	$pf = \dfrac{P}{\lvert S \rvert} = \dfrac{R}{\lvert Z \rvert} = \cos(\theta_z)$

6.13 Problems

6.1 Use the phasor transform to simplify the following sinusoidal expressions.

(a) $y_1(t) = 12\cos(200t + 15°) + 8.5\cos(200t - 30°)$

(b) $y_2(t) = 10\cos(1000t + 135°) - 24\cos(1000t - 135°)$

(c) $y_3(t) = 6\cos(400t + 25°) + 8\cos(1200t - 60°)$
$+ 10\cos(400t + 135°) + 12\cos(1200t - 135°)$

6.2 Find the equivalent impedance Z_{eq} for each of the following circuits. Express Z_{eq} in rectangular form and identify what the equivalent components are, *i.e.*, a resistor in series with a capacitor or a resistor in series with an inductor.

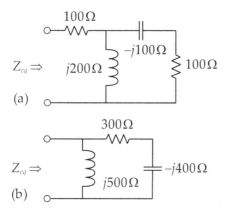

6.3 Find the equivalent impedance Z_{eq} of the circuit below and find the frequency ω where $Z_{eq} = R_{eq} + j0$.

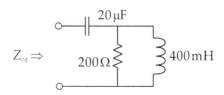

6.4 Find $i_1(t)$, $i_2(t)$, and $v_o(t)$ in the circuit below where $i_s(t) = 12\cos(10kt + 15°)$ mA. Note: 10k = 10 krad/s.

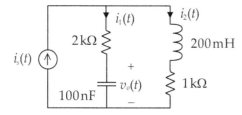

6.5 Find $v_o(t)$ in the following circuit (a) by applying nodal analysis, (b) by applying superposition, and (c) by performing source transformations and simplifications. The sources are $v_1(t) = 16\cos(8kt + 15°)$ V and $v_2(t) = 8\cos(8kt - 25°)$ V. Note: 8k = 8 krad/s.

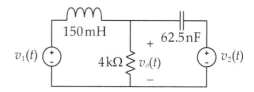

6.6 Find the Thévenin and Norton equivalent circuits for the circuit below (a) by finding the open circuit voltage $\underline{V}_{oc}$, short circuit current $\underline{I}_{sc}$, and equivalent impedance Z_{eq} seen looking into the terminals with the source shut OFF, and (b) by applying a sequence of source transformations and simplifications until the circuit becomes the desired results. The source is $v_s(t) = 40\cos(4kt)$ V. Note: 4k = 4 krad/s.

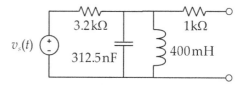

6.7 Find $v_o(t)$ in the circuit below where the sources are at different frequencies, $v_1(t) = 16\cos(4kt)$ V and $v_2(t) = 8\cos(16kt)$ V.

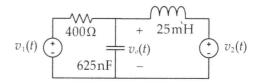

6.8 Find $v_o(t)$ in the circuit below if the input voltage is (a) $v_s(t) = \cos(10kt + 45°)$ V, (b) $v_s(t) = 2\cos(20kt - 45°)$ V.

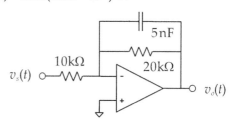

6.9 Find the node voltages $\underline{V}_1$ and $\underline{V}_2$ in the circuit below.

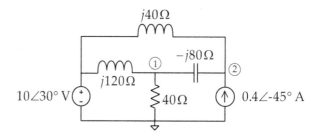

6.10 Find the Thévenin equivalent of the circuit below.

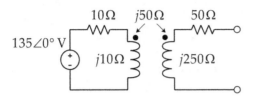

6.11 Find $v_o(t)$ in the circuit below if (a) $k = 0.2$, (b) $k = 0.5$, (c) $k = 1.0$. $v_s(t) = 20\cos(1000t)$ V.

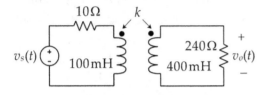

6.12 Find $v_o(t)$ in the circuit below if (a) $N_1/N_2 = 0.5$, (b) $N_1/N_2 = 2$, (c) $N_1/N_2 = 10$. $v_s(t) = 20\cos(1000t)$ V.

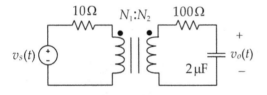

6.13 Repeat problem 6.12 above if the input voltage is $v_s(t) = 5 + 20\cos(1000t)$ V.

6.14 The voltage in Vrms units and current in Arms units associated with circuit elements are given below. Using this information, find (i) the average power P, (ii) the reactive power Q, (iii) the apparent power $|S|$, (iv) the complex power S, (v) the power factor pf, and (vi) the power factor angle θ_z.

(a) $v(t) = 120\cos(\omega t + 30°)$, $i(t) = 10\cos(\omega t - 20°)$

(b) $v(t) = 50\cos(\omega t + 120°)$, $i(t) = 16\cos(\omega t + 120°)$

(c) $v(t) = 85\cos(\omega t - 135°)$, $i(t) = 5\cos(\omega t + 10°)$

(d) $v(t) = -60\cos(\omega t + 20°)$, $i(t) = 30\cos(\omega t - 90°)$

6.15 In the following circuit $i_s(t) = 2\cos(2000t - 20°)$ mArms. Find (i) the complex power S in the source, (ii) the reactive powers Q in the capacitor and inductor, (iii) the average power P in each of the resistors, and (iv) the total complex power in the circuit.

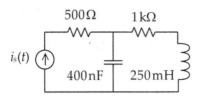

6.16 Consider the circuit below. (a) Let $X_c = \infty$ and find (i) the average power P in the 10 Ω load resistance, (ii) the reactive power Q in the $j4$ Ω load inductance, and (iii) the efficiency η with which power is delivered to the load. (b) find X_c so that the load has unity power factor, i.e., where the equivalent load impedance is resistive, $Z_{eq} = R_{eq} + j0$. With this value in place repeat all parts of (a) above. In addition, find (iv) the reactive power Q in X_c. Does the efficiency with which power is delivered to the load improve when X_c is chosen to maximize the power factor?

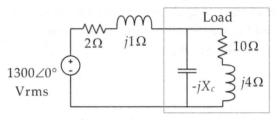

6.17 Find the average power P in each of the elements in the circuit below.

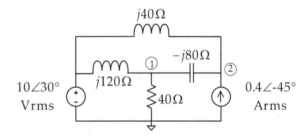

6.18 In the balanced circuit below $\underline{V}_{an} = 240\angle\,0°$ Vrms, $Z_l = 2 + j1$ Ω, and $Z_L = 10 + j4$ Ω. Find (i) $\underline{V}_{ab}$, (ii) $\underline{V}_{bc}$, (iii) $\underline{V}_{ca}$, (iv) $\underline{I}_{bB}$, (v) $\underline{V}_{AN}$, and (vi) $\underline{V}_{nN}$.

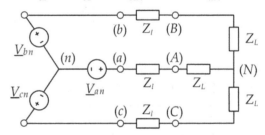

7 Frequency Response

Phasor analysis allows one to solve any circuit containing sinusoidal sources operating at a given frequency ω. In many cases, the frequency is either not known or may vary over a range of frequencies. When frequency is not specified, it becomes a variable, and numerical results cannot be computed. **This chapter explores techniques for solving and analyzing circuits where the operating frequency is not given. These circuits are commonly called filters. How filters respond as frequency varies is called the frequency response.**

7.1 Fundamental Ideas

Consider the following circuit where the input is composed of four sinusoids each at a different frequency,

$$v_1(t) = V_1 \cos(\omega_1 t + \theta_1)$$
$$v_2(t) = V_2 \cos(\omega_2 t + \theta_2)$$
$$v_3(t) = V_3 \cos(\omega_3 t + \theta_3)$$
$$v_4(t) = V_4 \cos(\omega_4 t + \theta_4)$$

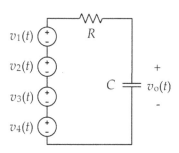

The solution $v_o(t)$ is the sum of four sinusoids that are found individually by applying superposition.

If $R = 10\ \text{k}\Omega$ and $C = 100\ \text{nF}$, and the four sources are

$$v_1(t) = 11\cos(500t + 0°)\ \text{V}$$
$$v_2(t) = 12\cos(1000t + 15°)\ \text{V}$$
$$v_3(t) = 13\cos(2000t + 30°)\ \text{V}$$
$$v_4(t) = 14\cos(5000t + 45°)\ \text{V}$$

the four phasor circuits to be solved are shown in the following circuits, where the capacitor's impedance $Z_c = -j1/(\omega C)$ is different for each input of the input frequencies.

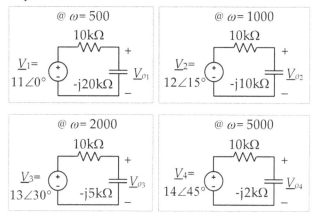

The individual solutions are found by applying the voltage division relationship

$$\underline{V}_o = \frac{Z_c}{R + Z_c}\underline{V}_i$$

Performing these steps for each of the four inputs leads to the following respective outputs

$$\underline{V}_{o1} = 9.84\angle-26.6°\ \text{V} \qquad \underline{V}_{o2} = 8.49\angle-30°\ \text{V}$$
$$\underline{V}_{o3} = 5.81\angle-33.4°\ \text{V} \qquad \underline{V}_{o4} = 2.75\angle-33.7°\ \text{V}$$

Each of these phasor solutions is transformed back to the time domain where the solutions are summed to give the final result,

$$v_o(t) = v_{o1}(t) + v_{o2}(t) + v_{o3}(t) + v_{o4}(t)$$
$$v_o(t) = 9.84\cos(500t - 26.6°)+$$
$$8.49\cos(1000t - 30°)+$$
$$5.81\cos(2000t - 33.4°)+$$
$$2.75\cos(5000t - 33.7°)\ \text{V}$$

Performing this analysis is tedious. It is even more tedious when the goal is to design a circuit that provides a desired result rather than simply performing analysis to find solutions. As a result, a different approach is needed to gain greater insight that makes circuit design possible.

The first thing to do is simply to analyze the circuit symbolically using variables rather than substituting numerical values. In this case, the phasor circuit becomes

As noted, the output voltage is found by applying voltage division as

$$V_o = \frac{Z_c}{R + Z_c} V_i$$

At this point, the expression for the capacitor impedance $Z_c = -j1/(\omega C)$ could be substituted in as

$$V_o = \frac{-j\dfrac{1}{\omega C}}{R - j\dfrac{1}{\omega C}} V_i$$

But this leads to a fraction divided by a fraction, which increases the likelihood of introducing algebra errors when further simplification is performed. It is much easier to simplify the original voltage division expression by recalling the relationship between capacitor impedance and admittance,

$$Z_c = -j\frac{1}{\omega C} = -j\left(\frac{j}{j}\right)\frac{1}{\omega C} = -j^2\frac{1}{j\omega C} = (+1)\frac{1}{j\omega C}$$

$$Y_c = \frac{1}{Z_c} = j\omega C$$

This relationship simplifies the original voltage division expression by multiplying through the numerator and denominator by $Y_c = 1/Z_c$ to give

$$V_o = \frac{Z_c}{R+Z_c}\left(\frac{Y_c}{Y_c}\right)V_i = \frac{1}{1+RY_c}V_i = \left(\frac{1}{1+j\omega RC}\right)V_i$$

The admittance of a capacitor $Y_c = j\omega C$ does not have a fractional part, so it is much easier to substitute for Y_c than to substitute for the impedance Z_c. **Whenever possible it is better to substitute Y_c rather than Z_c.**

The units work here as well. The product RC is the time constant, so it has units of seconds, whereas ω has units of radians per second. Therefore, the product ωRC is unitless as required since the term in parentheses above must be unitless so that the units

on both sides of the equal sign are volts. Radians are left in the overall product ωRC, but as noted in Chapter 1, radians has no physical meaning, so radians are dimensionless when assessing units in an equation.

For given values of R and C, the term in parentheses in the above expression is a function of frequency ω. As a result, this term is called the **frequency response** $H(\omega)$,

$$H(\omega) = \frac{1}{1 + j\omega RC}$$

and the relationship between the input voltage V_i and output voltage V_o becomes

$$V_o = H(\omega)V_i$$

Because $H(\omega)$ is a complex value for any given frequency ω, it can be written in polar form as

$$H(\omega) = |H(\omega)|\angle\theta(\omega)$$

Similarly, the input and output phasors are complex values that can be written in polar form as

$$V_i = |V_i|\angle\theta_i$$
$$V_o = |V_o|\angle\theta_o$$

Substituting these into the above relationship gives

$$V_o = H(\omega)\cdot V_i$$
$$|V_o|\angle\theta_o = \left(|H(\omega)|\angle\theta(\omega)\right)\cdot|V_i|\angle\theta_i$$

Multiplication of complex numbers in polar form allows the amplitude and phase of the output voltage to be written as

$$|V_o| = |H(\omega)|\cdot|V_i|$$
$$\angle\theta_o = \angle\theta(\omega) + \angle\theta_i$$

So the amplitude of the output is equal to the product of the amplitude or gain of the frequency response $|H(\omega)|$ and the amplitude of the input. The phase of the output is simply the sum of the input phase and the phase of the frequency response.

The amplitude expression can also be rewritten using decibels (dB) as

$$20\log\left(|V_o|\right) = 20\log\left(|H(\omega)|\cdot|V_i|\right)$$
$$20\log\left(|V_o|\right) = 20\log\left(|H(\omega)|\right) + 20\log\left(|V_i|\right)$$
$$|V_o|_{dB} = |H(\omega)|_{dB} + |V_i|_{dB}$$

In this case, when decibel scaling is used, the output amplitude is given by a sum as well.

In summary, the relationship between an input sinusoid and the corresponding output sinusoid is determined by the frequency response of the circuit that acts on the input to produce the output. This frequency response is a function of frequency because the impedance of inductors and capacitors changes with frequency. This relationship is shown in the diagram below.

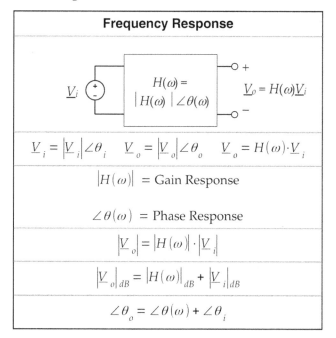

While the input and output can be any combination of voltages and currents, voltages are most common when using electricity to process analog information. The same is true for digital circuits where the presence or absence of a voltage denotes the two logic states True and False.

Frequency Response

$$\underline{V}_i = |\underline{V}_i| \angle \theta_i \quad \underline{V}_o = |\underline{V}_o| \angle \theta_o \quad \underline{V}_o = H(\omega)\cdot \underline{V}_i$$

$$|H(\omega)| = \text{Gain Response}$$

$$\angle \theta(\omega) = \text{Phase Response}$$

$$|\underline{V}_o| = |H(\omega)|\cdot |\underline{V}_i|$$

$$|\underline{V}_o|_{dB} = |H(\omega)|_{dB} + |\underline{V}_i|_{dB}$$

$$\angle \theta_o = \angle \theta(\omega) + \angle \theta_i$$

7.2 RC Circuits

Circuits containing one resistor in series with one capacitor appear frequently in circuit designs. The output voltage can be the voltage across the resistor or the capacitor as shown in the following circuits.

Without performing any mathematics, the basic behavior of these circuits can be determined by considering how the two frequency extremes $\omega = 0$ and $\omega = \infty$ impact the magnitude or gain of the frequency response,

$$|H(\omega)| = \frac{|\underline{V}_o|}{|\underline{V}_i|}$$

When $\omega = 0$, the capacitor impedance is infinite,

$$Z_c = -j\frac{1}{\omega C}\bigg|_{\omega=0} = -j\frac{1}{0\cdot C} = -j\infty = \infty = \text{open circuit}$$

That is, at zero frequency, i.e., DC, the capacitor is an open circuit and the two RC circuits become

Because the capacitor is an open circuit, there is no current flowing in either circuit. By Ohm's law, $v = iR = 0\cdot R = 0$, the voltage across the resistor is zero. Therefore, the output voltage in the circuit on the **left** is equal to the input voltage and $|H(0)| = 1$. The output voltage in the circuit on the **right** is zero and $|H(0)| = 0$.

At infinite frequency, the capacitor is a short,

$$Z_c = -j\frac{1}{\omega C}\bigg|_{\omega=\infty} = -j\frac{1}{\infty\cdot C} = -j0 = 0 = \text{short circuit}$$

and the two RC circuits become

Now the results are the opposite. The output voltage in the circuit on the **left** is zero and $|H(\infty)| = 0$. The output voltage in the circuit on the **right** is equal to the circuit input and $|H(\infty)| = 1$.

Capacitor Impedance Extreme Values

$$Z_c = -j\frac{1}{\omega C} \xrightarrow{@ \; \omega=0} \text{open circuit}$$

$$Z_c = -j\frac{1}{\omega C} \xrightarrow{@ \; \omega=\infty} \text{short circuit}$$

These points are shown graphically in the following figure.

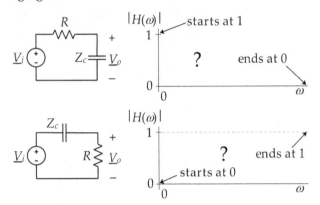

To find out what happens between these frequency extremes requires circuit analysis.

RC Lowpass Filter

Consider the circuit shown on the top left above.

The frequency response of this circuit was found as

$$\frac{V_o}{V_i} = H(\omega) = \frac{1}{1 + j\omega RC}$$

It is common to rewrite this equation using the substitution for the inverse of the RC circuit time constant, $\tau = RC$, as

$$\omega_c = \frac{1}{\tau} = \frac{1}{RC}$$

Then the frequency response becomes

$$\frac{V_o}{V_i} = H(\omega) = \frac{1}{1 + j\dfrac{\omega}{\omega_c}}$$

where ω_c is called the **critical frequency** or **cutoff frequency**. The time constant τ of the circuit and the critical frequency or cutoff frequency ω_c are inverses of each other.

Gain Response: Using basic complex arithmetic, where the magnitude of a complex number $a + jb$ is given by

$$|a + jb| = \sqrt{a^2 + b^2}$$

the **circuit gain response** can be written as

$$|H(\omega)| = \frac{1}{\sqrt{1 + \left(\dfrac{\omega}{\omega_c}\right)^2}}$$

This result agrees with our earlier circuit analysis results at $\omega = 0$

$$|H(0)| = \frac{1}{\sqrt{1 + \left(\dfrac{0}{\omega_c}\right)^2}} = \frac{1}{\sqrt{1}} = 1$$

and at $\omega = \infty$

$$|H(\infty)| = \frac{1}{\sqrt{1 + \left(\dfrac{\infty}{\omega_c}\right)^2}} = \frac{1}{\sqrt{\infty}} = 0$$

Between these two extreme values the gain varies from one to zero in a smooth transition. One particular value that is easily computed is $\omega = \omega_c$,

$$|H(\omega_c)| = \frac{1}{\sqrt{1 + \left(\dfrac{\omega_c}{\omega_c}\right)^2}} = \frac{1}{\sqrt{1 + 1}} = \frac{1}{\sqrt{2}} = 0.707$$

When this specific value is expressed in decibels, it becomes

$$20\log\left(\frac{1}{\sqrt{2}}\right) = -20\log\left(\sqrt{2}\right) = -3.01\,\text{dB} \approx -3\,\text{dB}$$

where the final integer result gives the universally accepted approximation. Because the gain at the cutoff frequency is –3 dB, the frequency ω_c is also often called the **3 dB frequency**. This frequency is also called the **half power frequency** because –3.01dB is equal to a power ratio of one half,

$$-3.01\,\text{dB} = 10\log(x)$$
$$\frac{-3.01}{10} = \log(x)$$
$$10^{-3.01/10} = 10^{\log(x)} = x$$
$$10^{-3.01/10} = \frac{1}{2} = x$$

Given the gain response $|H(\omega)|$, a typical plot illustrating its shape versus frequency is shown in the following figure where both axes are linearly scaled.

While this gain plot is correct, it is difficult to interpret accurately. In the region around ω_c, it is difficult to identify the frequencies associated with specific gain response values because the slope of the curve is so steep. In the region around and past $10\omega_c$, it is difficult to identify gain response values for specific frequencies because the curve is so close to zero. As a result, frequency response plots are seldom plotted with linearly scaled axes.

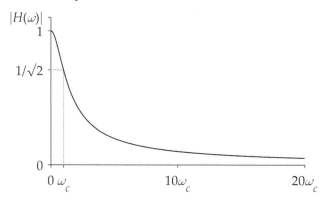

It is much more common to logarithmically scale the frequency axis where $|H(\omega)|$ is plotted versus $\log(\omega)$ rather than ω as illustrated below.

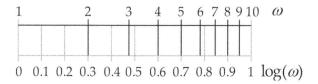

When this is done, the frequency axis is still labeled with the associated frequency values ω, not $\log(\omega)$, but the spacing between frequency values is based on $\log(\omega)$. This scaling makes every factor of ten in frequency occupy the same length along the horizontal axis.

For example, the distance between 10 and 100 rad/s is the same as that between 100 and 1000 rad/s because $\log(100) - \log(10) = \log(1000) - \log(100) = 1$. As a result of this logarithmic scaling, it is no longer possible to plot data for $\omega = 0$, because $\log(0) = -\infty$, but the frequency axis can extend to sufficiently low frequencies so this is not a problem.

In addition to scaling the frequency axis, it is also very common to express the gain in decibels, *i.e.*, $20\log(|H(\omega)|)$ and the vertical axis uses units of decibels or dB. Doing both of these things generates the following revised gain response plot.

The plot is much easier to read accurately over the entire range of frequencies plotted, especially if appropriate grid lines are added. The frequency axis starts at $\omega_c/10$ and extends three decades to $100\omega_c$, where the term **decade** refers to a factor of 10 in frequency.

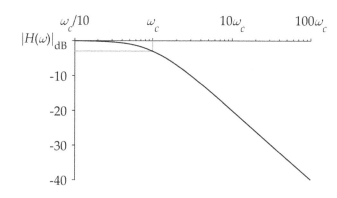

The added line on both plots marks the point were $\omega = \omega_c$. In terms of dB, this point is

$$\left|H(\omega_c)\right| = 1/\sqrt{2}$$
$$\left|H(\omega_c)\right|_{dB} = 20\log\left(1/\sqrt{2}\right) = -3.01\,\text{dB} \approx -3\,\text{dB}$$

where the final integer result -3 dB is the universally accepted approximation for this value.

Knowing that the amplitude of the output is related to the input by

$$\left|\underline{V}_o\right| = \left|H(\omega)\right| \cdot \left|\underline{V}_i\right|$$

you can identify two general regions on the frequency response plot. When the frequency of the input ω is less than ω_c, the amplitude of the output is not **reduced or attenuated** significantly because the gain $|H(\omega)|$ is closer to one. However, when the frequency of the input ω is greater than ω_c, the amplitude of the output is significantly reduced or attenuated because the gain $|H(\omega)|$ is closer to zero.

Gain versus Attenuation
Attenuation is the inverse of gain.
For example, a gain of 1/2 is equal to attenuation by 2.
When expressed in dB, attenuation has the opposite sign as gain. For example, −3 db Gain = 3 dB Attenuation.

While there is no clear frequency point where the transition from little attenuation to mostly attenuated occurs, common convention uses the cutoff frequency to mark this transition point. That is, inputs having frequencies less than ω_c essentially pass through to the filter output. This range or band of frequencies is called the **passband**. In addition, for lowpass filters, the width of the passband $0 \leq \omega \leq \omega_c$ is often called the filter **bandwidth**.

Inputs having frequencies greater than ω_c are essentially stopped; they do not reach the filter output. This range or band of frequencies is called the **stopband**.

The passband and stopband are shown on the frequency response plot below. With this definition of passband and stopband, the reason for calling ω_c the cutoff frequency becomes clear. It is the frequency where the filter starts cutting off the input.

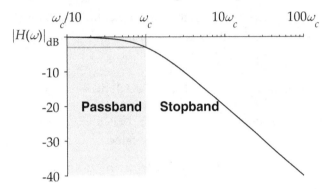

Because low frequencies, i.e., those less than ω_c, are those that pass through to the output, this circuit is called a **lowpass filter**. In addition, since the highest power of ω that appears in $H(\omega)$ is the first power, i.e., $\omega = \omega^1$, this is called a **first order filter**.

Phase Response: In most applications, a filter is designed to meet gain or attenuation requirements and the phase is not important. Nevertheless, it is beneficial to identify the basic characteristics of the phase response $\theta(\omega)$. Recall that the frequency response of the RC lowpass filter is

$$\frac{V_o}{V_i} = H(\omega) = \frac{1}{1 + j\dfrac{\omega}{\omega_c}}$$

Using basic complex mathematics where

$$\angle\left(\frac{1}{a+jb}\right) = -\angle(a+jb) = -\text{atan2}(b,a)$$

the phase response can be written as

$$\theta(\omega) = -\text{atan}2(\omega/\omega_c, 1) = -\text{atan}(\omega/\omega_c)$$

The phase starts at 0 degrees at $\omega = 0$,

$$\theta(0) = -\text{atan}(0/\omega_c) = -\text{atan}(0) = 0°$$

and reaches $-90°$ at $\omega = \infty$,

$$\theta(\infty) = -\text{atan}(\infty/\omega_c) = -\text{atan}(\infty) = -90°$$

At the cutoff frequency ω_c, the phase is

$$\theta(\omega_c) = -\text{atan}(\omega_c/\omega_c) = -\text{atan}(1) = -45°$$

The filter phase plot below uses the same logarithmic frequency axis as used for the gain response.

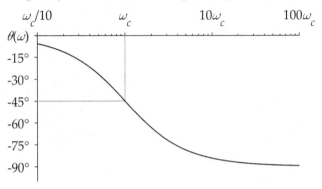

If the frequency axis started at lower frequencies, it would be more clear that the phase starts at 0 degrees.

Example: Reconsider the example that was considered at the beginning of this chapter, where the input to the circuit shown below is composed of four sinusoids, each at a different frequency,

$$v_1(t) = 11\cos(500t + 0°) \text{ V}$$
$$v_2(t) = 12\cos(1000t + 15°) \text{ V}$$
$$v_3(t) = 13\cos(2000t + 30°) \text{ V}$$
$$v_4(t) = 14\cos(5000t + 45°) \text{ V}$$

and $R = 10\text{ k}\Omega$ and $C = 100$ nF.

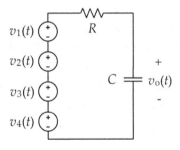

The cutoff frequency and frequency response of this filter circuit are

$$\omega_c = \frac{1}{RC} = \frac{1}{10\,\text{k}\cdot 100\,\text{n}} = 1000 \text{ rad/s} = 1 \text{ krad/s}$$

$$\frac{V_o}{V_i} = H(\omega) = \frac{1}{1 + j\dfrac{\omega}{\omega_c}} = \frac{1}{1 + j\dfrac{\omega}{1000}}$$

Using the frequency response relationship, the phasor outputs for each of the inputs are

$$\underline{V}_{o1}=H(\omega_1)\underline{V}_1=\cfrac{1}{1+j\cfrac{\omega_1}{1000}}\underline{V}_1=\cfrac{1}{1+j\cfrac{500}{1000}}\cdot(11\angle0°)$$

$$\underline{V}_{o1}=(0.8944\angle-26.57°)\cdot(11\angle0°)=\mathbf{9.84\angle-26.6°\ V}$$

$$\underline{V}_{o2}=H(\omega_2)\underline{V}_2=\cfrac{1}{1+j\cfrac{\omega_2}{1000}}\underline{V}_2=\cfrac{1}{1+j\cfrac{1000}{1000}}\cdot(12\angle15°)$$

$$\underline{V}_{o2}=(0.7071\angle-45°)\cdot(12\angle15°)=\mathbf{8.49\angle-30°\ V}$$

$$\underline{V}_{o3}=H(\omega_3)\underline{V}_3=\cfrac{1}{1+j\cfrac{\omega_3}{1000}}\underline{V}_3=\cfrac{1}{1+j\cfrac{2000}{1000}}\cdot(13\angle30°)$$

$$\underline{V}_{o3}=(0.4472\angle-63.43°)\cdot(13\angle30°)=\mathbf{5.81\angle-33.4°\ V}$$

$$\underline{V}_{o4}=H(\omega_4)\underline{V}_4=\cfrac{1}{1+j\cfrac{\omega_4}{1000}}\underline{V}_4=\cfrac{1}{1+j\cfrac{5000}{1000}}\cdot(14\angle45°)$$

$$\underline{V}_{o4}=(0.1961\angle-78.69°)\cdot(14\angle45°)=\mathbf{2.75\angle-33.7°\ V}$$

These phasor values are identical to those found by phasor analysis at the beginning of this chapter.

Design: Designing an RC lowpass filter involves choosing values for the resistance R and capacitance C so that the filter gain is equal to some desired value at some desired frequency. That is, if a desired gain $|H(\omega_d)|$ at the frequency $\omega=\omega_d$ must be met by the filter, the gain response expression at this frequency becomes

$$\left|H(\omega_d)\right|=\cfrac{1}{\sqrt{1+\left(\cfrac{\omega_d}{\omega_c}\right)^2}}$$

Using algebra, this expression can be solved for the required cutoff frequency, $\omega_c=1/(RC)$ that meets this specification. The result of that work leads to

$$\omega_c=\cfrac{1}{RC}=\cfrac{\omega_d\left|H(\omega_d)\right|}{\sqrt{1-\left|H(\omega_d)\right|^2}}$$

Substituting a desired gain $|H(\omega_d)|$ at a desired frequency ω_d into this expression gives the cutoff frequency ω_c required to meet the desired specification.

Example: Let the gain at the frequency $\omega_d=10$ krad/s be $|H(\omega_d)|_{dB}=-30$ dB, which is the same as saying that the filter must have 30 dB attenuation at this frequency.

To solve this problem, the gain must be converted from decibels to a gain value. In this case, decibel scaling is defined by

$$X_{dB}=20\log(x)\qquad x=10^{\frac{X_{dB}}{20}}$$

Therefore, $|H(\omega_d)|_{dB}=-30$ dB becomes

$$\left|H(\omega_d)\right|=10^{\frac{\left|H(\omega_d)\right|_{dB}}{20}}=10^{\frac{-30}{20}}=0.03162=31.62\,\text{m}$$

Substituting this value and $\omega_d=10$ krad/s into the design expression gives

$$\omega_c=\cfrac{1}{RC}=\cfrac{\omega_d\left|H(\omega_d)\right|}{\sqrt{1-\left|H(\omega_d)\right|^2}}=\cfrac{10\text{k}\cdot(31.62\,\text{m})}{\sqrt{1-(31.62\,\text{m})^2}}=316.4\,\text{rad/s}$$

If the resistor value $R=10$ kΩ is chosen, the capacitor value is

$$C=\cfrac{1}{R\,\omega_c}=\cfrac{1}{10\text{k}\cdot316.4}=316\,\text{nF}$$

The resulting filter gain response is shown below. As can be seen on the plot, the filter meets the specification of having 30 dB attenuation or −30 dB gain at $\omega_d=10$ krad/s. The value of the cutoff frequency ω_c is also correct.

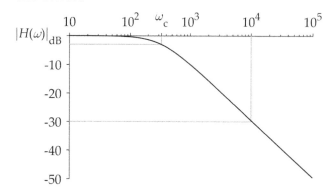

RC Highpass Filter

Consider the following RC circuit where the output voltage is measured across the resistor rather than the capacitor as it was for the lowpass filter.

Voltage division gives the output voltage as

$$\underline{V}_o=\cfrac{R}{Z_c+R}\underline{V}_i$$

First Order Lowpass Filter

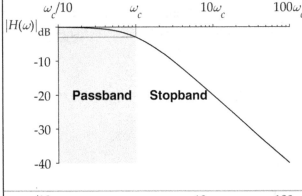

$$\frac{V_o}{V_i} = H(\omega) = |H(\omega)| \angle \theta(\omega) = \frac{1}{1 + j\frac{\omega}{\omega_c}}$$

Critical, Cutoff, or 3 dB frequency, and bandwidth

$$\omega_c = \frac{1}{RC}$$

$$|H(0)| = 1 = 0 \text{ dB}$$

$$|H(\omega_c)| = 1/\sqrt{2} = -3.01 \text{ dB} \approx -3 \text{ dB}$$

$$|H(\infty)| = 0 = -\infty \text{ dB}$$

Design Equation

$$\omega_c = \frac{1}{RC} = \frac{\omega_d |H(\omega_d)|}{\sqrt{1 - |H(\omega_d)|^2}}$$

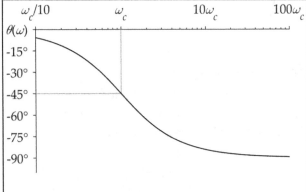

This equation is easily simplified by multiplying through the numerator and denominator by the admittance of the capacitor as derived earlier

$$Y_c = \frac{1}{Z_c} = j\omega C$$

Doing so gives

$$V_o = \frac{R}{Z_c + R}\left(\frac{Y_c}{Y_c}\right)V_i = \frac{RY_c}{1 + RY_c}V_i = \frac{j\omega RC}{1 + j\omega RC}V_i$$

Once again, letting the cutoff frequency be defined as

$$\omega_c = \frac{1}{\tau} = \frac{1}{RC}$$

the frequency response becomes

$$\frac{V_o}{V_i} = H(\omega) = |H(\omega)| \angle \theta(\omega) = \frac{j\frac{\omega}{\omega_c}}{1 + j\frac{\omega}{\omega_c}}$$

Gain Response: Using basic complex arithmetic where the magnitude of a complex number $a + jb$ is given by $|a + jb| = \sqrt{a^2 + b^2}$ the gain response can be written as

$$|H(\omega)| = \frac{\frac{\omega}{\omega_c}}{\sqrt{1 + \left(\frac{\omega}{\omega_c}\right)^2}}$$

This gain matches that found earlier, *i.e.*, at DC,

$$|H(0)| = \frac{0}{\sqrt{1 + (0)^2}} = \frac{0}{\sqrt{1}} = 0$$

and at infinite frequency, $\omega = \infty$,

$$|H(\infty)| = \lim_{\omega \to \infty} \frac{\frac{\omega}{\omega_c}}{\sqrt{1 + \left(\frac{\omega}{\omega_c}\right)^2}} = \lim_{\omega \to \infty} \frac{\frac{\omega}{\omega_c}}{\sqrt{\left(\frac{\omega}{\omega_c}\right)^2}} = \lim_{\omega \to \infty} \frac{\frac{\omega}{\omega_c}}{\frac{\omega}{\omega_c}} = 1$$

The gain value at the cutoff frequency ω_c is the same as that for the RC lowpass filter, namely

$$|H(\omega_c)| = \frac{\frac{\omega_c}{\omega_c}}{\sqrt{1 + \left(\frac{\omega_c}{\omega_c}\right)^2}} = \frac{1}{\sqrt{1 + 1}} = \frac{1}{\sqrt{2}} = -3 \text{ dB}$$

The following plot shows the gain response and includes labeling of the passband and stopband.

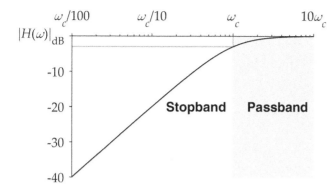

Since this filter lets inputs at high frequencies pass through and rejects or stops low frequencies, this is called a **highpass filter**. There is no bandwidth associated with highpass filters since the width of the passband is infinite, *i.e.*, from ω_c to ∞.

Phase Response: In most applications a filter is designed to meet gain and attenuation requirements and the phase is not important. Nevertheless, it is beneficial to identify the basic characteristics of the phase $\theta(\omega)$.

Using complex mathematics, the phase of the frequency response can be written as

$$\theta(\omega) = \angle(j\,\omega/\omega_c) - \text{atan}(\omega/\omega_c)$$
$$\theta(\omega) = 90° - \text{atan}(\omega/\omega_c)$$

The phase starts at 90 ° degrees at $\omega = 0$,

$$\theta(0) = 90° - \text{atan}(0/\omega_c) = 90°$$

and reaches 0 ° at $\omega = \infty$,

$$\theta(\infty) = 90° - \text{atan}(\infty/\omega_c) = 90° - 90° = 0°$$

At the cutoff frequency ω_c, the phase is

$$\theta(\omega_c) = 90° - \text{atan}(\omega_c/\omega_c) = 90° - 45° = 45°$$

The following plot illustrates the phase response using the same logarithmic frequency axis used earlier.

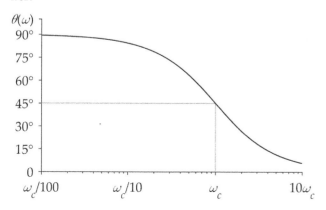

Design: Designing an RC highpass filter involves choosing values for the resistance R and capacitance C so that a gain specification is met. If a desired gain $|H(\omega_d)|$ at the frequency $\omega = \omega_d$, is given, the gain response becomes

$$|H(\omega_d)| = \frac{\dfrac{\omega_d}{\omega_c}}{\sqrt{1 + \left(\dfrac{\omega_d}{\omega_c}\right)^2}}$$

Using algebra, this expression can be solved for the cutoff frequency. The result of that work leads to

$$\omega_c = \frac{1}{RC} = \frac{\omega_d\sqrt{1 - |H(\omega_d)|^2}}{|H(\omega_d)|}$$

Substituting a desired gain $|H(\omega_d)|$ at a desired frequency ω_d into this expression gives the cutoff frequency ω_c required to meet a desired specification.

Example: For example, let the gain at $\omega_d = 1$ krad/s be $|H(\omega_d)|_{dB} = -10$ dB. To solve this problem, the gain must be converted from decibels to a common value. In this case, decibel scaling is defined by

$$X_{dB} = 20\log(x) \qquad x = 10^{\frac{X_{dB}}{20}}$$

Therefore, $|H(\omega_d)|_{dB} = -10$ dB becomes

$$|H(\omega_d)| = 10^{\frac{|H(\omega_d)|_{dB}}{20}} = 10^{\frac{-10}{20}} = 0.3162 = 316.2\,\text{m}$$

Substituting this value and $\omega_d = 1$ krad/s into the design expression gives

$$\omega_c = \frac{1}{RC} = \frac{\omega_d\sqrt{1 - |H(\omega_d)|^2}}{|H(\omega_d)|} = \frac{1000\sqrt{1 - 0.3162^2}}{0.3162}$$
$$\omega_c = 3{,}000\,\text{rad/s} = 3\,\text{krad/s}$$

If the resistor value $R = 1.2$ kΩ is chosen, the capacitor value is

$$C = \frac{1}{R\omega_c} = \frac{1}{1.2\,\text{k} \cdot 3\,\text{k}} = 278\,\text{nF}$$

The gain response of this filter is shown in the following plot. As can be seen on the plot, the filter meets the specification of having 10 dB of attenuation or −10 dB of gain at $\omega_d = 1$ krad/s. The value of the cutoff frequency is also correct.

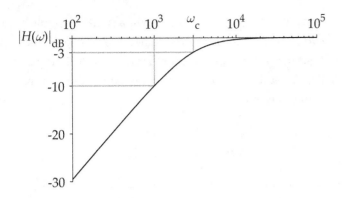

7.3 RL Circuits

First order filters can also be constructed using an inductor and a resistor as shown below.

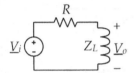 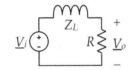

These filters are much less common than RC filters because inductors are generally occupy more volume and are more expensive than capacitors. Because of this, the use of inductors in circuits that process information is infrequent. However, inductors are very common in filters used to filter power. RL filters are presented here for the sake of completeness.

When $\omega = 0$, the impedance of the inductor is zero,

$$Z_L = j\omega L \Big|_{\omega=0} = j0 = 0 = \text{short circuit}$$

That is, at zero frequency, i.e., DC, the inductor is a short circuit and the two RL circuits become

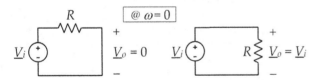

The output voltage in the circuit on the **left** is equal to zero because of the short and the circuit gain is zero, $|H(0)| = 0$. The output voltage in the circuit on the **right** is equal to the input voltage and the gain is one, $|H(0)| = 1$.

At infinite frequency, the inductor is an open circuit,

$$Z_L = -j\omega L \Big|_{\omega=\infty} = j\infty \cdot L = j\infty = \infty = \text{open circuit}$$

and the two circuits are as shown below the highpass filter summary table in the right column of this page.

First Order Highpass Filter

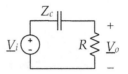

$$\frac{V_o}{V_i} = H(\omega) = |H(\omega)| \angle \theta(\omega) = \frac{j\frac{\omega}{\omega_c}}{1 + j\frac{\omega}{\omega_c}}$$

Critical, Cutoff, or 3 dB frequency

$$\omega_c = \frac{1}{RC}$$

$$|H(0)| = 0 = -\infty \text{ dB}$$
$$|H(\omega_c)| = 1/\sqrt{2} = -3.01 \text{ dB} \approx -3 \text{ dB}$$
$$|H(\infty)| = 1 = 0 \text{ dB}$$

Design Equation

$$\omega_c = \frac{1}{RC} = \frac{\omega_d \sqrt{1 - |H(\omega_d)|^2}}{|H(\omega_d)|}$$

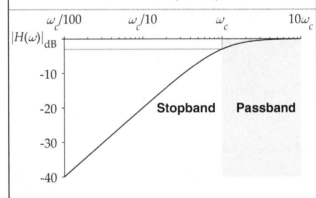

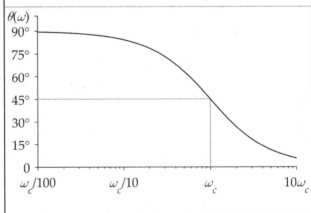

Now the results are the opposite. The output voltage in the circuit on the **left** is equal to the input voltage, so $|H(\infty)| = 1$. The output voltage in the circuit on the **right** is equal to zero, so $|H(\infty)| = 0$.

These points are shown graphically in the following figure.

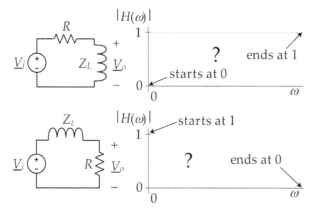

Based on similar analysis of the RC circuits, these are highpass and lowpass filters respectively.

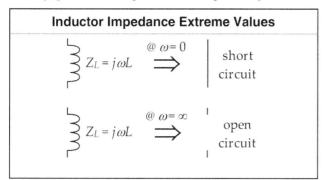

RL Highpass

Consider the RL circuit illustrated in the following figure.

Applying voltage division gives the relationship between the input and output voltages as

$$\frac{V_o}{V_i} = H(\omega) = \frac{Z_L}{R + Z_L}$$

The impedance of an inductor does not contain a fraction, i.e., $Z_L = j\omega L$, so it can be substituted in and the equation can be simplified to give the frequency response

$$H(\omega) = \frac{j\omega L}{R + j\omega L} = \frac{j\omega L}{R + j\omega L} \cdot \left(\frac{1/R}{1/R}\right) = \frac{j\omega \frac{L}{R}}{1 + j\omega \frac{L}{R}}$$

By defining the cutoff frequency as the inverse of the time constant, $\tau = L/R$, as

$$\omega_c = \frac{1}{\tau} = \frac{R}{L}$$

the frequency response becomes

$$H(\omega) = \frac{j\frac{\omega}{\omega_c}}{1 + j\frac{\omega}{\omega_c}}$$

This is a first order highpass frequency response expression because it is identical to the expression for the RC first order highpass filter analyzed earlier.

RL Lowpass

The other RL circuit repeated in the following figure provides a lowpass characteristic.

Applying voltage division gives the frequency response as

$$\frac{V_o}{V_i} = H(\omega) = \frac{R}{R + Z_L}$$

Substituting $Z_L = j\omega L$ and simplifying leads to

$$H(\omega) = \frac{R}{R + j\omega L} = \frac{R}{R + j\omega L}\left(\frac{1/R}{1/R}\right) = \frac{1}{1 + j\omega \frac{L}{R}} = \frac{1}{1 + j\frac{\omega}{\omega_c}}$$

where the cutoff frequency is the inverse of the circuit time constant, $\omega_c = R/L$.

This frequency response expression is first order lowpass because it is identical to the expression for the RC first order lowpass filter analyzed earlier.

Once an RL filter is written in either of the standard forms with the cutoff frequency, the analysis and properties of RL filters match those of their equivalent RC filters. The preceding frequency response plots and design equations still apply.

7.4 Resonant Circuits

In addition to RC and RL filters, circuits containing one resistor, one inductor, and one capacitor can be used to construct filters. As was the case with second order transient circuits, the inductor and capacitor can be connected in series or in parallel. Each of these configurations is useful and each produces resonance at a resonant frequency ω_o.

Series Resonance

Consider the following circuit where an inductor is in series with a capacitor.

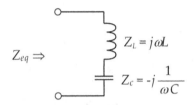

The equivalent impedance Z_{eq} measured across this series combination is

$$Z_{eq} = Z_L + Z_c = j\omega L - j\frac{1}{\omega C} = j\left(\omega L - \frac{1}{\omega C}\right) = j\left(X_L - X_c\right)$$

Since the signs on the inductor and capacitor impedances differ, **there is a frequency $\omega = \omega_o$, called the resonant frequency**, where the equivalent series impedance is zero,

$$\left(\omega_o L - \frac{1}{\omega_o C}\right) = 0$$

$$\omega_o L = \frac{1}{\omega_o C} \rightarrow \omega_o^2 L = \frac{1}{C} \rightarrow \omega_o^2 = \frac{1}{LC} \rightarrow \omega_o = \frac{1}{\sqrt{LC}}$$

This last result is the same as that found when considering second order transients. This frequency is the resonant frequency.

Series Resonance

$$@\,\omega = \omega_o = \frac{1}{\sqrt{LC}}$$

$Z_L = j\omega_o L$

$Z_c = -j\dfrac{1}{\omega_o C}$

$\Leftrightarrow$ short circuit

When a circuit containing an inductor in series with a capacitor is being excited by a sinusoidal source at the resonant frequency, the circuit is said to be **in resonance** or **operating at resonance**.

In addition to the mathematical analysis above, it is informative to consider the sum

$$X_L - X_c = \omega L - \frac{1}{\omega C}$$

graphically. In particular, it is useful to plot the individual inductive reactance $X_L = \omega L$ and capacitive reactance as $X_c = -1/(\omega C)$, in addition to plotting their sum, $X_L + X_c = \omega L - 1/(\omega C)$. Doing so leads to the following plot.

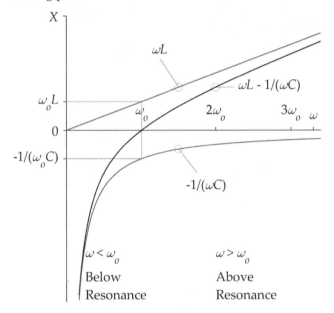

At $\omega = \omega_o$ the inductive and capacitive reactances are equally separated on opposite sides of the horizontal axis where $X = 0$ because their sum is zero as shown.

Below resonance where $\omega < \omega_o$ the capacitor dominates, so the net reactance is negative and the series combination appears capacitive. This is especially true as the frequency approaches zero where the inductive reactance is negligible, $X_L = \omega L \approx 0$.

Above resonance where $\omega > \omega_o$ the inductor dominates, so the net reactance is positive and the series combination appears inductive. This is especially true as the frequency approaches infinity where the capacitive reactance is negligible, $X_c = -1/(\omega C) \approx 0$.

At zero frequency, *i.e.*, DC, the inductor plays no role because it is a short at DC, $j\omega L = j0L = 0$. As frequency increases, the inductor starts to play a larger and larger role in the equivalent impedance Z_{eq}. At resonance, the inductive and capacitive reactances cancel each other out. As frequency increases further, the capacitor plays a smaller and smaller role because its reactance is decreasing while the inductor's is increasing. The higher the frequency goes the less impact the capacitor has.

> **In summary, an inductor in series with a capacitor appears capacitive below resonance, and inductive above resonance.**

Quality Factor Q: With this understanding of series resonance, consider the following circuit where a voltage source and series resistor provide excitation to an inductor and capacitor in series. Furthermore, let the voltage source be sinusoidal at the resonant frequency ω_o.

Voltage division gives the voltage $\underline{V}_{LC}$ as

$$\underline{V}_{LC} = \underline{V}_L + \underline{V}_c$$

$$\underline{V}_{LC} = \frac{Z_L}{R+Z_L+Z_c}\underline{V}_i + \frac{Z_c}{R+Z_L+Z_c}\underline{V}_i$$

$$\underline{V}_{LC} = \frac{Z_L + Z_c}{R + Z_L + Z_c}\underline{V}_i$$

But, by the definition of the resonant frequency ω_o, the impedance of the inductor and capacitor sum to zero at resonance, *i.e.*,

$$Z_L + Z_c = 0$$

Therefore, the voltage $\underline{V}_{LC}$ simplifies to the expected value of zero

$$\underline{V}_{LC} = \frac{Z_L + Z_c}{R + Z_L + Z_c}\underline{V}_i = \frac{0}{R+0}\underline{V}_i = 0$$

What is more interesting is the relative amplitude of the inductor and capacitor voltages. These voltages have the same amplitude, but the opposite sign because $Z_L = -Z_c$ at resonance.

At resonance, the inductor voltage is

$$\underline{V}_L = \frac{Z_L}{R+Z_L+Z_c}\underline{V}_i = \frac{Z_L}{R+0}\underline{V}_i = \frac{j\omega_o L}{R+0}\underline{V}_i = j\frac{\omega_o L}{R}\underline{V}_i$$

Dividing both sides by $\underline{V}_i$, and expressing the magnitude gives the relative amplitude of the inductor voltage as

$$\left|\frac{\underline{V}_L}{\underline{V}_i}\right| = \left|j\frac{\omega_o L}{R}\right| = \frac{\omega_o L}{R} = \frac{X_L}{R}$$

Depending on the component values chosen, the inductive reactance $X_L = \omega_o L$ in the numerator can be many times greater than the resistance R in the denominator. When this happens, the voltages across the inductor and across the capacitor are many times greater in amplitude than the input voltage $\underline{V}_i$. As a result, resonance can amplify the input voltage to produce very large voltages across the inductor and across the capacitor.

This ratio of the inductive reactance to the resistance is called the **quality factor** or **Q** of the circuit,

$$Q = \frac{\omega_o L}{R}$$

As will be shown in the following sections, Q plays a fundamental role in the frequency response of filters constructed using inductors and capacitors.

Example: Let $L = 10$ mH and $C = 1$ μF. Then the resonant frequency is

$$\omega_o = \frac{1}{\sqrt{LC}} = \frac{1}{\sqrt{10^{-2}\cdot 10^{-6}}} = \frac{1}{\sqrt{10^{-8}}} = \frac{1}{10^{-4}} = 10\,\text{krad/s}$$

If the resistance is $R = 10\,\Omega$, the quality factor is

$$Q = \frac{\omega_o L}{R} = \frac{10^4 \cdot 10^{-2}}{10} = \frac{10^2}{10} = 10$$

In this case, at resonance, the voltage across the inductor and across the capacitor is ten times larger than the amplitude of the voltage exciting the circuit.

Series RLC Bandpass Filter

Series resonance can be used to produce a number of different filters. The most common filter structure is shown in the following circuit where the output voltage is taken across the resistor.

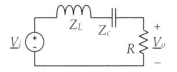

Before computing the output voltage, consider what the circuit looks like at three frequencies. First consider zero frequency, *i.e.*, DC. At $\omega = 0$, the inductor is a short circuit,

$$Z_L = j\omega L \Big|_{\omega=0} = j0 = 0 = \text{short circuit}$$

and the capacitor is an open circuit,

$$Z_c = -j\frac{1}{\omega C}\Big|_{\omega=0} = -j\frac{1}{0\cdot C} = -j\infty = \infty = \text{open circuit}$$

Under these conditions, the circuit becomes

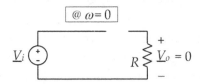

and the output voltage is zero. In terms of gain, the gain $|H(0)| = |\underline{V}_o/\underline{V}_i|$ is zero.

Next consider infinite frequency, $\omega = \infty$. At this frequency the inductor is an open circuit,

$$Z_L = j\omega L \Big|_{\omega=\infty} = j\infty = \infty = \text{open circuit}$$

and the capacitor is a short circuit,

$$Z_c = -j\frac{1}{\omega C}\Big|_{\omega=\infty} = -j\frac{1}{\infty\cdot C} = -j0 = 0 = \text{short circuit}$$

Under these conditions, the circuit becomes

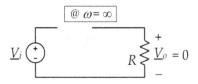

and the output is zero yet again since there is no connection between the input and output. So the gain is zero again as well, *i.e.*, $|H(\infty)| = |\underline{V}_o/\underline{V}_i|$ is zero.

Finally, consider the resonant frequency. In this case, the inductive and capacitive reactances cancel each other out, leaving a short circuit. Under these conditions, the circuit becomes

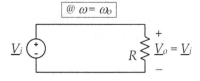

Now the output voltage is equal to the input voltage and the gain $|H(\omega_o)| = |\underline{V}_o/\underline{V}_i|$ is equal to one.

The gains at these three frequencies are shown in the following figure.

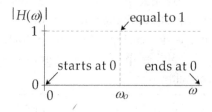

Because the gain reaches one only at the resonant frequency and is zero at DC and infinite frequencies, this filter cannot be a lowpass or highpass filter. This filter passes a band of frequencies around the resonant frequency, so it is called a **bandpass filter**.

Frequency Response: Further insight requires circuit analysis. Voltage division gives the output voltage as

$$\underline{V}_o = \frac{R}{R + Z_L + Z_c}\underline{V}_i$$

So the frequency response is

$$\frac{\underline{V}_o}{\underline{V}_i} = H(\omega) = \frac{R}{R + Z_L + Z_c}$$

which simplifies as

$$H(\omega) = \frac{R}{R + Z_L + Z_c}\cdot\frac{Y_c}{Y_c}$$

$$H(\omega) = \frac{RY_c}{RY_c + Z_L Y_c + 1}$$

$$H(\omega) = \frac{j\omega RC}{j\omega RC + j\omega L\cdot j\omega C + 1}$$

$$H(\omega) = \frac{j\omega RC}{j\omega RC + j\omega L\cdot j\omega C + 1}$$

$$H(\omega) = \frac{j\omega RC}{j\omega RC - \omega^2 LC + 1}\cdot\frac{1/(LC)}{1/(LC)}$$

$$H(\omega) = \frac{j\omega\dfrac{R}{L}}{j\omega\dfrac{R}{L} - \omega^2 + \dfrac{1}{LC}}$$

Just as there were standard forms for the first order RC and RL filter responses considered earlier, there is a standard form for this filter as well. The standard form is found by rewriting $H(\omega)$ as

$$H(\omega) = \frac{j\omega \dfrac{R}{L}}{\dfrac{1}{LC} - \omega^2 + j\omega \dfrac{R}{L}}$$

then substituting

$$\omega_o = \frac{1}{\sqrt{LC}}$$

which is the resonant frequency or filter **center frequency**, and

$$\beta = \frac{R}{L}$$

which is the filter **bandwidth**.

Making these substitutions gives the standard form

$$H(\omega) = \frac{j\omega\beta}{\left(\omega_o^2 - \omega^2\right) + j\omega\beta} = |H(\omega)| \angle \theta(\omega)$$

The response of this filter at the resonant frequency ω_o is

$$H(\omega_o) = \frac{j\omega_o\beta}{\left(\omega_o^2 - \omega_o^2\right) + j\omega_o\beta} = \frac{j\omega_o\beta}{j\omega_o\beta} = 1$$

which agrees with the earlier circuit analysis. The gain is one at the resonant frequency.

The **bandwidth** β is equal to the distance between the two cutoff frequencies ω_{c1} and ω_{c2} where the gain is $1/\sqrt{2}$ or -3 dB,

$$\beta = \omega_{c2} - \omega_{c1}$$

as shown in the gain response plot below. This plot does not use decibel scaling for the gain, nor does it use logarithmic frequency axis scaling. Thus, the response peak is easily seen.

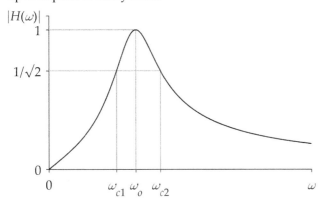

This is a **second order bandpass filter** because the highest power of ω in the denominator is ω^2.

It is tedious to compute the values for the two cutoff frequencies. And they are generally not of much use in practice, but in any case they are given by

$$\omega_{c1}, \omega_{c2} = \mp \frac{\beta}{2} + \sqrt{\left(\frac{\beta}{2}\right)^2 + \omega_o^2}$$

Perhaps most interesting is the fact that the two cutoff frequencies are not equally spaced about the resonant or center frequency. That is, the center frequency ω_o is **not equal** to the arithmetic mean

$$\omega_o \ne \left(\omega_{c1} + \omega_{c2}\right)/2$$

This is apparent in the preceding gain plot where ω_{c1} is closer to ω_o than ω_{c2} is. Rather, it is possible to show that the resonant or center frequency is equal to the geometric mean of the two cutoff frequencies,

$$\omega_o = \sqrt{\omega_{c1}\omega_{c2}}$$

Quality Factor Q: Recalling the expression for the quality factor Q,

$$Q = \frac{\omega_o L}{R}$$

and rearranging this expression leads to another relationship for Q,

$$Q = \frac{\omega_o L}{R} = \frac{\omega_o}{R/L} = \frac{\omega_o}{\beta}$$

The quality factor is the ratio of the resonant frequency to the bandwidth. Therefore, Q is an indication of how peaked or narrow the bandwidth is. The higher the Q, the narrower the bandwidth relative to the center frequency ω_o. And from earlier, the higher the Q, the larger the voltage across the inductor and across the capacitor at resonance.

Gain Response: Given the frequency response, the gain of the frequency response can be written as

$$|H(\omega)| = \frac{|j\omega\beta|}{\left|\left(\omega_o^2 - \omega^2\right) + j\omega\beta\right|} = \frac{\omega\beta}{\sqrt{\left(\omega_o^2 - \omega^2\right)^2 + (\omega\beta)^2}}$$

Phase Response: The associated phase of the frequency response $\theta(\omega)$ can be written as

$$\theta(\omega) = \angle(j\omega\beta) - \angle\left(\omega_o^2 - \omega^2 + j\omega\beta\right)$$

$$\theta(\omega) = 90° - \operatorname{atan}2\left(\omega\beta, \omega_o^2 - \omega^2\right)$$

The angle plot associated with the preceding gain plot is shown below. The angle starts at 90 °, passes through 0 ° at the resonant frequency, and goes to −90 ° as frequency goes to infinity. The angles at the two cutoff frequencies are ±45 ° respectively.

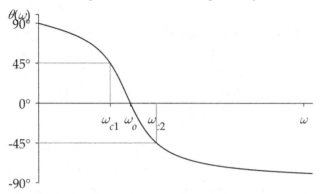

Design: The frequency response of series RLC filters is governed by two parameters, the center frequency ω_o and the bandwidth β. The filter component values can be found once these are determined.

The specifications for a bandpass filter often include the center frequency ω_o and the desired gain $|H(\omega_d)|$ required at some other frequency ω_d. Given these two specifications, the bandwidth β can be determined.

Substituting $\omega = \omega_d$ into the gain expression gives

$$|H(\omega_d)| = \frac{\omega_d \beta}{\sqrt{\left(\omega_o^2 - \omega_d^2\right)^2 + \left(\omega_d \beta\right)^2}}$$

Though tedious, this expression can be solved for the bandwidth using symbolic analysis software. The result of that work leads to

$$\beta = \frac{|H(\omega_d)| \cdot |\omega_o^2 - \omega_d^2|}{\omega_d \sqrt{1 - |H(\omega_d)|^2}}$$

Substituting the desired specifications into this equation gives the bandwidth required to meet the specifications. Once the bandwidth is known, the circuit components are chosen by selecting component values using the relationships

$$LC = \frac{1}{\omega_o^2} \qquad \frac{R}{L} = \beta$$

Since there are three component values and two specifications or constraints, one component value can be chosen as desired and the other two found from the above relationships.

Example: Let the center frequency of the filter be $\omega_o = 10$ krad/s and let the gain at $\omega_d = 40$ krad/s be $|H(\omega_d)|_{dB} = -30$ dB. To solve this problem, the gain must be converted from decibels to a common value. In this case, decibel scaling is defined by

$$X_{dB} = 20 \log(x)$$

Solving this expression for x gives

$$x = 10^{\frac{X_{dB}}{20}}$$

Therefore, $|H(\omega_d)|_{dB} = -30$ dB becomes

$$|H(\omega_d)| = 10^{\frac{|H(\omega_d)|_{dB}}{20}} = 10^{\frac{-30}{20}} = 0.03162 = 31.62\,\text{m}$$

Substituting this value and $\omega_d = 40$ krad/s into the expression for the bandwidth gives

$$\beta = \frac{31.62\,\text{m} \cdot \left|\left(10^4\right)^2 - \left(4 \cdot 10^4\right)^2\right|}{\left(4 \cdot 10^4\right) \cdot \sqrt{1 - \left(31.62\,\text{m}\right)^2}} = 1{,}186 \text{ rad/s}$$

The resulting gain response is shown in the following figure where the gain is given in decibels and the frequency axis is logarithmically scaled.

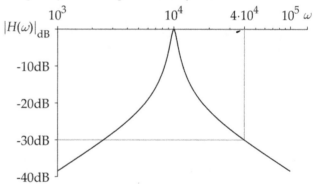

Interestingly, the bandpass response is visually symmetric around the center frequency when the frequency axis is logarithmically scaled.

The Q of this filter is

$$Q = \frac{\omega_o}{\beta} = \frac{10^4}{1186} = 8.43$$

In general, a filter having a Q of 10 or more is considered a high Q filter. So this filter has moderate Q.

There is no unique or best way to choose component values. For this example, let the inductance be equal to $L = 0.1$ H. Then the capacitance value is

$$C = \frac{1}{\omega_o^2 L} = \frac{1}{\left(10^4\right)^2 \cdot 10^{-1}} = \frac{1}{10^7} = 10^{-7}\,F = 100\ nF$$

and the resulting resistance value is

$$\frac{R}{L} = \beta \quad \Rightarrow \quad R = \beta L = 1186 \cdot 0.1 = 118.6\ \Omega = 119\ \Omega$$

The designed filter is shown in the following circuit.

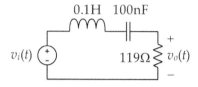

Parallel Resonance

Consider the following circuit where an inductor is in parallel with a capacitor.

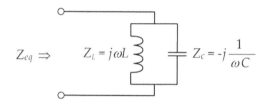

The equivalent impedance Z_{eq} looking into the parallel combination of L and C is given by

$$\frac{1}{Z_{eq}} = \frac{1}{Z_L} + \frac{1}{Z_c}$$

$$\frac{1}{Z_{eq}} = \frac{1}{j\omega L} + j\omega C$$

$$\frac{1}{Z_{eq}} = -j\frac{1}{\omega L} + j\omega C$$

$$\frac{1}{Z_{eq}} = j\left(\omega C - \frac{1}{\omega L}\right)$$

Rather than invert this last equation to obtain Z_{eq}, it is more convenient to leave this equation in the form of the equivalent admittance Y_{eq},

$$Y_{eq} = \frac{1}{Z_{eq}} = j\left(\omega C - \frac{1}{\omega L}\right) = j\left(B_c + B_L\right)$$

Since the signs on the capacitive and inductive terms differ, there is a frequency $\omega = \omega_o$ called the resonant frequency where the equivalent admittance is zero, i.e.,

$$\left(\omega_o C - \frac{1}{\omega_o L}\right) = 0$$

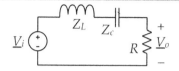

Series RLC Bandpass Filter

$$H(\omega) = \frac{j\omega\beta}{\left(\omega_o^2 - \omega^2\right) + j\omega\beta}$$

Center Frequency $\quad \omega_o = \dfrac{1}{\sqrt{LC}}$

Bandwidth $\quad \beta = \dfrac{R}{L} = \omega_{c2} - \omega_{c1}$

Quality Factor $\quad Q = \dfrac{\omega_o}{\beta}$

$$|H(0)| = 0 = -\infty\ dB,$$
$$|H(\omega_o)| = 1 = 0\ dB,$$
$$|H(\infty)| = 0 = -\infty\ dB$$

Design Equation

$$\beta = \frac{\left|H(\omega_d)\right| \cdot \left|\omega_o^2 - \omega_d^2\right|}{\omega_d \sqrt{1 - \left|H(\omega_d)\right|^2}}$$

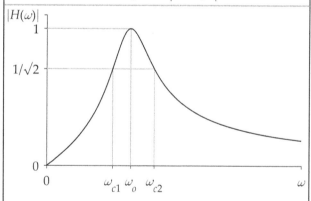

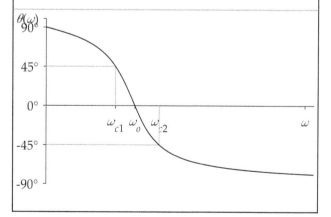

Solving for the resonant frequency gives

$$\omega_o C = \frac{1}{\omega_o L} \rightarrow \omega_o^2 C = \frac{1}{L} \rightarrow \omega_o^2 = \frac{1}{LC} \rightarrow \omega_o = \frac{1}{\sqrt{LC}}$$

This result is the same as that found for the series RLC circuit and when considering second order transients. **This is the resonant frequency.**

When a circuit containing an inductor in parallel with a capacitor is being excited by a sinusoidal source at the resonant frequency, the circuit is said to be **in resonance** or **operating at resonance**.

At the resonant frequency, the equivalent admittance is zero, so the equivalent impedance is infinity,

$$Z_{eq} = \frac{1}{Y_{eq}} = \frac{1}{j\left(\omega_o C - \frac{1}{\omega_o L}\right)} = \frac{1}{j0} = \infty$$

In addition to the mathematical analysis above, it is informative to consider the sum of susceptances

$$B_c + B_L = \omega C - \frac{1}{\omega L}$$

graphically. In particular, it is useful to plot the individual capacitive susceptance $B_c = \omega C$ and the individual inductive susceptance $B_L = -1/(\omega L)$, in addition to plotting their sum. Doing so leads to the following plot.

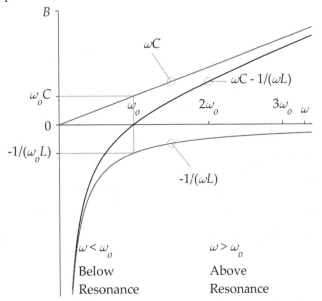

At $\omega = \omega_o$ the inductive and capacitive susceptances are equally separated on opposite sides of the axis where $B = 0$ because their sum is zero as shown.

The equivalent reactance X_{eq} associated with the circuit susceptance $B_c + B_L$ is given by

$$\frac{1}{j\left(\omega C - \frac{1}{\omega L}\right)} = -j\frac{1}{\left(\omega C - \frac{1}{\omega L}\right)} = jX_{eq}$$

A plot of the equivalent reactance X_{eq} is shown in the following figure.

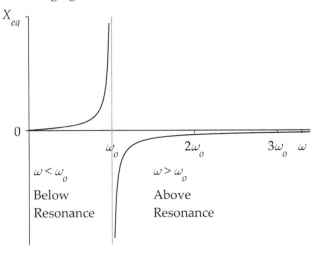

This figure illustrates the reactance versus frequency, just as was done for the series RLC case investigated earlier. Here, the reactance starts at zero and increases just as the reactance of an inductor does, so the circuit is inductive below resonance. Above resonance, the reactance starts at negative infinity and goes toward zero just as the reactance of a capacitor does. So, when an inductor is in parallel with a capacitor, the circuit is inductive below resonance and capacitive above resonance. This is the opposite of what happens for the series RLC case.

In summary, an inductor in parallel with a capacitor appears inductive below resonance and capacitive above resonance.

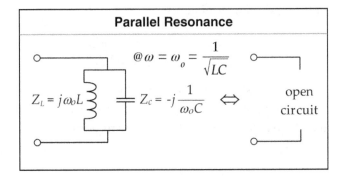

Quality Factor Q: With this understanding of parallel resonance, consider the following circuit where a voltage source operating at the resonant frequency ω_o and a series resistor R provide excitation to an inductor and capacitor in parallel.

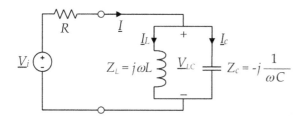

At zero frequency, $\omega = 0$, the source current $\underline{I}$ is maximum because the impedance of the inductor is zero at zero frequency, i.e., $Z_L = j\omega L = j(0){\cdot}L = 0$. Using this fact, the maximum current is

$$\underline{I}_{max} = \frac{\underline{V}_i}{R}$$

or in terms of the input voltage

$$\underline{V}_i = \underline{I}_{max} R$$

This maximum current also exists at infinite frequency, because the capacitor becomes a short at infinite frequency.

The voltage $\underline{V}_{LC}$ across the parallel inductor and capacitor is

$$\underline{V}_{LC} = \frac{Z_{eq}}{Z_{eq} + R}\underline{V}_i$$

$$\underline{V}_{LC} = \frac{Z_{eq}}{Z_{eq} + R}\cdot\left(\frac{Y_{eq}}{Y_{eq}}\right)\underline{V}_i$$

$$\underline{V}_{LC} = \frac{1}{1 + R Y_{eq}}\underline{V}_i$$

$$\underline{V}_{LC} = \frac{\underline{V}_i}{1 + jR\left(\omega_o C - \dfrac{1}{\omega_o L}\right)}$$

But, by the definition of the resonant frequency ω_o, the admittances of the inductor and capacitor sum to zero at resonance, i.e.,

$$\omega_o C - \frac{1}{\omega_o L} = 0$$

so the voltage $\underline{V}_{LC}$ is equal to the applied voltage at resonance,

$$\underline{V}_{LC} = \frac{\underline{V}_i}{1 + jR\left(\omega_o C - \dfrac{1}{\omega_o L}\right)} = \frac{\underline{V}_i}{1 + jR{\cdot}(0)} = \underline{V}_i$$

This equality, or gain of one, occurs because the admittance Y_{eq} of the parallel inductor and capacitor is zero at resonance. Because of this, the source current $\underline{I}$ is zero at resonance

$$\underline{I}\Big|_{\omega = \omega_o} = \underline{V}_{LC}{\cdot}Y_{eq} = \underline{V}_{LC}{\cdot}0 = 0$$

While the source current is zero at resonance, the inductor and capacitor currents, $\underline{I}_L$ and $\underline{I}_c$ are not zero. They are equal in magnitude and opposite in sign so that their sum is zero as required. The capacitor current is

$$\underline{I}_c = \left(j\omega_o C\right)\underline{V}_i$$

The expression for $\underline{I}_c$ can be written in terms of the maximum current $\underline{I}_{max}$ by substituting the relationship shown earlier, $\underline{V}_i = \underline{I}_{max}R$

$$\underline{I}_c = j\omega_o C\underline{V}_i = j\omega_o C\left(\underline{I}_{max}R\right) = j\omega_o R C \underline{I}_{max}$$

Dividing both sides by $\underline{I}_{max}$ and by considering the magnitude only leads to

$$\left|\frac{\underline{I}_c}{\underline{I}_{max}}\right| = \left|j\omega_o R C\right| = \omega_o R C$$

Depending on the component values chosen, this product can be much greater than one. When this happens, the currents through the inductor and through the capacitor are many times greater than the maximum current $\underline{I}_{max}$. Resonance can amplify the maximum source current to produce very large currents through the inductor and through the capacitor.

The above ratio of the capacitor current to the maximum current is defined as the **quality factor** or Q of the circuit,

$$Q = \omega_o R C$$

As will be shown in the following sections, Q plays a fundamental role in the frequency response of filters constructed using inductors and capacitors.

Example: Let $L = 10\text{ mH}$ and $C = 1\ \mu\text{F}$ as they were for the previous example. Then the resonant frequency is

$$\omega_o = \frac{1}{\sqrt{LC}} = \frac{1}{\sqrt{10^{-2} \cdot 10^{-6}}} = \frac{1}{\sqrt{10^{-8}}} = \frac{1}{10^{-4}} = 10^4 \, \text{rad/s}$$

If the resistance is $R = 1 \, \text{k}\Omega$, then the quality factor is

$$Q = \omega_o RC = 10^4 \cdot 10^3 \cdot 10^{-6} = 10$$

In this case, at resonance, the current through the inductor and through the capacitor is ten times larger than the maximum current I_{max}.

Parallel RLC Bandreject Filter

Parallel resonance can be used to produce a number of different filters. One such filter structure is shown in the following figure where the output voltage is taken across the resistor.

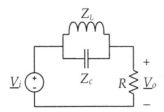

Before computing the output voltage, consider what the circuit looks like at three frequencies. First consider zero frequency, i.e., DC. At $\omega = 0$, the inductor is a short circuit,

$$Z_L = j\omega L \Big|_{\omega=0} = j0 = 0 = \text{short circuit}$$

and the capacitor is an open circuit,

$$Z_c = -j\frac{1}{\omega C}\Big|_{\omega=0} = -j\frac{1}{0 \cdot C} = -j\infty = \infty = \text{open circuit}$$

Under these conditions, the circuit becomes

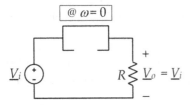

and the output voltage is equal to the input voltage since there is a short between the input and output. The gain $|H(0)| = |V_o/V_i|$ is equal to one.

Next consider infinite frequency, $\omega = \infty$. At this frequency the inductor is an open circuit,

$$Z_L = j\omega L \Big|_{\omega=\infty} = j\infty = \infty = \text{open circuit}$$

and the capacitor is a short circuit,

$$Z_c = -j\frac{1}{\omega C}\Big|_{\omega=\infty} = -j\frac{1}{\infty \cdot C} = -j0 = 0 = \text{short circuit}$$

Under these conditions, the circuit becomes

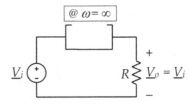

and the output is equal to one since there is a short between the input and output. Therefore, the gain $|H(\infty)| = |V_o/V_i|$ is equal to one.

Finally, consider the resonant frequency. In this case, the inductive and capacitive reactances cancel each other out, leaving an open circuit. Under these conditions, the circuit becomes

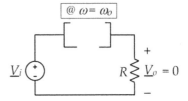

Now the output voltage is equal to zero since there is no connection between the input and output. Therefore the gain $|H(\omega_o)| = |V_o/V_i|$ is equal to zero.

The gains at these three frequencies are shown in the following figure. This filter rejects a band of frequencies around the resonant frequency, so it is called a **bandreject filter**.

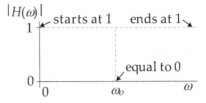

Frequency Response: Further insight requires circuit analysis. Voltage division gives the output voltage as

$$V_o = \frac{R}{R + Z_{eq}} V_i$$

So the frequency response is

$$\frac{V_o}{V_i} = H(\omega) = \frac{R}{R + Z_{eq}} = \frac{R}{R + Z_{eq}}\left(\frac{Y_{eq}}{Y_{eq}}\right) = \frac{RY_{eq}}{RY_{eq} + 1}$$

Using the expression for Y_{eq}

$$Y_{eq} = j\left(\omega C - \frac{1}{\omega L}\right)$$

the frequency response becomes

$$H(\omega) = \frac{R j\left(\omega C - \dfrac{1}{\omega L}\right)}{R j\left(\omega C - \dfrac{1}{\omega L}\right) + 1}$$

This frequency response expression can be put in standard form by simplifying and rewriting $H(\omega)$ as

$$H(\omega) = \frac{R j\left(\omega C - \dfrac{1}{\omega L}\right)}{R j\left(\omega C - \dfrac{1}{\omega L}\right) + 1} \cdot \left(\frac{j\dfrac{\omega}{RC}}{j\dfrac{\omega}{RC}}\right)$$

$$H(\omega) = \frac{j^2\left(\omega^2 - \dfrac{1}{LC}\right)}{j^2\left(\omega^2 - \dfrac{1}{LC}\right) + j\dfrac{\omega}{RC}}$$

$$H(\omega) = \frac{\left(\dfrac{1}{LC} - \omega^2\right)}{\left(\dfrac{1}{LC} - \omega^2\right) + j\dfrac{\omega}{RC}}$$

which can be rewritten as

$$H(\omega) = \frac{\left(\omega_o^2 - \omega^2\right)}{\left(\omega_o^2 - \omega^2\right) + j\omega\beta}$$

where the resonant or filter **center frequency** is

$$\omega_o = \frac{1}{\sqrt{LC}}$$

and the **bandwidth β** is

$$\beta = \frac{1}{RC}$$

The bandwidth or passband width is equal to the distance between the two cutoff frequencies ω_{c1} and ω_{c2} where the gain is $1/\sqrt{2}$ or -3 dB

$$\beta = \omega_{c2} - \omega_{c1}$$

as shown in the following figure.

This is a **second order bandreject filter** because the highest power of ω in the denominator is ω^2.

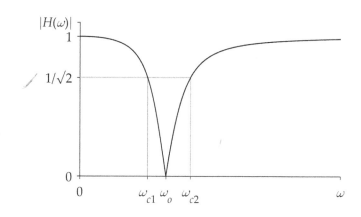

It is tedious to compute the values for the two cutoff frequencies. And they are generally not of much use in practice, but in any case they are

$$\omega_{c1}, \omega_{c2} = \mp\frac{\beta}{2} + \sqrt{\left(\frac{\beta}{2}\right)^2 + \omega_o^2}$$

Perhaps most interesting is the fact that the two cutoff frequencies are not equally spaced about the resonant or center frequency. That is, the center frequency is **not equal** to the arithmetic mean

$$\omega_o \neq \left(\omega_{c1} + \omega_{c2}\right)/2$$

This is apparent in the preceding gain plot where ω_{c1} is closer to ω_o than ω_{c2} is. Rather, it is possible to show that the resonant or center frequency is equal to the geometric mean of the two cutoff frequencies,

$$\omega_o = \sqrt{\omega_{c1}\omega_{c2}}$$

Quality Factor Q: Recalling the expression for the quality factor Q as

$$Q = \omega_o RC$$

and rearranging this expression leads to another relationship for Q,

$$Q = \omega_o RC = \frac{\omega_o}{1/(RC)} = \frac{\omega_o}{\beta}$$

The quality factor is the ratio of the resonant frequency to the bandwidth. Therefore, Q is an indication of how peaked or narrow the bandreject region is. The higher the Q, the narrower the bandwidth relative to the center frequency ω_o. And from earlier, the higher the Q, the larger the current through the inductor and through the capacitor at resonance.

Gain Response: Given the frequency response form, the gain response can be written as

$$|H(\omega)| = \frac{|\omega_o^2 - \omega^2|}{|(\omega_o^2 - \omega^2) + j\omega\beta|}$$

$$|H(\omega)| = \frac{(\omega_o^2 - \omega^2)}{\sqrt{(\omega_o^2 - \omega^2)^2 + (\omega\beta)^2}}$$

Phase Response: The associated phase $\theta(\omega)$ can be written as

$$\theta(\omega) = \angle(\omega_o^2 - \omega^2) - \angle(\omega_o^2 - \omega^2 + j\omega\beta)$$

$$\theta(\omega) = \angle(\omega_o^2 - \omega^2) - \mathrm{atan2}(\omega\beta, \omega_o^2 - \omega^2)$$

where $\omega_o^2 - \omega^2$ is a real value, so its angle is simply

$$\angle(\omega_o^2 - \omega^2) = \begin{cases} 0° & (\omega_o^2 - \omega^2) > 0 \\ 180° & (\omega_o^2 - \omega^2) < 0 \end{cases}$$

This can be stated mathematically as

$$\angle(\omega_o^2 - \omega^2) = 90° - 90° \cdot \mathrm{sign}(\omega_o^2 - \omega^2)$$

where the function sign(x) returns the sign of its argument. If $x > 0$, sign(x) = 1; if $x < 0$, sign(x) = –1.

The angle plot associated with the gain plot on the preceding page is shown in the following figure. The angle starts at zero degrees and goes –90 ° at resonance where it jumps 180 ° to 90 °, then decreases to zero degrees as frequency goes to infinity. The angles at the two cutoff frequencies are ±45 °.

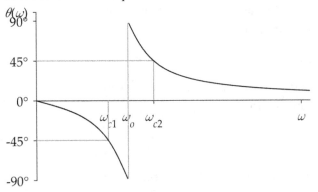

Design: The frequency response of a bandreject parallel RLC filter is governed by two parameters, the center frequency ω_o and the bandwidth β. The filter component values can be found once these are determined.

The specifications for a bandreject filter often include the center frequency ω_o and the desired gain $|H(\omega_d)|$ required at some other frequency ω_d. Given

these two specifications, the bandwidth β must be determined.

Substituting $\omega = \omega_d$ into the gain expression gives

$$H(\omega_d) = \frac{(\omega_o^2 - \omega_d^2)}{(\omega_o^2 - \omega_d^2) + j\omega_d\beta}$$

Though tedious, this expression can be solved for the bandwidth. The result of that work leads to

$$\beta = \frac{|\omega_o^2 - \omega_d^2|}{\omega_d |H(\omega_d)|} \sqrt{1 - |H(\omega_d)|^2}$$

Substituting the desired specifications into this equation gives the bandwidth required to meet the specifications. Once the bandwidth is known, the circuit components are chosen by selecting component values using the relationships

$$LC = \frac{1}{\omega_o^2} \qquad \frac{1}{RC} = \beta$$

Since there are three component values and two specifications or constraints, one component value can be chosen as desired and the other two found from the above relationships.

Example: Let the center frequency of the filter be $\omega_o = 10$ krad/s and let the gain at $\omega_d = 8$ krad/s be $|H(\omega_d)|_{dB} = -1$ dB so that little attenuation is provided at this frequency. To solve this problem, the gain must be converted from decibels to a common value. In this case, decibel scaling is defined by

$$X_{dB} = 20\log(x) \qquad x = 10^{\frac{X_{dB}}{20}}$$

Therefore, $|H(\omega_d)|_{dB} = -1$ dB becomes

$$|H(\omega_d)| = 10^{\frac{|H(\omega_d)|_{dB}}{20}} = 10^{\frac{-1}{20}} = 0.8913 = 891.3 \text{ m}$$

Substituting this value and $\omega_d = 8$ krad/s into the expression for the bandwidth gives

$$\beta = \frac{|(10^4)^2 - (8 \cdot 10^3)^2|}{8 \cdot 10^3 \cdot 0.8913}\sqrt{1 - (0.8913)^2} = 2{,}289 \text{ rad/s}$$

The resulting gain response is shown in the following figure where the gain is in decibels and the frequency axis is linearly scaled rather than logarithmically scaled. The fact that ω_d is so close to

ω_o makes the linear scale more visually appropriate in this case.

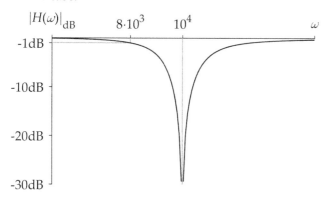

The Q of this filter is

$$Q = \frac{\omega_o}{\beta} = \frac{10^4}{2289} = 4.37$$

In general, a filter having a Q of 10 or more is considered a high Q filter. So this filter has a moderate Q.

There is no unique or best way to choose component values. Of course extreme values should be avoided, and what constitutes extreme values depends on the application. For this example, let the inductance be equal to 1 henry, $L = 0.1$ H. Then the capacitance value is

$$C = \frac{1}{\omega_o^2 L} = \frac{1}{\left(10^4\right)^2 \cdot 10^{-1}} = \frac{1}{10^7} = 10^{-7}\,\text{F} = 100\,\text{nF}$$

and the resulting resistance value is

$$R = \frac{1}{\beta C} = \frac{1}{2289 \cdot 10^{-7}} = 4.37\ \text{k}\Omega$$

7.5 Real World Filters

The preceding work illustrated only very basic filter concepts. The fundamental properties of representative and simple lowpass, highpass, bandpass, and bandreject filters were presented.

Filters are important, fundamental, and ubiquitous both in the processing of information and in the processing of power.

When processing information, filters separate desired information in one frequency band from unwanted information in others. For example, when you listen to a radio station or TV channel, the station or channel you select is separated from other stations and channels by a bandpass filter. The desired information gets through the filter and the rest is rejected.

Parallel RLC Bandreject Filter

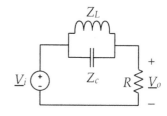

$$H(\omega) = \frac{\left(\omega_o^2 - \omega^2\right)}{\left(\omega_o^2 - \omega^2\right) + j\omega\beta} = |H(\omega)|\,\angle\theta(\omega)$$

Center Frequency $\quad \omega_o = \dfrac{1}{\sqrt{LC}}$

Bandwidth $\quad \beta = \dfrac{1}{RC} = \omega_{c2} - \omega_{c1}$

Quality Factor $\quad Q = \dfrac{\omega_o}{\beta}$

$|H(0)| = 1 = 0$ dB,

$|H(\omega_o)| = 0 = -\infty$ dB,

$|H(\infty)| = 1 = 0$ dB

Design Equation

$$\beta = \frac{\left|\omega_o^2 - \omega_d^2\right|}{\omega_d\,\left|H(\omega_d)\right|}\sqrt{1 - \left|H(\omega_d)\right|^2}$$

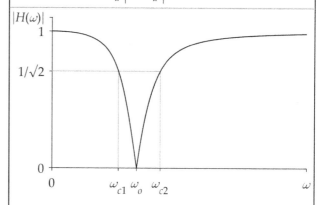

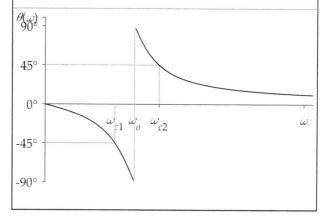

Because information carrying signals vary from audio frequencies in the kHz range to broadcast signals in the GHz range, the technology used to implement these filters varies widely. At audio frequencies, active filters and digital filters are common. At radio frequencies (RF), distributed parameter filter technologies and piezoelectric technologies are common. These RF filters do not contain inductors and capacitors.

Active filters are generally constructed using op amps, resistors, and capacitors. No inductors are used. There are numerous op amp circuit topologies for implementing active filters, including Sallen-Key, multiple feedback, biquad, state variable, leap frog, and switched capacitor. The op amps in active filters require power supplies to operate, so they can only be used when appropriate power supplies are available. Dedicated active filter integrated circuits also exist that provide easily implemented filters.

Digital filters are common when signals are sampled using an analog to digital (A/D) converter. Once signals are sampled, a processor utilizes a digital filter algorithm to process the incoming samples. After being filtered, the signal samples may be further processed or perhaps converted back to an analog signal through a digital to analog (D/A) converter. Digital filtering is limited by the capabilities of the analog to digital converter and by processor speed and capabilities.

Filters also appear in the processing of power. For example, they play an important role in power supplies that convert the AC voltage at a wall outlet into the DC supply voltage for devices that contain electronic circuitry. Such devices include the power supply in a computer and battery chargers for electronics devices such as tablets and cell phones. They also appear in the circuitry that interfaces renewable energy sources, such as wind generators and photovoltaics, to the AC power line. Most of these applications require lowpass filters, which are constructed from inductors and capacitors. Resistors are generally not used since they absorb power, which reduces efficiency, whereas inductors and capacitors ideally do not.

The process of designing filters, *i.e.*, filter synthesis, is well known and well beyond the scope of this text. Filters are characterized by their frequency response

characteristics, such as lowpass, highpass, bandpass, bandreject, and other less common characteristics.

Filters are also characterized by their order, which describes how quickly the filter transitions from the passband to the stopband. The higher the filter order, the faster this transition occurs and the steeper the gain response falls off. The RC lowpass and highpass filters discussed previously were first order filters, whereas the resonant circuit filters were second order. Higher order filters are created by cascading filters together. That is, the output of one filter becomes the input to the next and so on as desired.

Filters are also characterized by finer attributes of their frequency response, such as gain ripple in the passband or stopband or both, as well as the linearity and slope of the phase response. These characteristics depend on the class of polynomials or functions used in their design. These polynomials and functions include Bessel, Butterworth, Chebyshev, and elliptic.

A wealth of information regarding filter design can be found online and in numerous textbooks. It is not uncommon to find one or more engineering courses that focus on filter design as well.

7.6 Filter Examples

RC Filter with Loading

Consider the circuit below where the filter input is driven by a voltage source in series with a resistor and the filter output is loaded by a load resistor.

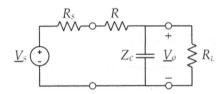

The frequency response of this filter is different from the ideal RC lowpass filter considered earlier. To find out how it is different requires circuit analysis.

To analyze this circuit, it is perhaps easiest to simplify the circuit by swapping the positions of the capacitor and the load resistor as shown below.

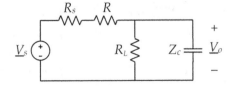

Then replace the source and three resistors by their Thévenin equivalent as shown below.

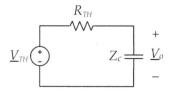

Ignoring the capacitor because it is not part of the Thévenin equivalent, voltage division gives the open circuit or Thévenin voltage as

$$\underline{V}_{TH} = \frac{R_L}{R_s + R + R_L}\,\underline{V}_s$$

and the Thévenin resistance is found by shutting off the source $\underline{V}_s$, and expressing it as the equivalent resistance seen looking toward the source as

$$R_{TH} = \left(R_s + R\right) \| R_L = \frac{\left(R_s + R\right)\cdot R_L}{R_s + R + R_L}$$

The simplified circuit now has the form of the original RC lowpass. Therefore, this filter is described by the frequency response relationship

$$\underline{V}_o = \frac{1}{1 + j\omega R_{TH} C}\,\underline{V}_{TH}$$

Substituting in the above expression for the Thévenin voltage gives

$$\underline{V}_o = \frac{1}{1 + j\omega R_{TH} C} \cdot \left(\frac{R_L}{R_s + R + R_L}\,\underline{V}_s\right)$$

The frequency response is then given by

$$H(\omega) = \frac{\underline{V}_o}{\underline{V}_i} = \frac{1}{1 + j\omega R_{TH} C} \cdot \left(\frac{R_L}{R_s + R + R_L}\right)$$

Evaluating this at DC, $\omega = 0$ gives

$$H(0) = \left(\frac{R_L}{R_s + R + R_L}\right)$$

So, the expression for the frequency response can be written as

$$H(\omega) = H(0)\cdot\left(\frac{1}{1 + j\omega R_{TH} C}\right)$$

This result differs from the ideal RC filter frequency response of

$$H(\omega) = \frac{1}{1 + j\omega RC}$$

But the two expressions are equal if R_s is set equal to zero and R_L is set equal to infinity. In this case $R_{TH} = R$ and the DC gain is equal to one

$$H(0) = \frac{R_L}{0 + 0 + R_L} = \frac{R_L}{R_L} = 1$$

Given the frequency response for the filter in this example, the critical or cutoff frequency is

$$\omega_c = \frac{1}{R_{TH} C}$$

and the frequency response can be rewritten as

$$H(\omega) = H(0) \cdot \frac{1}{1 + j\dfrac{\omega}{\omega_c}} = |H(\omega)| \angle\theta(\omega)$$

The gain response is

$$|H(\omega)| = H(0) \cdot \frac{1}{\left|1 + j\dfrac{\omega}{\omega_c}\right|}$$

and the gain at the cutoff frequency is

$$|H(\omega_c)| = H(0)\cdot \frac{1}{\left|1 + j\dfrac{\omega_c}{\omega_c}\right|} = H(0)\cdot \frac{1}{|1 + j1|} = H(0)\cdot \frac{1}{\sqrt{2}}$$

which can be written in decibels as

$$|H(\omega_c)|_{dB} = H(0)|_{dB} + \left.\frac{1}{\sqrt{2}}\right|_{dB} = H(0)|_{dB} - 3\,dB$$

The gain at the cutoff frequency is 3 dB lower than the DC gain $H(0)$. As a result, ω_c is still called the 3 dB frequency because the gain is 3 dB lower than the zero frequency or DC gain.

Except for the change in the cutoff frequency, the phase of the frequency response is unchanged from the earlier circuit,

$$\theta(\omega) = \angle\left(\frac{H(0)}{1 + j\dfrac{\omega}{\omega_c}}\right) = -atan\left(\frac{\omega}{\omega_c}\right)$$

Example: Let $R = 10\ k\Omega$, $C = 100\ nF$, $R_L = 10\ k\Omega$, and $R_s = 100\ \Omega$. Then,

$$R_{TH} = \left(R_s + R\right) \| R_L = \frac{\left(100 + 10k\right)\cdot 10k}{100 + 10k + 10k} = 5.025\ k\Omega$$

and the cutoff frequency is

$$\omega_c = \frac{1}{R_{TH}C} = \frac{1}{5.025\,\text{k}\cdot100\,\text{n}} = 1{,}990 \text{ rad/s}$$

and the DC gain is

$$H(0) = \frac{R_L}{R_s+R+R_L} = \frac{10\,\text{k}}{100+10\,\text{k}+10\,\text{k}} = 0.4975$$

The resulting frequency response is

$$H(\omega) = \frac{H(0)}{1+j\dfrac{\omega}{\omega_c}} = \frac{0.4975}{1+j\dfrac{\omega}{1990}}$$

When the source resistance is zero, $R_s = 0$, and the load resistance is infinite, $R_L = \infty$, the cutoff frequency is $\omega_c = 1/(RC) = 1/(10\,\text{k}\cdot100\,\text{n}) = 1{,}000$ rad/s, and the ideal frequency response is

$$H_{ideal}(\omega) = \frac{1}{1+j\dfrac{\omega}{\omega_c}} = \frac{1}{1+j\dfrac{\omega}{1000}}$$

The following plot shows the gain $|H(\omega)|$ of the "loaded" filter and the gain $|H_{ideal}(\omega)|$ of the ideal unloaded filter.

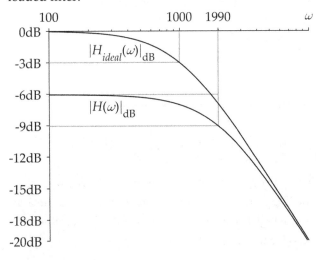

The passband gains of the two filters are significantly different because of the **loading** produced by the voltage division between the load resistor and the equivalent source resistance. The loaded filter starts with a gain equal to $20\log(0.4975) = -6.06$ dB ≈ -6 dB, whereas the ideal filter starts with a gain of 0 dB. In addition, the cutoff frequencies of the two filters are significantly different, 1,000 rad/s versus 1,990 rad/s. However, the stopband gains of the two filters approach each other as frequency extends beyond 10 krad/s.

Active Lowpass Filter

Active filters generally eliminate loading issues since they produce an output that is independent of the load connected to the op amp, provided the output voltage and current are within the limits of the chosen op amp. The following circuit illustrates the active filter equivalent of the ideal RC lowpass filter.

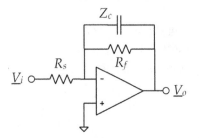

The gain of this op amp circuit is simply

$$\frac{V_o}{V_i} = H(\omega) = -\frac{Z_f}{R_s}$$

where

$$Z_f = R_f \parallel Z_c$$

$$\frac{1}{Z_f} = Y_f = \frac{1}{R_f} + j\omega C$$

Combining these equations leads to

$$H(\omega) = -\frac{Z_f}{R_s}\cdot\left(\frac{Y_f}{Y_f}\right) = -\frac{1}{R_s Y_f}$$

$$H(\omega) = -\frac{1}{R_s\left(\dfrac{1}{R_f}+j\omega C\right)}$$

$$H(\omega) = -\frac{1}{\dfrac{R_s}{R_f}+j\omega R_s C}$$

Further simplification allows the frequency response to more closely resemble that of the passive RC lowpass filter,

$$H(\omega) = -\frac{1}{\dfrac{R_s}{R_f}+j\omega R_s C}\cdot\left(\dfrac{\dfrac{R_f}{R_s}}{\dfrac{R_f}{R_s}}\right)$$

$$H(\omega) = -\frac{R_f}{R_s}\frac{1}{1+j\omega R_f C} = -\frac{R_f}{R_s}\cdot\left(\frac{1}{1+j\dfrac{\omega}{\omega_c}}\right)$$

where the cutoff frequency is

$$\omega_c = \frac{1}{R_f C}$$

The term in parentheses in the frequency response expression $H(\omega)$ is equal to that of the standard passive RC lowpass filter. The term to the left of the parentheses in $H(\omega)$ is equal to the DC gain of the inverting op amp, *i.e.*, the gain when the capacitor is removed. Because of the gain term, this filter can amplify signals in addition to providing filtering.

Active filters are also easy to cascade as shown in the following figure where both **filter stages or sections** are identical in this example.

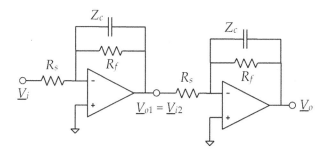

The output of the first filter stage is simply the input to the second filter. Because the second filter stage does not load or change the frequency response of the first filter, the frequency response $H_o(\omega)$ of the combined filters is simply

$$\frac{V_o}{V_i} = H_o(\omega) = H(\omega) \cdot H(\omega) = \left(-\frac{R_f}{R_s} \cdot \frac{1}{1 + j\frac{\omega}{\omega_c}} \right)^2$$

Example: Let $R_s = R_f = 10\,\text{k}\Omega$ and $C = 100\,\text{nF}$. Then the cutoff frequency is

$$\omega_c = \frac{1}{R_f C} = \frac{1}{10\,\text{k} \cdot 100\,\text{n}} = 1000\ \text{rad/s} = 1\,\text{krad/s}$$

The frequency response of the single stage filter is

$$H(\omega) = -\frac{R_f}{R_s} \cdot \left| \frac{1}{1 + j\frac{\omega}{\omega_c}} \right|$$

$$H(\omega) = -\frac{10\,\text{k}}{10\,\text{k}} \cdot \left(\frac{1}{1 + j\frac{\omega}{1000}} \right)$$

$$H(\omega) = \frac{-1}{1 + j\frac{\omega}{1000}}$$

and the frequency response of two cascaded op amp filters as illustrated above is simply

$$H_o(\omega) = \frac{1}{\left(1 + j\frac{\omega}{1000}\right)^2}$$

The following plot shows the gain $|H(\omega)|$ of the single stage filter and the gain $|H_o(\omega)|$ of the cascaded filter.

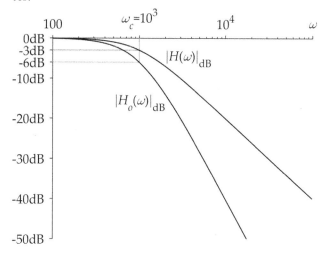

Because the two filters are cascaded, the cascaded filter has a gain of −6 dB at ω_c. This occurs because each filter stage contributes −3 dB at ω_c. The gain of the cascaded filter also has a much steeper slope in the stop band because the input is filtered twice, once by the first stage and again by the second stage.

Based on this example, it should be clear that any number of active filter stages, each with its own frequency response, can be cascaded to produce whatever filter characteristic is desired.

Passive Second Order RC Filter

Consider the following filter that is formed by cascading two RC lowpass filters. Because the second RC loads the first RC, the overall frequency response is not the product of the two individual RC frequency responses as it was earlier for the two stage active lowpass filter.

The frequency response of this circuit is found by applying nodal analysis and writing KCL for the center node

$$\frac{V_1 - V_i}{R_1} + \frac{V_1}{Z_{c1}} + \frac{V_1 - V_o}{R_2} = 0$$

Voltage division gives the output voltage $\underline{V}_o$ in terms of $\underline{V}_1$ as

$$\underline{V}_o = \frac{Z_{c2}}{R_2 + Z_{c2}} \underline{V}_1$$

which can be solved for $\underline{V}_1$ as

$$\underline{V}_1 = \frac{R_2 + Z_{c2}}{Z_{c2}} \underline{V}_o$$

This equation can be substituted into the nodal analysis equation to eliminate $\underline{V}_1$ and solve for the frequency response $H(\omega) = \underline{V}_o / \underline{V}_i$. Doing so is tedious algebra that can be made less prone to error by using symbolic algebra software. The result of that work gives the frequency response in a standard second order form as

$$H(\omega) = \frac{\omega_o^2}{\left(\omega_o^2 - \omega^2\right) + j\omega\beta}$$

where

$$\omega_o^2 = \frac{1}{R_1 R_2 C_1 C_2}$$

and

$$\beta = \frac{1}{R_1 C_1} + \frac{1}{R_2 C_2} + \frac{1}{R_2 C_1}$$

The gain or amplitude of the frequency response is

$$|H(\omega)| = \left| \frac{\omega_o^2}{\left(\omega_o^2 - \omega^2\right) + j\omega\beta} \right| = \frac{\omega_o^2}{\sqrt{\left(\omega_o^2 - \omega^2\right)^2 + \left(\omega\beta\right)^2}}$$

There is no simple way to identify the cutoff frequency ω_c where the gain is $1/\sqrt{2} = -3\,\text{dB}$.

The values of β and ω_o have no particular significance in this circuit like they did in resonant circuits where they identified the bandwidth and center frequency of a bandpass or bandreject filter. The filter response is written in this form solely to maintain uniform notation for second order filter forms.

The gain at $\omega = \omega_o$ is

$$|H(\omega_o)| = \frac{\omega_o^2}{\sqrt{\left(\omega_o^2 - \omega_o^2\right)^2 + \left(\omega_o\beta\right)^2}} = \frac{\omega_o^2}{\sqrt{\left(\omega_o\beta\right)^2}} = \frac{\omega_o}{\beta}$$

So ω_o could be the cutoff frequency if components are chosen so that

$$\frac{\omega_o}{\beta} = \frac{1}{\sqrt{2}} = -3\,\text{dB}$$

Using symbolic analysis software, an expression for the cutoff frequency can be found, but the resulting expression does not provide useful insight for choosing component values.

Example: Let $R_1 = R_2 = 5\,\text{k}\Omega$ and $C_1 = C_2 = 100\,\text{nF}$. Then, the filter is described by

$$\omega_o^2 = \frac{1}{R_1 R_2 C_1 C_2} = \frac{1}{5\,\text{k} \cdot 5\,\text{k} \cdot 100\,\text{n} \cdot 100\,\text{n}} = 4 \cdot 10^6 \, (\text{rad/s})^2$$

$$\omega_o = \sqrt{4 \cdot 10^6} = 2000 \, \text{rad/s}$$

and

$$\beta = \frac{1}{R_1 C_1} + \frac{1}{R_2 C_2} + \frac{1}{R_2 C_1}$$

$$\beta = \frac{1}{5\,\text{k} \cdot 100\,\text{n}} + \frac{1}{5\,\text{k} \cdot 100\,\text{n}} + \frac{1}{5\,\text{k} \cdot 100\,\text{n}} = 6000 \, \text{rad/s}$$

Given these values, the gain at $\omega = \omega_o$ is

$$|H(\omega_o)| = \frac{\omega_o}{\beta} = \frac{2000}{6000} = \frac{1}{3} = -9.54\,\text{dB}$$

Therefore, the cutoff frequency for this example filter will be significantly less than ω_o.

The following plot shows the gain response $|H(\omega)|$ of the filter having these parameters. Numerical interpolation of the plot shows that the gain is -3 dB at approximately $\omega_c = 748$ rad/s.

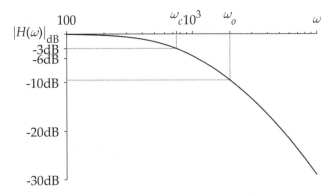

Resonant Second Order Lowpass Filter

A common passive lowpass filter that appears in power supplies is shown in the following figure.

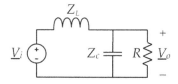

The resistor R in this circuit models the load connected to the filter composed of an inductor and capacitor.

Let the capacitor impedance in parallel with the load resistor R be the impedance Z_{eq} where

$$\frac{1}{Z_{eq}} = Y_{eq} = j\omega C + \frac{1}{R}$$

Then the frequency response is given by voltage division

$$\frac{V_o}{V_i} = H(\omega) = \frac{Z_{eq}}{Z_{eq} + Z_L} = \frac{Z_{eq}}{Z_{eq} + Z_L} \cdot \left(\frac{Y_{eq}}{Y_{eq}}\right) = \frac{1}{1 + Z_L Y_{eq}}$$

which simplifies to

$$H(\omega) = \frac{1}{1 + j\omega L\left(j\omega C + \frac{1}{R}\right)}$$

$$H(\omega) = \frac{1}{1 - \omega^2 LC + j\omega\frac{L}{R}}$$

$$H(\omega) = \frac{1}{1 - \omega^2 LC + j\omega\frac{L}{R}} \cdot \left(\frac{\frac{1}{LC}}{\frac{1}{LC}}\right)$$

$$H(\omega) = \frac{\frac{1}{LC}}{\frac{1}{LC} - \omega^2 + j\omega\frac{1}{RC}}$$

$$H(\omega) = \frac{\omega_o^2}{\left(\omega_o^2 - \omega^2\right) + j\omega\beta}$$

where

$$\omega_o^2 = \frac{1}{LC} \qquad \beta = \frac{1}{RC}$$

This frequency response has the same form as the passive second order RC filter considered earlier. **The** values of β and ω_o here have no particular significance in this circuit like they did in resonant circuits where they identified the bandwidth and center frequency of a bandpass or bandreject filter.

There is no simple way to identify the cutoff frequency ω_c where the gain is $1/\sqrt{2} = -3\,\text{dB}$. An expression for the cutoff frequency can be found, but its usefulness is not significant. This is especially true if the load resistor R varies dynamically as the load on the power supply changes.

For plotting purposes it is convenient to define a quality factor Q as

$$Q = \frac{\omega_o}{\beta}$$

and to rewrite the frequency response as

$$H(\omega) = \frac{\omega_o^2}{\left(\omega_o^2 - \omega^2\right) + j\omega\frac{\omega_o}{Q}} \cdot \left(\frac{\frac{1}{\omega_o^2}}{\frac{1}{\omega_o^2}}\right)$$

$$H(\omega) = \frac{1}{1 - \left(\frac{\omega}{\omega_o}\right)^2 + j\frac{1}{Q}\left(\frac{\omega}{\omega_o}\right)}$$

The response is now characterized by the two parameters, ω_o and Q. The following plot shows example gain response plots, $|H(\omega)|$ for several illustrative Q values. Because resonance occurs in this circuit between the inductor and capacitor, the gain of this circuit $|H(\omega)|$ exceeds one near ω_o for Q values greater than $1/2$.

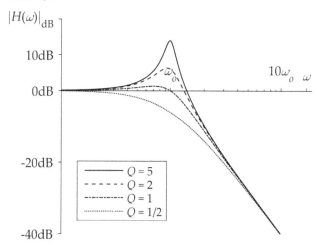

So, amazingly this is one situation where voltage division leads to an increase in voltage rather than the decrease that must occur when circuits contain resistors only. In any case, all frequency responses eventually fall off in the stop band beyond ω_o in the same way and at the same slope.

Active Allpass Filter

Consider the following active filter where the first op amp section on the left is simply a gain of –1, so its output is the negative of the input voltage $\underline{V}_i$. The second op amp section on the right is a difference amplifier with both inputs being the same voltage.

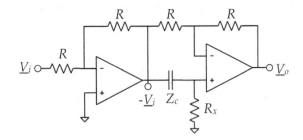

The second op amp section is shown below. The gain of this circuit is easily found by applying super-position.

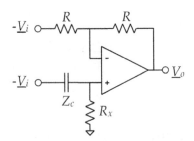

First, shut OFF the lower $-\underline{V}_i$ source, giving the following circuit.

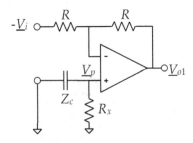

The voltage at the positive (+) terminal is zero, *i.e.*, $\underline{V}_p = 0$, since there is no current flowing into the op amp. As a result, this is an inverting amplifier and the output voltage $\underline{V}_{o1}$ is simply

$$\underline{V}_{o1} = \frac{-R}{R}\left(-\underline{V}_i\right) = \underline{V}_i$$

Next, shut OFF the upper $-\underline{V}_i$ source, giving the following circuit.

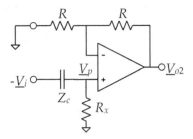

The voltage at the positive (+) terminal $\underline{V}_p$ is given by voltage division as

$$\underline{V}_p = \frac{R_x}{Z_c + R_x}\left(-\underline{V}_i\right) = \frac{-R_x}{Z_c + R_x}\underline{V}_i$$

Using this result, the output voltage $\underline{V}_{o2}$ is given by the noninverting amplifier relationship

$$\underline{V}_{o2} = \left(1 + \frac{R}{R}\right)\underline{V}_p = 2\underline{V}_p = 2\frac{-R_x}{Z_c + R_x}\underline{V}_i$$

The actual or net circuit output $\underline{V}_o$ is the sum of the two partial solutions,

$$\underline{V}_o = \underline{V}_{o1} + \underline{V}_{o2}$$

$$\underline{V}_o = \underline{V}_i + 2\frac{-R_x}{Z_c + R_x}\underline{V}_i$$

$$\underline{V}_o = \left(1 - 2\frac{R_x}{Z_c + R_x}\right)\underline{V}_i$$

Therefore the frequency response of this circuit is

$$\frac{\underline{V}_o}{\underline{V}_i} = H(\omega) = 1 - \frac{2R_x}{Z_c + R_x}$$

This expression does not provide any useful insight. However, combining terms over a common denominator and using the capacitor admittance $Y_c = j\omega C$ leads to the following

$$H(\omega) = 1 - \frac{2R_x}{Z_c + R_x}$$

$$H(\omega) = \left(\frac{Z_c + R_x}{Z_c + R_x}\right) - \frac{2R_x}{Z_c + R_x}$$

$$H(\omega) = \frac{Z_c - R_x}{Z_c + R_x}$$

which can be further simplified as

$$H(\omega) = \frac{Z_c - R_x}{Z_c + R_x} \cdot \left(\frac{Y_c}{Y_c}\right)$$

$$H(\omega) = \frac{1 - R_x Y_c}{1 + R_x Y_c}$$

$$H(\omega) = \frac{1 - j\omega R_x C}{1 + j\omega R_x C}$$

$$H(\omega) = \frac{1 - j\frac{\omega}{\omega_x}}{1 + j\frac{\omega}{\omega_x}} = |H(\omega)| \angle\theta(\omega)$$

where

$$\omega_x = \frac{1}{R_x C}$$

The gain response is

$$|H(\omega)| = \frac{\left|1 - j\frac{\omega}{\omega_x}\right|}{\left|1 + j\frac{\omega}{\omega_x}\right|} = \frac{\sqrt{1 + \left(\frac{-\omega}{\omega_x}\right)^2}}{\sqrt{1 + \left(\frac{\omega}{\omega_x}\right)^2}} = \frac{\sqrt{1 + \left(\frac{\omega}{\omega_x}\right)^2}}{\sqrt{1 + \left(\frac{\omega}{\omega_x}\right)^2}} = 1$$

The gain of the circuit is equal to one at all frequencies! Therefore, this is called an **allpass filter**.

This filter is used for its phase response,

$$\theta(\omega) = \angle\left(1 - j\frac{\omega}{\omega_x}\right) - \angle\left(1 + j\frac{\omega}{\omega_x}\right)$$

$$\theta(\omega) = \text{atan}\left(\frac{-\omega}{\omega_x}\right) - \text{atan}\left(\frac{\omega}{\omega_x}\right)$$

$$\theta(\omega) = -2\,\text{atan}\left(\frac{\omega}{\omega_x}\right)$$

At $\omega = 0$, the phase is

$$\theta(0) = -2\,\text{atan}\left(\frac{0}{\omega_x}\right) = -2\,\text{atan}(0) = -2\cdot 0 = 0°$$

At $\omega = \omega_x$, the phase is

$$\theta(\omega_x) = -2\,\text{atan}\left(\frac{\omega_x}{\omega_x}\right) = -2\,\text{atan}(1) = -2\cdot 45° = -90°$$

And at $\omega = \infty$, the phase is

$$\theta(\infty) = -2\,\text{atan}\left(\frac{\infty}{\omega_x}\right) = -2\,\text{atan}(\infty) = -2\cdot 90° = -180°$$

The following plot illustrates the phase response where the frequency axis is logarithmically scaled.

The utility of this circuit is that there are signal processing applications where both the cosine and sine are required at a specific frequency. If the input to this circuit is

$$v_i(t) = V_m \cos(\omega_x t) \Leftrightarrow \underline{V}_i = V_m \angle 0°$$

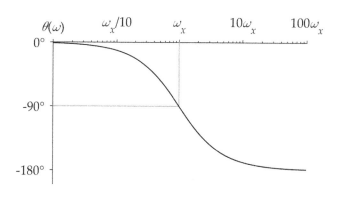

the output is

$$\underline{V}_o = H(\omega_x)\underline{V}_i = \left(|H(\omega_x)| \angle\theta(\omega_x)\right)\cdot\underline{V}_i$$

$$\underline{V}_o = \left(1 \angle -90°\right)\cdot V_m \angle 0°$$

$$\underline{V}_o = V_m \angle -90°$$

which is the time domain voltage

$$v_o(t) = V_m \cos(\omega_x t - 90°) = V_m \sin(\omega_x t)$$

A cosine input produces a sine output.

Active Bandpass Filter

Consider the following **multiple feedback active filter** circuit where the two capacitors have the same value.

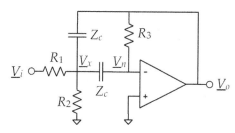

The utility of this circuit is not visually apparent. The filter type can be determined by considering the capacitor impedance at zero frequency, *i.e.*, DC, and infinite frequency.

At zero frequency, the capacitor is an open circuit,

$$Z_c = -j\frac{1}{\omega C}\bigg|_{\omega=0} = -j\frac{1}{0\cdot C} = -j\infty = \infty = \text{open circuit}$$

Under these conditions, the filter appears as the following circuit.

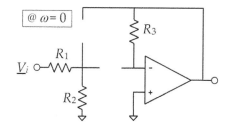

There is no connection between the input and the output, so the output is zero and the gain is zero at DC, $|H(0)| = 0$.

At infinite frequency, the capacitor is a short circuit,

$$Z_c = -j\frac{1}{\omega C}\Big|_{\omega=\infty} = -j\frac{1}{\infty \cdot C} = -j0 = 0 = \text{short circuit}$$

Under these conditions, the filter appears as the following circuit.

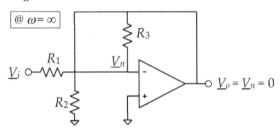

Now there is a short between the output and the negative (–) terminal, which is at zero volts because the positive (+) terminal is connected to reference. Once again, the output is zero and the gain is zero, $|H(\infty)| = 0$.

Since the gains are zero at both DC and infinite frequencies, this must be a bandpass filter.

The frequency response of this filter is found by using nodal analysis. Applying KCL at the essential node labeled $\underline{V}_x$ in the original circuit gives

$$\frac{\underline{V}_x - \underline{V}_i}{R_1} + \frac{\underline{V}_x}{R_2} + \frac{\underline{V}_x - \underline{V}_o}{Z_c} + \frac{\underline{V}_x - 0}{Z_c} = 0$$

Applying KCL at the negative terminal (–) gives

$$\frac{0 - \underline{V}_x}{Z_c} + \frac{0 - \underline{V}_o}{R_3} = 0$$

This equation can be simplified to become

$$\frac{\underline{V}_x}{Z_c} + \frac{\underline{V}_o}{R_3} = 0$$

$$\frac{\underline{V}_x}{Z_c} = -\frac{\underline{V}_o}{R_3}$$

$$\underline{V}_x = \frac{-Z_c}{R_3}\underline{V}_o$$

The frequency response is then found by substituting this relationship into the preceding KCL equation at the node labeled $\underline{V}_x$ and simplifying the result.

Once again, to maximize productivity and minimize errors, this algebra is best performed using symbolic analysis software. The result of that work leads to

$$\frac{\underline{V}_o}{\underline{V}_i} = H(\omega) = -K\left(\frac{j\omega\beta}{\omega_o^2 - \omega^2 + j\omega\beta}\right)$$

where

$$\beta = \frac{2}{R_3 C}$$

$$K = \frac{R_3}{2R_1}$$

$$\omega_o^2 = \frac{1}{R_{eq}R_3 C^2}$$

$$R_{eq} = R_1 \| R_2 = \frac{R_1 R_2}{R_1 + R_2}$$

The term in parentheses in the frequency response equation is equal to the standard frequency response expression found earlier in this chapter for the bandpass filter constructed using a series RLC circuit. No inductor appears in this active filter circuit. The terms in the frequency response have the same meaning here. The center frequency is ω_o, and the bandwidth is β. The quality factor is $Q = \omega_o/\beta$. The term $-K$ shows that this circuit is an inverting amplifier and has a center frequency gain of K, i.e.,

$$|H(\omega_o)| = \left|-K\left(\frac{j\omega_o\beta}{\omega_o^2 - \omega_o^2 + j\omega_o\beta}\right)\right| = K\left|\left(\frac{j\omega_o\beta}{j\omega_o\beta}\right)\right| = K$$

There are four component values to be chosen in this design, the three resistances and one capacitance. And there are three parameters, ω_o, β, and K. Since there are three constraints and four unknowns, one of the parameter values can be chosen, and then the others follow accordingly. Several test cases may be needed to achieve reasonable component values.

Example: Let the specifications for the bandpass filter be

$$\omega_o = 10 \text{ krad/s}$$
$$Q = 10$$
$$K = 2 = 6\,\text{dB}$$

Since it is generally easier to find resistor values than it is to find capacitor values, choose the capacitance first, then find the resistances.

Use the fact that the center frequency gain is two to find the ratio between R_1 and R_3,

$$K = 2 = \frac{R_3}{2R_1}$$

$$4 = \frac{R_3}{R_1}$$

$$R_1 = \frac{R_3}{4}$$

The bandwidth β is given by

$$\beta = \frac{\omega_o}{Q} = \frac{10^4}{10} = 1000 = 1 \text{ krad/s}$$

Let the capacitance be $C = 100$ nF $= 10^{-7}$ F. Then R_3 can be computed from the bandwidth relationship

$$\beta = \frac{2}{R_3 C}$$

$$R_3 = \frac{2}{\beta C} = \frac{2}{10^3 \cdot 10^{-7}} = \frac{2}{10^{-4}} = 2 \cdot 10^4 = 20 \text{ k}\Omega$$

The resistance R_1 is then

$$R_1 = \frac{R_3}{4} = \frac{20 \text{k}}{4} = 5 \text{ k}\Omega$$

Then the equivalent resistance R_{eq} is found from

$$\omega_o^2 = \frac{1}{R_{eq} R_3 C^2}$$

$$R_{eq} = \frac{1}{\omega_o^2 R_3 C^2} = \frac{1}{10^8 \cdot 2 \cdot 10^4 \cdot 10^{-14}} = \frac{1}{2 \cdot 10^2} = 50 \ \Omega$$

The final resistance R_2 is then related to R_{eq} by

$$R_{eq} = R_1 \| R_2 = \frac{R_1 R_2}{R_1 + R_2} \quad \text{or} \quad \frac{1}{R_{eq}} = \frac{1}{R_1} + \frac{1}{R_2}$$

Therefore R_2 is found by solving the equation,

$$\frac{1}{R_{eq}} = \frac{1}{R_1} + \frac{1}{R_2}$$

$$\frac{1}{R_2} = \frac{1}{R_{eq}} - \frac{1}{R_1}$$

$$\frac{1}{R_2} = \frac{1}{50} - \frac{1}{5000} = \frac{1}{50.51}$$

So $R_2 = 50.51 \ \Omega \approx 50 \ \Omega$. If $R_2 = 50 \ \Omega$ is used, the revised equivalent resistance is

$$R_{eq} = \frac{R_1 R_2}{R_1 + R_2} = \frac{5k \cdot 50}{5k + 50} = 49.5 \ \Omega$$

and the center frequency changes to

$$\omega_o^2 = \frac{1}{R_{eq} R_3 C^2} = \frac{1}{49.5 \cdot 20 \text{ k} \cdot 10^{-14}} = 1.01 \cdot 10^8$$

so $\omega_o = 10.05$ krad/s.

The final time domain circuit and a plot of the gain response are shown in the following figures.

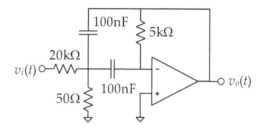

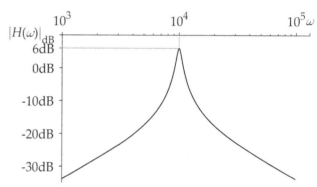

7.7 Bode Plots

Clearly, a great deal of insight is gained by the visual representation of the frequency response. This is true about many many things. Visual pictures or representations play an important role in understanding the world we live in. A very early example is the ~17,000 year old cave paintings in Lascaux France. While engineering does not involve cave painting, engineers commonly make plots to solve problems and explain phenomena because doing so facilitates greater insight. Where would circuit analysis be if we did not draw circuit schematics on paper?

All plots of the gain response $|H(\omega)|$ and phase $\theta(\omega)$ versus frequency ω illustrated here have been generated using computer software. How were such plots made before computers existed? How were such plots made before calculators existed?

Plotting the frequency response $|H(\omega)|$ and $\theta(\omega)$ versus frequency ω is vitally important in understanding frequency response and filtering in general. Before the advent of calculators and computers with graphics capability, these plots had to be made by hand. One such technique for making these plots was established in 1938 by Hendrik W. Bode (1905-1982). **These hand drawn plots are called Bode plots.**

> The key to understanding Bode's approximations is realizing that Bode had a **ruler**, **graph paper**, and a **pencil**. Nothing more. Even simple calculators did not exist.

Frequency response is composed of two components, the gain $|H(\omega)|$ and the phase $\theta(\omega)$ versus frequency ω,

$$H(\omega) = |H(\omega)| \angle \theta(\omega)$$

Without the benefit of any electronic computation capabilities, Bode found a way to approximate plots of both $|H(\omega)|$ and $\theta(\omega)$. His approximations were and are sufficiently accurate for many applications.

Given how easy it is to generate frequency response plots using a computer, it may seem that Bode's approximations are no longer needed. In a sense that is true, but understanding Bode's approximations allows one to quickly identify the general shape of the gain and phase responses without resorting to computer generated plots. This often facilitates quicker filter design.

First Order Lowpass

As derived earlier, the frequency response of a first order lowpass filter is

$$H(\omega) = \cfrac{1}{1 + j\cfrac{\omega}{\omega_c}} = |H(\omega)| \angle \theta(\omega)$$

The magnitude or gain $|H(\omega)|$ is

$$|H(\omega)| = \left| \cfrac{1}{1 + j\cfrac{\omega}{\omega_c}} \right| = \cfrac{1}{\left|1 + j\cfrac{\omega}{\omega_c}\right|} = \cfrac{1}{\sqrt{1 + \left(\cfrac{\omega}{\omega_c}\right)^2}}$$

In decibels, the gain is $|H(\omega)|_{dB}$ is

$$|H(\omega)|_{dB} = \left| \cfrac{1}{1 + j\cfrac{\omega}{\omega_c}} \right|_{dB}$$

The associated phase $\theta(\omega)$ is

$$\theta(\omega) = -\mathrm{atan}\left(\cfrac{\omega}{\omega_c}\right)$$

Bode Gain Plot: As illustrated in this chapter, it is common to plot gain in decibels on a logarithmically scaled frequency axis. In doing so, wide ranges in values are compressed so that the plot is easily interpreted.

Bode approximated the gain in decibels by considering the two extremes in frequency. First, consider the case

$$\omega \ll \omega_c$$

When this is true, ω/ω_c is negligible compared to one, and the gain is approximated by

$$|H(\omega)|_{dB} = \left| \cfrac{1}{1 + j\cfrac{\omega}{\omega_c}} \right|_{dB} \approx \left| \cfrac{1}{1 + j0} \right|_{dB} = |1|_{dB} = 0_{dB}$$

Next, consider the case

$$\omega \gg \omega_c$$

When this is true, one is negligible compared to ω/ω_c, and the gain is approximated by

$$|H(\omega)|_{dB} = \left| \cfrac{1}{1 + j\cfrac{\omega}{\omega_c}} \right|_{dB}$$

$$|H(\omega)|_{dB} \approx \left| \cfrac{1}{0 + j\cfrac{\omega}{\omega_c}} \right|_{dB}$$

$$|H(\omega)|_{dB} \approx \left| \cfrac{1}{\cfrac{\omega}{\omega_c}} \right|_{dB} = \left| \left(\cfrac{\omega}{\omega_c}\right)^{-1} \right|_{dB}$$

$$|H(\omega)|_{dB} \approx -\left| \cfrac{\omega}{\omega_c} \right|_{dB}$$

To get an idea of what the gain in decibels is in this case, let $\omega = 10\omega_c$, then

$$|H(\omega)|_{dB} \approx -\left| \cfrac{\omega}{\omega_c} \right|_{dB} = -\left| \cfrac{10^1 \omega_c}{\omega_c} \right|_{dB} = -|10^1|_{dB} = -20\,dB$$

Increasing frequency by a factor of 10 to $\omega = 100\omega_c$ gives

$$|H(\omega)|_{dB} \approx -\left|\frac{\omega}{\omega_c}\right|_{dB} = -\left|\frac{10^2\omega_c}{\omega_c}\right|_{dB} = -\left|10^2\right|_{dB} = -40\,dB$$

Increasing frequency by another factor of 10 to $\omega = 1000\omega_c$ gives

$$|H(\omega)|_{dB} \approx -\left|\frac{\omega}{\omega_c}\right|_{dB} = -\left|\frac{10^3\omega_c}{\omega_c}\right|_{dB} = -\left|10^3\right|_{dB} = -60\,dB$$

Every time the frequency increases by a factor of 10, the gain decreases by 20 dB: –20 dB to –40 dB to –60 dB. **A factor of 10 in frequency is called a decade**, so the above relationship describes a straight line on a logarithmic frequency axis having a slope of **–20 dB per decade** (dB/dec) in frequency.

On the other hand, doubling the frequency from $\omega = 10\omega_c$ to $\omega = 20\omega_c$ gives

$$|H(\omega)|_{dB} \approx -\left|\frac{\omega}{\omega_c}\right|_{dB} = -\left|\frac{2\cdot10\omega_c}{\omega_c}\right|_{dB}$$

or

$$|H(\omega)|_{dB} = -\left|2\cdot10\right|_{dB} = -\left|10^1\right|_{dB} - \left|2\right|_{dB}$$
$$|H(\omega)|_{dB} = -20\,dB - 6\,dB = -26\,dB$$

Doubling frequency again to $\omega = 40\omega_c$ gives

$$|H(\omega)|_{dB} \approx -\left|\frac{\omega}{\omega_c}\right|_{dB} = -\left|\frac{4\cdot10\omega_c}{\omega_c}\right|_{dB}$$

or

$$|H(\omega)|_{dB} = -\left|2^2\cdot10\right|_{dB}$$
$$|H(\omega)|_{dB} = -\left|10^1\right|_{dB} - \left|2^2\right|_{dB}$$
$$|H(\omega)|_{dB} = -20\,dB - 2\cdot\left|2\right|_{dB}$$
$$|H(\omega)|_{dB} = -20\,dB - 2\cdot(6\,dB) = -32\,dB$$

Every time the frequency increases by a factor of 2, the gain decreases by 6 dB: –20 dB to –26 dB to –32 dB. **A factor of two in frequency is called an octave**, so the above relationship describes a straight line on a logarithmic frequency axis having a slope of **–6 dB per octave** (dB/oct) in frequency.

> It is curious that a factor of **two** is considered an octave when the prefix "**oct**" is normally associated with the number 8, not 2. In music there are eight notes in the major scale, *i.e.*, "**do-re-mi-fa-sol-la-ti-do**," separating every factor of two in frequency. Thus, the reason why a factor of two is an octave.

For example, middle 'C' on a piano keyboard is twice the frequency of the 'C' key to the left on a piano keyboard and one half the frequency of the 'C' key to the right on the piano keyboard. Given this explanation, using the term octave to describe a factor of two in frequency makes sense.

To summarize, when

$$\omega \ll \omega_c$$
$$|H(\omega)|_{dB} = 0\,dB$$

and when

$$\omega \gg \omega_c$$
$$|H(\omega)|_{dB} = -\left|\frac{\omega}{\omega_c}\right|_{dB}$$

These two relationships describe straight lines on a logarithmic frequency axis. These lines commonly called **asymptotes**. The first is a horizontal line at 0 dB, and the second is a line having slope –20 dB/dec or –6 dB/oct that crosses 0 dB at $\omega = \omega_c$.

Bode drew both of these lines using a ruler. The horizontal line at 0 dB is drawn from left to right and the sloped line is drawn from right to left until the two lines intersect at 0 dB at $\omega = \omega_c$ as shown in the following figure.

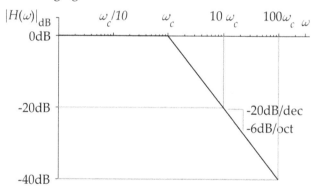

This straight line approximation compares favorably with the actual gain plot superimposed on the Bode plot as shown in the following figure. The greatest error occurs at $\omega = \omega_c$ where the actual gain is –3 dB. Because the point $\omega = \omega_c$ forms a corner in the Bode approximation, the frequency ω_c is also referred to as the **corner frequency**.

> To summarize, ω_c is known as the *critical* frequency, the *cutoff* frequency, the *3 dB* frequency, the *half power* frequency, and the *corner* frequency.

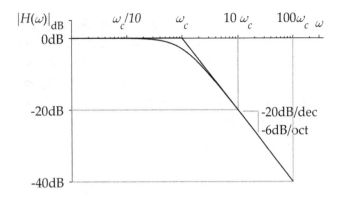

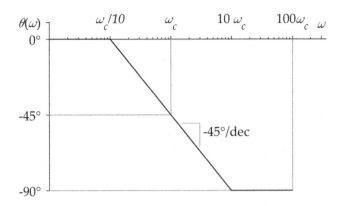

The Bode gain plot approximates the gain response by two straight lines. When all you have is a ruler, graph paper, and a pencil, this is a very good approximation. Even when a computer is readily available, Bode's approximation provides quick results and valuable insight into the fundamental characteristics of the gain response.

Bode Phase Plot: The phase response $\theta(\omega)$ is given by

$$\theta(\omega)=-\text{atan}\left(\frac{\omega}{\omega_c}\right)$$

Bode approximated this relationship by considering three cases. First, let

$$\omega \leq \frac{\omega_c}{10}$$

then the phase is approximated as

$$\theta(\omega)=-\text{atan}\left(\frac{\omega}{\omega_c}\right) \approx -\text{atan}\left(\frac{1}{10}\right) \approx 0°$$

Next, let

$$\omega \geq 10\,\omega_c$$

then the phase is approximated as

$$\theta(\omega)=-\text{atan}\left(\frac{\omega}{\omega_c}\right) \approx -\text{atan}\left(10\right) \approx -90°$$

Finally, let

$$\omega = \omega_c$$

then

$$\theta(\omega_c)=-\text{atan}\left(\frac{\omega_c}{\omega_c}\right) = -\text{atan}\left(1\right) = -45°$$

This $-45°$ point is used to mark the midway point in a straight line connecting the limiting values of $0°$ and $-90°$. The associated straight line approximation for the phase plot is shown in the following figure.

As shown in the following figure, this straight line approximation compares favorably with the actual phase plot superimposed on the Bode plot. The greatest error occurs at the corners at $\omega = \omega_c/10$ and $\omega = 10\omega_c$ where the magnitude of the error is equal to

$$|e| = \left|-\text{atan}\left(\frac{\omega_c/10}{\omega_c}\right)\right| = \text{atan}\left(\frac{1}{10}\right) = 5.7°$$

Once again, when all you have is a ruler, graph paper, and a pencil, this is a very good approximation.

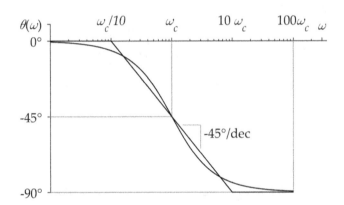

The process of finding the Bode approximations for the gain and phase of the frequency response applies to other filter types as well.

First Order Highpass
The frequency response of the first order highpass is

$$H(\omega) = \frac{j\frac{\omega}{\omega_c}}{1 + j\frac{\omega}{\omega_c}} = |H(\omega)| \angle\theta(\omega)$$

Bode Gain Plot: The gain in decibels is

$$|H(\omega)|_{dB} = \left|\frac{j\frac{\omega}{\omega_c}}{1 + j\frac{\omega}{\omega_c}}\right|_{dB} = \left(\left|j\frac{\omega}{\omega_c}\right| \cdot \left|\frac{1}{1 + j\frac{\omega}{\omega_c}}\right|\right)_{dB}$$

which simplifies to

$$\left|H(\omega)\right|_{dB} = \left|j\frac{\omega}{\omega_c}\right|_{dB} + \left|\frac{1}{1+j\dfrac{\omega}{\omega_c}}\right|_{dB}$$

When written in this way as the sum of two terms in decibels, the gain response has two terms, one associated with the numerator and the other associated with the denominator. The latter term is equal to that of the first order lowpass just analyzed. Therefore, if the gain of the numerator term is found, it can simply be added to that of the denominator.

The gain of the numerator term is

$$\left|H(\omega)\right|_{dB} = \left|j\frac{\omega}{\omega_c}\right|_{dB} = \left|\frac{\omega}{\omega_c}\right|_{dB}$$

At $\omega = \omega_c$ the gain is

$$\left|H(\omega_c)\right|_{dB} = \left|\frac{\omega_c}{\omega_c}\right|_{dB} = \left|1\right|_{dB} = \left|10^0\right|_{dB} = 0\,dB$$

At $\omega = 10\omega_c$ the gain is

$$\left|H(\omega_c)\right|_{dB} = \left|\frac{10\,\omega_c}{\omega_c}\right|_{dB} = \left|10^1\right|_{dB} = 20\,dB$$

And at $\omega = 100\omega_c$ the gain is

$$\left|H(\omega_c)\right|_{dB} = \left|\frac{100\,\omega_c}{\omega_c}\right|_{dB} = \left|10^2\right|_{dB} = 40\,dB$$

Given these results, **the gain of the numerator term is a line having slope equal to 20 dB/dec or equivalently 6 dB/oct** passing through 0 dB at $\omega = \omega_c$ as shown in the following figure.

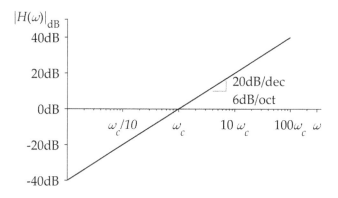

Superimposing this line for the numerator term over that for the denominator term, which was found earlier as the first order lowpass gain, leads to the following plot.

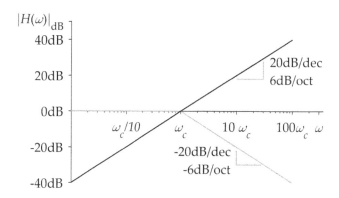

The sum of these two curves gives the final high-pass filter result as shown below. At each point along the frequency axis, the two curves are added together to get the net result.

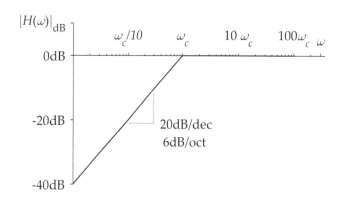

For example, at $\omega = \omega_c/10$ the two values are 0 dB and –20 dB, giving the result $0 - 20 = -20$ dB. And at $\omega = 10\omega_c$ the two values are 20 dB and –20 dB, given the result $20 - 20 = 0$ dB. Below $\omega = \omega_c$, the upward slope of the numerator curve adds to the 0 dB of the denominator term. Beyond $\omega = \omega_c$, the upward slope of 20 dB/dec of the numerator curve cancels the downward slope of –20 dB/dec of the denominator curve giving a horizontal line at 0 dB.

This straight line approximation compares favorably with the actual gain plot superimposed on the Bode plot as shown below. The greatest error occurs at $\omega = \omega_c$ where the actual gain is –3 dB.

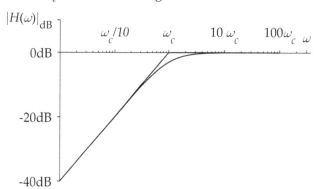

Bode Phase Plot: The phase of the first order high-pass filter was found earlier in this chapter as

$$\theta(\omega) = \angle(j\omega/\omega_c) - \text{atan}(\omega/\omega_c)$$

$$\theta(\omega) = 90° - \text{atan}(\omega/\omega_c)$$

The first component above is due to the numerator term in $H(\omega)$ and the second is due to the denominator term. Therefore, each component can be plotted on a common frequency axis and summed to produce the desired result. The approximation for the denominator term matches that for the previous first order lowpass filter. The two components to the phase response are shown in the following plot.

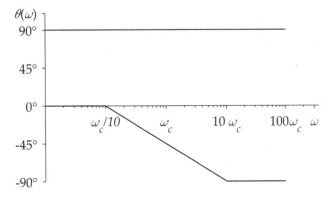

The plot below shows the sum of the two curves above as well as the actual phase response. This straight line approximation compares favorably with the actual phase plot superimposed on the Bode plot result. The greatest error occurs at the corners at $\omega = \omega_c/10$ and $\omega = 10\omega_c$ where the magnitude of the error is equal to $5.7°$.

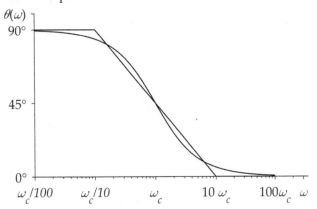

Second Order Lowpass

Bode's approximations for second order terms do not work as well, but still provides useful information. For example, consider the second order lowpass frequency response analyzed earlier

$$H(\omega) = \frac{\omega_o^2}{\left(\omega_o^2 - \omega^2\right) + j\omega\beta} = |H(\omega)| \angle\theta(\omega)$$

This can be put in Bode form by substituting $\beta = \omega_o/Q$ in the form of $1/Q = \beta/\omega_o$, and rewriting $H(\omega)$ as

$$H(\omega) = \frac{\omega_o^2}{\left(\omega_o^2 - \omega^2\right) + j\omega\beta} \cdot \left|\frac{\dfrac{1}{\omega_o^2}}{\dfrac{1}{\omega_o^2}}\right|$$

$$H(\omega) = \frac{1}{1 - \left(\dfrac{\omega}{\omega_o}\right)^2 + j\dfrac{1}{Q}\left(\dfrac{\omega}{\omega_o}\right)}$$

The gain response in dB is then

$$|H(\omega)|_{dB} = \left|\frac{1}{1 - \left(\dfrac{\omega}{\omega_o}\right)^2 + j\dfrac{1}{Q}\left(\dfrac{\omega}{\omega_o}\right)}\right|_{dB}$$

Following Bode's approach, consider the case where

$$\omega \ll \omega_o$$

When this is true, ω/ω_o is negligible compared to one, and the gain is approximated by

$$|H(\omega)|_{dB} \approx \left|\frac{1}{1 - (0)^2 + j\dfrac{1}{Q}(0)}\right|_{dB} = |1|_{dB} = |10^0|_{dB} = 0\,dB$$

This is a horizontal line at 0 dB.

Next, consider the case where

$$\omega \gg \omega_o$$

When this is true, only the term $(\omega/\omega_o)^2$ remains significant, so the gain is approximated by

$$|H(\omega)|_{dB} \approx \left|\frac{1}{\left(\dfrac{\omega}{\omega_o}\right)^2}\right|_{dB} = \left|\left(\frac{\omega}{\omega_o}\right)^{-2}\right|_{dB} = -2\cdot\left|\frac{\omega}{\omega_o}\right|_{dB}$$

To get an idea of what the gain in decibels is in this case, let $\omega = 10\omega_o$. Then

$$|H(10\,\omega_o)|_{dB} \approx -2\cdot\left|\frac{10\,\omega_o}{\omega_o}\right|_{dB} = -2\cdot|10^1|_{dB} = -40\,dB$$

And if $\omega = 100\omega_o$, then

$$\left| H(100\,\omega_o) \right|_{dB} \approx -2 \cdot \left| \frac{100\,\omega_o}{\omega_o} \right|_{dB} = -2 \cdot \left| 10^2 \right|_{dB} = -80\,dB$$

Based on these results, every time the frequency increases by a factor of 10, the gain decreases by 40 dB. **So this is a line having slope equal to −40 dB/dec.**

To summarize, when

$$\omega \ll \omega_o$$

$$\left| H(\omega) \right|_{dB} = 0\,dB$$

and when

$$\omega \gg \omega_c$$

$$\left| H(\omega) \right|_{dB} = -2 \cdot \left| \frac{\omega}{\omega_o} \right|_{dB}$$

These two relationships describe straight lines on a logarithmic frequency axis. The first is a horizontal line at 0 dB, and the second is a line having slope −40 dB/dec or −12 dB/oct that crosses 0 dB at $\omega = \omega_o$.

Bode drew both of these lines using a ruler. The horizontal line at 0 dB is drawn from left to right and the sloped line is drawn from right to left until the two lines intersected at 0 dB at $\omega = \omega_o$ as shown in the following figure.

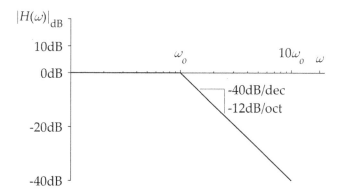

This Bode approximation ignores the impact of Q on the plot in the region around the resonant frequency ω_o as illustrated in the actual gain plot shown in the following figure. However, the approximation works well for frequencies substantially beyond the resonant frequency where it accurately captures the −40 dB/dec slope.

Of course there are detailed analytic techniques for correcting the Bode plot as a function of Q, but given the ease with which computer generated plots can be

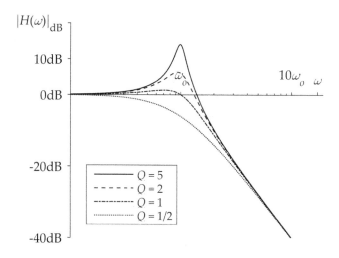

made, these techniques are generally no longer a productive use of one's time.

The phase response for second order terms can also be approximated. This approximation suffers from the same issue as the gain. The approximation works well except for the region around the resonant frequency. Since the phase response of a filter has generally little importance in many applications, the Bode approximation for phase response for second order terms is not covered here.

Second Order Bandpass

Finally, consider the frequency response of the active bandpass filter as derived earlier

$$H(\omega) = -K\left(\frac{j\omega\beta}{\omega_o^2 - \omega^2 + j\omega\beta} \right) = \left| H(\omega) \right| \angle\theta(\omega)$$

This can be put in Bode form by substituting $\beta = \omega_o/Q$ and rewriting $H(\omega)$ as

$$H(\omega) = -K\left(\frac{j\omega\dfrac{\omega_o}{Q}}{\omega_o^2 - \omega^2 + j\omega\dfrac{\omega_o}{Q}} \right) \cdot \left| \frac{\dfrac{1}{\omega_o^2}}{\dfrac{1}{\omega_o^2}} \right|$$

$$H(\omega) = -\frac{K}{Q}\left(\frac{j\dfrac{\omega}{\omega_o}}{1 - \left(\dfrac{\omega}{\omega_o}\right)^2 + j\dfrac{1}{Q}\dfrac{\omega}{\omega_o}} \right)$$

The gain response in dB is then

$$\left| H(\omega) \right|_{dB} = \left| \left(\frac{-K}{Q} \right) \frac{j\left(\dfrac{\omega}{\omega_o}\right)}{1 - \left(\dfrac{\omega}{\omega_o}\right)^2 + j\dfrac{1}{Q}\left(\dfrac{\omega}{\omega_o}\right)} \right|_{dB}$$

Using the product property of logarithms, the gain response can be written as

$$|H(\omega)|_{dB} = \left| \frac{-K}{Q} \right|_{dB} + \left| j\frac{\omega}{\omega_o} \right|_{dB} + \left| \frac{1}{1 - \left(\frac{\omega}{\omega_o}\right)^2 + j\frac{1}{Q}\left(\frac{\omega}{\omega_o}\right)} \right|_{dB}$$

Plotting the gain in decibels versus frequency is simply a matter of plotting each term on the right hand side in this equation, and then adding them graphically as Bode did.

The **first term** on the right hand side above is a constant gain, which becomes a horizontal line at $|K/Q|_{dB}$ on the frequency response plot.

The **second term** on the right hand side was considered earlier when the Bode plot for the high pass filter was considered. This term is a straight line as shown in the following figure having a slope of 20 dB/dec or 6 dB/oct, crossing through 0 dB at $\omega = \omega_o$.

The **last term** on the right hand side is equal to the second order low pass filter response considered earlier.

These three components are illustrated in the following figure for $K = 1$, $Q = 1/2$, $\omega_o = 10$ krad/s. In this case, $|K/Q|_{dB} = |2|_{dB} = 6$ dB.

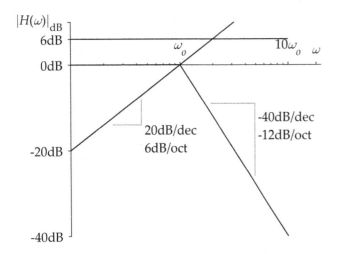

The sum of these three components gives the following gain response plot. This is followed by a subsequent plot of the actual gain response.

Comparing the Bode approximation to the actual response, the approximation accurately captures the 20 dB/dec slope below the center frequency and the −20 dB/dec slope above the center frequency. The

Bode approximation exhibits the greatest error in the region surrounding the center frequency.

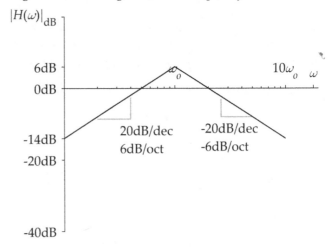

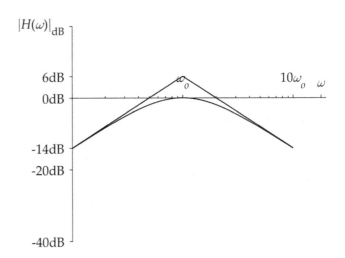

As with the preceding second order lowpass response, the Bode approximation performs more poorly around the center or resonant frequency as the quality factor Q increases.

The following plot shows the Bode approximation and actual gain response for the case $K = 1$, $Q = 4$, $\omega_o = 10$ krad/s.

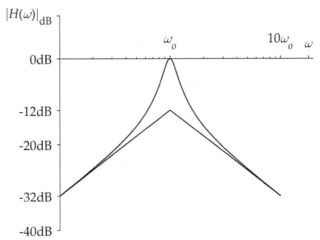

While it may be disappointing that the Bode approximation does poorly around resonances, Bode provided analysis for identifying specific points in the resonance region. Given the ease with which gain response and phase plots can be created using a computer, this added analysis is no longer important.

What is fundamentally important about Bode's approximation is the ± 20 dB/dec = ± 6 dB/oct slope associated with the gain response asymptotes. These asymptotes are created by each of the terms in the numerator and denominator of $H(\omega)$.

Even when a computer is readily available, Bode's approximations provide quick results and valuable insight into the fundamental characteristics of the gain response.

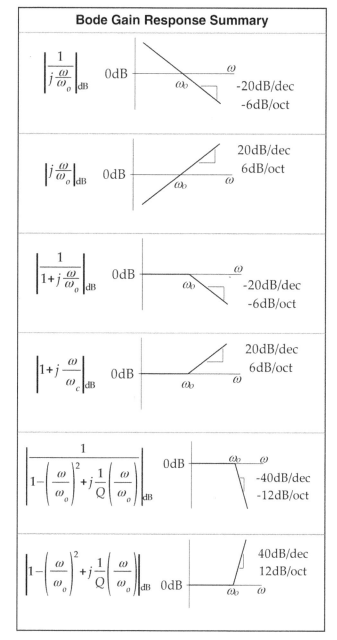

Bode Gain Response Summary

7.8 Standard Filter Forms

The preceding sections identified a number of filters. These filters were described in terms of standard first and second order forms. To summarize this work, it is beneficial to consider standard forms for the frequency response of lowpass, highpass, bandpass, and bandreject filters.

These forms can be written in terms of ω as is done throughout this chapter. They can also be written using the Laplace variable s, which is related to ω by

$$s = j\omega$$

In this case, the square of s is

$$s^2 = (j\omega)^2 = j^2\omega^2 = -\omega^2$$

In later courses, it is generally more common to write responses in terms of s. When this is done, the response is called the transfer function, denoted $H(s)$, rather than the frequency response $H(\omega)$. In any case, making the substitution $s = j\omega$ gives the frequency response

$$H(\omega) = H(s)\big|_{s=j\omega}$$

Given this background, standard forms for common filters are given in the following tables, where K is a gain constant that may or may not appear.

Lowpass Filter Response Forms

First Order

$$H(\omega) = K\frac{1}{1 + j\frac{\omega}{\omega_c}} \qquad H(s) = K\frac{\omega_c}{s + \omega_c}$$

Second Order

$$H(\omega) = K\frac{\omega_0^2}{\omega_0^2 - \omega^2 + j\omega\beta} \qquad H(s) = K\frac{\omega_0^2}{s^2 + \beta s + \omega_0^2}$$

Highpass Filter Response Forms

First Order

$$H(\omega) = K\frac{j\frac{\omega}{\omega_c}}{1 + j\frac{\omega}{\omega_c}} \qquad H(s) = K\frac{s}{s + \omega_c}$$

Second Order

$$H(\omega) = K\frac{-\omega^2}{\omega_0^2 - \omega^2 + j\omega\beta} \qquad H(s) = K\frac{s^2}{s^2 + \beta s + \omega_0^2}$$

Bandpass Filter Response Forms

$$H(\omega) = K \frac{j\omega\beta}{\omega_o^2 - \omega^2 + j\omega\beta} \qquad H(s) = K \frac{\beta s}{s^2 + \beta s + \omega_o^2}$$

Bandreject Filter Response Forms

$$H(\omega) = K \frac{\omega_o^2 - \omega^2}{\omega_o^2 - \omega^2 + j\omega\beta} \qquad H(s) = K \frac{s^2 + \omega_o^2}{s^2 + \beta s + \omega_o^2}$$

7.9 Summary

Frequency Response

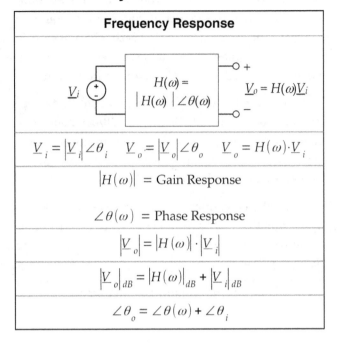

$$\underline{V}_i = |\underline{V}_i| \angle \theta_i \qquad \underline{V}_o = |\underline{V}_o| \angle \theta_o \qquad \underline{V}_o = H(\omega) \cdot \underline{V}_i$$

$$|H(\omega)| = \text{Gain Response}$$

$$\angle \theta(\omega) = \text{Phase Response}$$

$$|\underline{V}_o| = |H(\omega)| \cdot |\underline{V}_i|$$

$$|\underline{V}_o|_{dB} = |H(\omega)|_{dB} + |\underline{V}_i|_{dB}$$

$$\angle \theta_o = \angle \theta(\omega) + \angle \theta_i$$

Capacitor Impedance Extreme Values

$$Z_C = -j\frac{1}{\omega C} \quad \overset{@\ \omega = 0}{\Longrightarrow} \quad \text{open circuit}$$

$$Z_C = -j\frac{1}{\omega C} \quad \overset{@\ \omega = \infty}{\Longrightarrow} \quad \text{short circuit}$$

Inductor Impedance Extreme Values

$$Z_L = j\omega L \quad \overset{@\ \omega = 0}{\Longrightarrow} \quad \text{short circuit}$$

$$Z_L = j\omega L \quad \overset{@\ \omega = \infty}{\Longrightarrow} \quad \text{open circuit}$$

First Order Lowpass Filter	**First Order Highpass Filter**
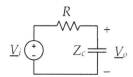	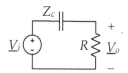
$$\frac{V_o}{V_i} = H(\omega) = |H(\omega)| \angle \theta(\omega) = \frac{1}{1 + j\frac{\omega}{\omega_c}}$$	$$\frac{V_o}{V_i} = H(\omega) = |H(\omega)| \angle \theta(\omega) = \frac{j\frac{\omega}{\omega_c}}{1 + j\frac{\omega}{\omega_c}}$$
Critical, Cutoff, or 3 dB frequency $$\omega_c = \frac{1}{RC}$$	Critical, Cutoff, or 3 dB frequency $$\omega_c = \frac{1}{RC}$$
$|H(0)| = 1 = 0$ dB $|H(\omega_c)| = 1/\sqrt{2} = -3.01$ dB ≈ -3 dB $|H(\infty)| = 0 = -\infty$ dB	$|H(0)| = 0 = -\infty$ dB $|H(\omega_c)| = 1/\sqrt{2} = -3.01$ dB ≈ -3 dB $|H(\infty)| = 1 = 0$ dB
Design Equation $$\omega_c = \frac{1}{RC} = \frac{\omega_d |H(\omega_d)|}{\sqrt{1 - |H(\omega_d)|^2}}$$	Design Equation $$\omega_c = \frac{1}{RC} = \frac{\omega_d \sqrt{1 - |H(\omega_d)|^2}}{|H(\omega_d)|}$$
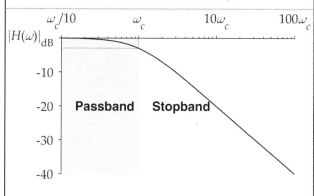	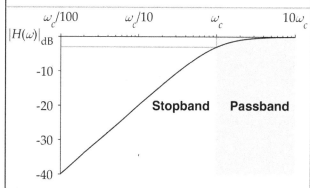
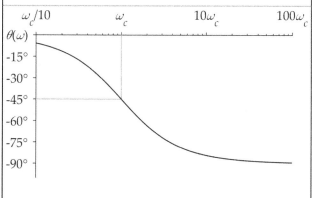	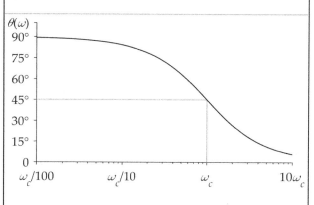

Series RLC Bandpass Filter

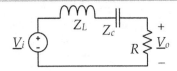

$$H(\omega) = \frac{j\omega\beta}{\left(\omega_o^2 - \omega^2\right) + j\omega\beta} = |H(\omega)| \angle\theta(\omega)$$

Center Frequency $\quad \omega_o = \dfrac{1}{\sqrt{LC}}$

Bandwidth $\quad \beta = \dfrac{R}{L} = \omega_{c2} - \omega_{c1}$

Quality Factor $\quad Q = \dfrac{\omega_o}{\beta}$

$|H(0)| = 0 = -\infty$ dB,

$|H(\omega_o)| = 1 = 0$ dB,

$|H(\infty)| = 0 = -\infty$ dB

Design Equation

$$\beta = \frac{|H(\omega_d)| \cdot |\omega_o^2 - \omega_d^2|}{\omega_d \sqrt{1 - |H(\omega_d)|^2}}$$

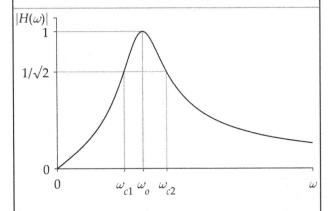

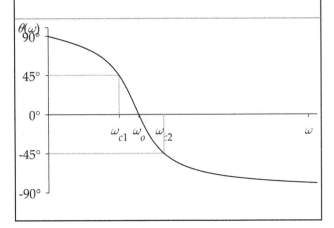

Parallel RLC Bandreject Filter

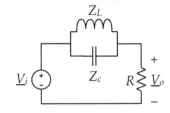

$$H(\omega) = \frac{\left(\omega_o^2 - \omega^2\right)}{\left(\omega_o^2 - \omega^2\right) + j\omega\beta} = |H(\omega)| \angle\theta(\omega)$$

Center Frequency $\quad \omega_o = \dfrac{1}{\sqrt{LC}}$

Bandwidth $\quad \beta = \dfrac{1}{RC} = \omega_{c2} - \omega_{c1}$

Quality Factor $\quad Q = \dfrac{\omega_o}{\beta}$

$|H(0)| = 1 = 0$ dB,

$|H(\omega_o)| = 0 = -\infty$ dB,

$|H(\infty)| = 1 = 0$ dB

Design Equation

$$\beta = \frac{|\omega_o^2 - \omega_d^2|}{\omega_d |H(\omega_d)|} \sqrt{1 - |H(\omega_d)|^2}$$

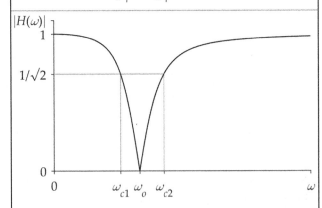

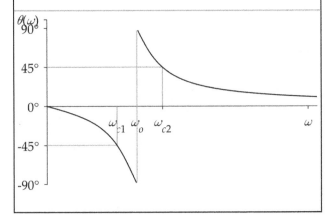

Series Resonance

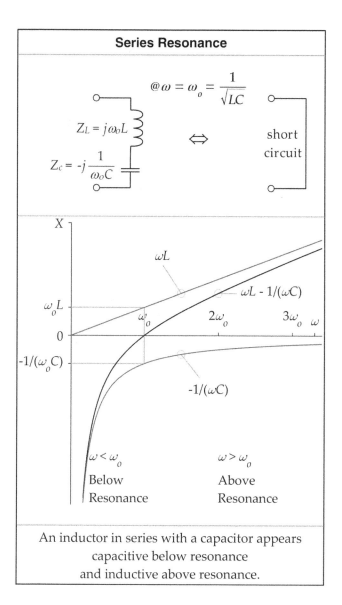

$$@ \omega = \omega_o = \frac{1}{\sqrt{LC}}$$

$Z_L = j\omega_o L$

$Z_c = -j\dfrac{1}{\omega_o C}$

$\Longleftrightarrow$ short circuit

An inductor in series with a capacitor appears
capacitive below resonance
and inductive above resonance.

Parallel Resonance

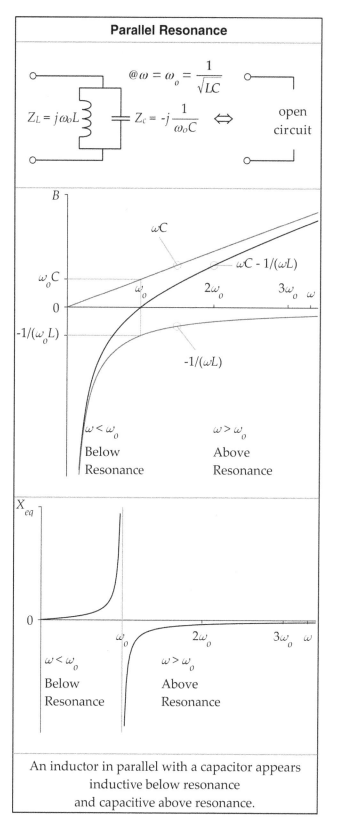

$$@ \omega = \omega_o = \frac{1}{\sqrt{LC}}$$

$Z_L = j\omega_o L$ $Z_c = -j\dfrac{1}{\omega_o C}$

$\Longleftrightarrow$ open circuit

An inductor in parallel with a capacitor appears
inductive below resonance
and capacitive above resonance.

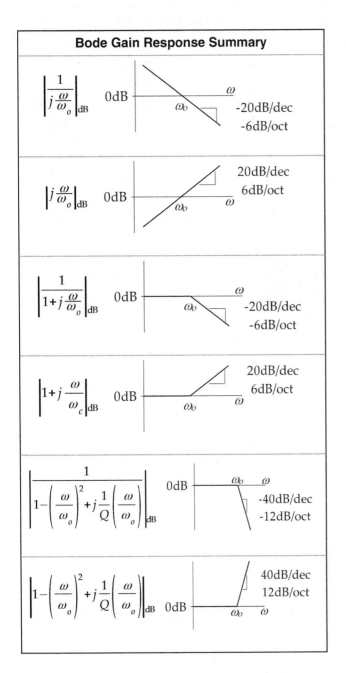

Bode Gain Response Summary

Frequency Factors

Decade, dec	A factor of **ten**.
Octave, oct	A factor of **two**.

Gain versus Attenuation

Attenuation is the inverse of gain.

For example,
a gain of 1/2 is equal to attenuation by 2.

When expressed in dB,
attenuation has the opposite sign as gain.
For example,
–3 db Gain = 3 dB Attenuation.

7.10 Problems

7.1 For the *lowpass* filter below, find $H(\omega) = \underline{V}_o/\underline{V}_i$, then compute ω_c, $|H(0)|$, $|H(\omega_c)|$, and $|H(\infty)|$ when $R_L = R$, $2R$, $5R$, $10R$, $20R$, $50R$, $100R$, and ∞.

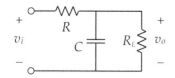

7.2 For the filter below, find $H(\omega) = \underline{V}_o/\underline{V}_i$. Let $\omega_c = 1/RC$, then compute $|H(0)|$, $|H(\omega_c)|$, and $|H(\infty)|$ when $R_p = R$, $2R$, $5R$, $10R$, $20R$, $50R$, $100R$, and ∞.

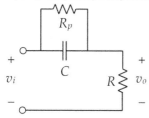

7.3 Design an **RC** *lowpass* filter using practical component values and using your resulting $H(\omega)$ expression find ω_c, $|H(\omega_c)|_{dB}$ and $|H(\omega_d)|_{dB}$ for

(a) $|H(\omega_d)|_{dB} = -30$ dB and $f_d = \omega_d/(2\pi) = 10$ kHz,

(b) $|H(\omega_d)|_{dB} = -50$ dB and $f_d = \omega_d/(2\pi) = 10$ kHz.

Find the filter response to $v_i(t) = 10\cos(2\pi\cdot4\text{k}t) + 10\cos(2\pi\cdot20\text{k}t)$ V.

7.4 Design an **RL** *lowpass* filter using practical component values and using your resulting $H(\omega)$ expression find ω_c, $|H(\omega_c)|_{dB}$ and $|H(\omega_d)|_{dB}$ for

(a) $|H(\omega_d)|_{dB} = -30$ dB and $f_d = \omega_d/(2\pi) = 10$ kHz,

(b) $|H(\omega_d)|_{dB} = -50$ dB and $f_d = \omega_d/(2\pi) = 10$ kHz.

Find the filter response to $v_i(t) = 10\cos(2\pi\cdot4\text{k}t) + 10\cos(2\pi\cdot20\text{k}t)$ V.

7.5 Design an **RC** *highpass* filter using practical component values and using your resulting $H(\omega)$ expression find ω_c, $|H(\omega_c)|_{dB}$ and $|H(\omega_d)|_{dB}$ for

(a) $|H(\omega_d)|_{dB} = -30$ dB and $f_d = \omega_d/(2\pi) = 5$ kHz,

(b) $|H(\omega_d)|_{dB} = -40$ dB and $f_d = \omega_d/(2\pi) = 5$ kHz,

Find the filter response to $v_i(t) = 10\cos(2\pi\cdot10\text{k}t) + 10\cos(2\pi\cdot60\text{k}t)$ V.

7.6 Design a series **RLC** *bandpass* filter using practical component values with $f_o = \omega_o/(2\pi) = 10$ kHz and find

β, Q, ω_{c1}, ω_{c2}, and compute $|H(\omega_d)|_{dB}$ from your resulting $H(\omega)$ expression for

(a) $|H(\omega_d)|_{dB} = -40$ dB and $f_d = \omega_d/(2\pi) = 15$ kHz,

(b) $|H(\omega_d)|_{dB} = -50$ dB and $f_d = \omega_d/(2\pi) = 15$ kHz.

Find the filter response to $v_i(t) = 10\cos(2\pi\cdot10\text{k}t) + 10\cos(2\pi\cdot20\text{k}t)$ V.

7.7 Design a parallel **RLC** *bandreject* filter using practical component values with $f_o = \omega_o/(2\pi) = 4$ kHz and find β, Q, ω_{c1}, ω_{c2}, and compute $|H(\omega_d)|_{dB}$ from your resulting $H(\omega)$ expression for

(a) $|H(\omega_d)|_{dB} = -3$ dB and $f_d = \omega_d/(2\pi) = 2$ kHz,

(b) $|H(\omega_d)|_{dB} = -6$ dB and $f_d = \omega_d/(2\pi) = 2$ kHz.

Find the filter response to $v_i(t) = 8\cos(2\pi\cdot8\text{k}t) + 8\cos(2\pi\cdot2\text{k}t)$ V.

7.8 Choose practical component values for the active *lowpass* filter below so that $|H(0)|_{dB} = 10$ dB and the cutoff frequency is $f_c = \omega_c/(2\pi) = 12$ kHz. Find the filter response to $v_i(t) = 2\cos(2\pi\cdot4\text{k}t) + 2\cos(2\pi\cdot40\text{k}t)$ V.

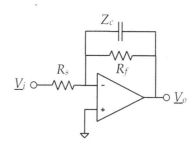

7.9 Design the resonant second order *lowpass* filter shown below using practical component values so that $f_o = \omega_o/(2\pi) = 10$ Hz and $Q = 2$. Find $|H(\omega_o)|_{dB}$ and $|H(\omega_d)|_{dB}$ for $f_d = \omega_d/(2\pi) = 100$ Hz. Find the response of the filter to $v_i(t) = 10\cos(20t) + 10\cos(2\pi\cdot200t)$ V.

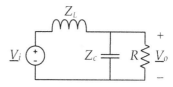

7.10 Design the active bandpass filter shown in the following circuit using practical component values given $|H(\omega_o)|_{dB} = 12$ dB, $f_o = \omega_o/(2\pi) = 10$ kHz. and $Q = 15$, Compute $|H(\omega_o-\beta/2)|_{dB}$ and $|H(\omega_o+\beta/2)|_{dB}$. From this data, are the frequencies $\omega = \omega_o\pm\beta/2$ good approximations for the two cutoff frequencies ω_{c1} and ω_{c2}? Find the response of the filter to $v_i(t) = 2\cos(2\pi\cdot1\text{k}t) + 2\cos(2\pi\cdot10\text{k}t)$ V.

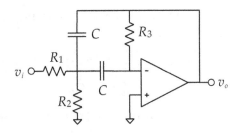

7.11 By considering capacitive and inductive impedances at DC and infinite frequencies, as well as possible resonant frequencies, identify the following filters where $H(\omega) = \underline{V}_o/\underline{V}_i$ as lowpass (LP), highpass (HP), bandpass (BP), bandreject (BR), or none-of-the-above (NA).

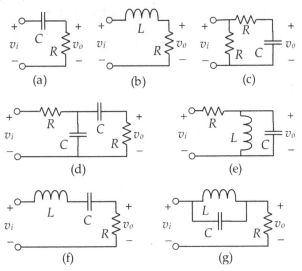

7.12 Find the frequency response $H(\omega) = \underline{V}_o/\underline{V}_i$ of the op amp filter below. Put your result in the standard form

$$H(\omega) = K \frac{j\omega\beta}{\omega_0^2 - \omega^2 + j\omega\beta}$$

Find K, β, and ω_o in terms of the circuit components. What is the quality factor Q of this filter? Choose practical component values so that the center frequency is $f_o = \omega_o/(2\pi) = 10$ kHz.

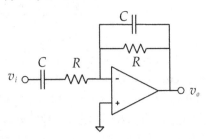

7.13 Find the frequency response $H(\omega) = \underline{V}_o/\underline{V}_i$ of the following op amp filter. Put your result in the standard form

$$H(\omega) = K \frac{j\omega/\omega_c}{1 + j\omega/\omega_c}$$

Find K, and ω_c in terms of the circuit components. Choose practical component values so that the passband gain is $|H(\infty)|_{dB} = 6$ dB and $f_c = \omega_c/(2\pi) = 6$ kHz.

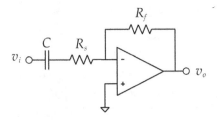

7.14 Sketch the Bode magnitude plots of the following frequency responses on semilog graph paper with appropriately scaled and labeled axes. Use a ruler and be sure to clearly show each of the components that contribute to the final result.

(a) $H(\omega) = 10 \dfrac{j\dfrac{\omega}{10}}{1 + j\dfrac{\omega}{20}}$

(b) $H(\omega) = 4 \dfrac{1 + j\dfrac{\omega}{10}}{\left(1 + j\dfrac{\omega}{40}\right)\left(1 + j\dfrac{\omega}{100}\right)}$

(c) $H(\omega) = \dfrac{10}{\left(1 + j\dfrac{\omega}{4}\right)\left(1 + j\dfrac{\omega}{10}\right)}$

(d) $H(\omega) = \dfrac{20}{\left(j\dfrac{\omega}{4}\right)\left(1 + j\dfrac{\omega}{10}\right)}$

(e) $H(\omega) = 10 \dfrac{j\dfrac{\omega}{100}}{\left(1 + j\dfrac{\omega}{100}\right)\left(1 + j\dfrac{\omega}{100}\right)}$

(f) $H(\omega) = 4 \dfrac{\left(1 + j\dfrac{\omega}{80}\right)\left(1 + j\dfrac{\omega}{200}\right)}{\left(1 + j\dfrac{\omega}{20}\right)\left(1 + j\dfrac{\omega}{800}\right)}$

7.15 Given $H(\omega) = \underline{V}_o/\underline{V}_i$ below, sketch the Bode magnitude and phase plots on semilog graph paper with appropriately scaled and labeled axes. From the plots, find the output of the circuit $v_o(t)$ if the input is $v_i(t) = 2\cos(20t) + 2\cos(200t)$ V.

$$H(\omega) = \frac{10}{1 + j\dfrac{\omega}{50}}$$

8 Periodic Sources

Sinusoidal sources are the most fundamental periodic AC sources that appear in electric circuits. However, they are not the only commonly appearing sources in electric circuits. This chapter covers other periodic sources and shows that these sources are equivalent to the sum of an infinite number of sinusoidal sources at harmonically related frequencies.

8.1 Common Periodic Sources

Other than sinusoidal sources, the most common periodic voltage or current sources, $f(t)$, are shown in the following figure.

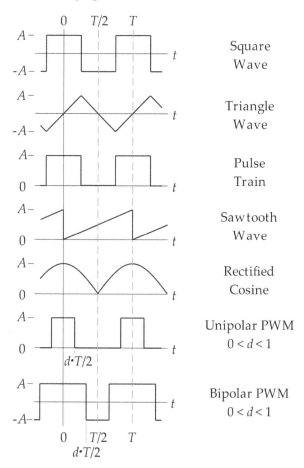

Sinusoidal waveforms along with the **square wave** and **triangle wave** shown above are the three common waveforms, signals, or voltages available from a function generator, which is a common laboratory waveform source.

The **pulse train** commonly appears in digital circuits as a clock signal that alternates periodically between two logic levels.

The **sawtooth waveform** provides a linear and repeating ramp signal.

The **rectified cosine** is simply the absolute value of a sinusoid, $f(t) = |\cos(\omega t)|$. Because of the absolute value, the period of this waveform is one half that of the sinusoid. Rectifying, meaning take the absolute value, is often the first step in converting the AC sinusoidal voltage at wall outlets to a DC source for powering electronic circuitry.

The final two signals are **pulse-width-modulated (PWM) waveforms** where the **duty cycle d** varies over time. The duty cycle expresses the ratio of the time the waveform has its peak value to the waveform period T. The **unipolar PWM waveform** is a common microcontroller output where the duty cycle d varies over time in response to some internally generated digital value. When the duty cycle of this waveform is one half, $d = 1/2$, it becomes the pulse train. The **bipolar PWM waveform** commonly appears in power electronic circuitry where the duty cycle d varies over time to control the voltage across or current through some load. When the duty cycle of this waveform is one half, $d = 1/2$, it becomes the square wave. Class D audio amplifiers are a common application where the bipolar PWM is used.

8.2 Basic Properties

All of these waveforms are characterized by their amplitudes as shown in the figure, and by their period T. The period is defined as the smallest time value T where the source $f(t)$ obeys

$$f(t) = f(t + T)$$

for all time t. As demonstrated for sinusoidal sources, the period T is related to the associated frequency as $f = 1/T$ in Hz, or as $\omega = 2\pi/T$ in rad/s.

Fundamental Frequency

In the more general case of other periodic waveforms, the frequency associated with the inverse of the period T is called the fundamental frequency and is given in hertz and rad/s as

$$f_o = \frac{1}{T}, \text{Hz} \qquad \omega_o = \frac{2\pi}{T}, \text{rad/s}$$

Average or DC Values

The average or DC value of a periodic waveform is given by

$$F_{dc} = \frac{1}{T} \int_{t_o}^{t_o+T} f(t)\, dt$$

for any starting value t_o. The integral by itself is simply the area under the function over one period. When $f(t) > 0$, the area is positive, and when $f(t) < 0$, the area is negative.

> The average value is not a function of the period T or fundamental frequency ω_o of the waveform. The average is also not a function of where the vertical $t = 0$ axis appears. The average value is directly proportional to the waveform amplitude.

When a waveform has equal area above and below the horizontal $f(t) = 0$ axis, the integral is zero. So the resulting average or DC value is zero as well. Because of this, the average value of a sinusoid is zero as shown in Chapter 1. The average or DC value of the square wave and triangle waves as shown below is zero as well.

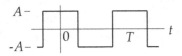

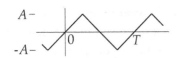

The average or DC value of the pulse train waveform shown in the following figure is given by the area of the rectangle formed by a pulse divided by the period

$$F_{dc} = \frac{1}{T}\left(A \cdot \frac{T}{2}\right) = \frac{A}{2}$$

This value is simply one half the amplitude A of the waveform.

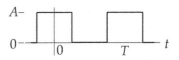

The sawtooth waveform shown below forms a right triangle over one period.

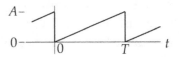

The area of this triangle is one half the product of its base and height. Therefore, the average or DC value of the sawtooth is

$$F_{dc} = \frac{1}{T}\left(\frac{1}{2}T \cdot A\right) = \frac{A}{2}$$

If the sawtooth is redrawn as shown below so that it extends from $-A/2$ to $A/2$, rather than from 0 to A, the average or DC value is now zero because there is equal area above and below the horizontal axis.

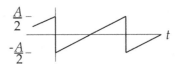

This sawtooth is equal to the former sawtooth with the average removed or subtracted. **Shifting a waveform up or down vertically simply changes its average value.**

The average or DC value of the rectified cosine shown below is not visually apparent.

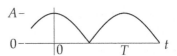

In this case, letting $T = \pi$, the integral expression becomes and is simplified as follows.

$$F_{dc} = \frac{1}{\pi} \int_{-\pi/2}^{\pi/2} A\cos(\theta)\, d\theta = \frac{A}{\pi}\sin(\theta)\Big|_{-\pi/2}^{\pi/2}$$

$$F_{dc} = \frac{A}{\pi}\left[\sin(\pi/2) - \sin(-\pi/2)\right] = \frac{A}{\pi}[1-(-1)] = \frac{2A}{\pi}$$

The average or DC value of the unipolar PWM waveform shown in the following figure is equal to the area of the rectangle formed by the waveform divided by the period.

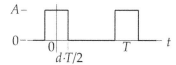

That is, the average value is given by

$$F_{dc} = \frac{1}{T}(A \cdot d \cdot T) = Ad$$

Therefore the DC value is directly proportional to the duty cycle d and the average varies between 0 and A.

The average or DC value of the bipolar PWM waveform shown below is equal to the difference in the areas of the rectangles formed above and below the $f(t) = 0$ axis, divided by the period.

Therefore, the average value is

$$F_{dc} = \frac{1}{T}[A \cdot d \cdot T - A(1-d)T]$$

$$F_{dc} = \frac{1}{T}A \cdot T(2d-1) = A(2d-1)$$

The average or DC value now varies between $-A$ and A. For example, when the duty cycle is 50%, *i.e.*, $d = 1/2$, the waveform becomes the square wave and has an average value of zero, $F_{dc} = A(2 \cdot (1/2) - 1) = 0$.

RMS Values

The effective or RMS value of a waveform conveys information about the average power a voltage or current can produce. For sinusoids, the effective value was computed earlier and is given by

$$F_{rms} = \frac{F}{\sqrt{2}}$$

where F is the amplitude of the sinusoid.

> As with the DC value, the RMS value is not a function of the period, frequency, or phase of the waveform. The RMS value is directly proportional to the waveform amplitude. The RMS value is equal to an equivalent or effective DC value that has no period, no frequency, and no phase, but produces the same average power in a resistor.

The RMS value of a waveform is computed using the root-mean-square expression derived earlier,

$$F_{rms} = \sqrt{\frac{1}{T}\int_{t_o}^{t_o+T} f^2(t)\,dt}$$

Because of the complexity of this expression, it is generally not easy to find the RMS value visually or intuitively. The most straightforward way is to substitute the waveform $f(t)$ into the above expression and compute the result. This is most easily done by using symbolic analysis software. The following figure summarizes the waveforms, their average or DC values, and their RMS values.

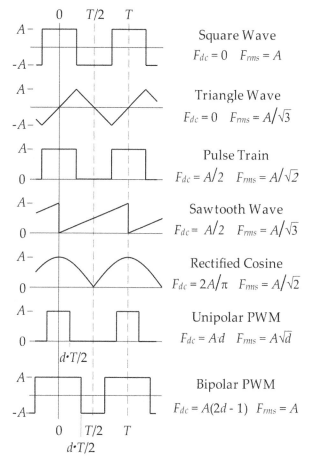

The RMS values above provide some interesting insight. For example, both the square wave and the bipolar PWM waveform have RMS values equal to their peak value A. This occurs because the square of both waveforms, $f^2(t)$, is the constant value A^2, which is leads to the final result $\sqrt{A^2} = A$.

The RMS value of the rectified cosine is equal to the RMS value of the standard sinusoid simply because the squaring process makes $f^2(t)$ equal for both waveforms.

Separating AC from DC

Earlier, two sawtooth waveforms were considered. The first, as shown below, has an average value of $A/2$.

The second sawtooth is equal to the first with the average value removed as shown below. This sawtooth has zero average value.

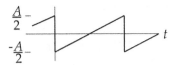

As shown in this example, it is possible to split any periodic waveform into the sum of two parts, one DC and the other AC, where the AC part has zero average value. Mathematically, this can be written as

$$f(t) = F_{dc} + f_{ac}(t)$$

where F_{dc} is the average or DC value of $f(t)$, and $f_{ac}(t)$ is the AC component having zero average value, i.e.,

$$F_{dc} = \frac{1}{T} \int_{t_o}^{t_o+T} f(t)\, dt$$

$$0 = \frac{1}{T} \int_{t_o}^{t_o+T} f_{ac}(t)\, dt$$

It is interesting to see how the RMS value of the original waveform $f(t)$ is related to the RMS values of the DC part F_{dc} and to the AC part $f_{ac}(t)$.

The RMS value of $f(t)$ is

$$F_{rms} = \sqrt{\frac{1}{T} \int_{t_o}^{t_o+T} f(t)^2\, dt}$$

and the square of the RMS value is

$$F_{rms}^2 = F_{ms} = \frac{1}{T} \int_{t_o}^{t_o+T} f(t)^2\, dt$$

By expressing the square of the RMS value, called the **mean square value** F_{ms}, the square root is eliminated from the analysis for the time being. Doing so simplifies the following analysis.

Substituting $f(t)$ into this expression gives

$$F_{rms}^2 = \frac{1}{T} \int_{t_o}^{t_o+T} \left(F_{dc} + f_{ac}(t)\right)^2 dt$$

Simplifying this expression leads to

$$F_{rms}^2 = \frac{1}{T} \int_{t_o}^{t_o+T} \left(F_{dc}^2 + 2F_{dc}f_{ac}(t) + f_{ac}^2(t)\right) dt$$

$$F_{rms}^2 = \frac{1}{T} \int_{t_o}^{t_o+T} F_{dc}^2\, dt$$
$$+ \frac{1}{T} \int_{t_o}^{t_o+T} 2F_{dc}f_{ac}(t)\, dt$$
$$+ \frac{1}{T} \int_{t_o}^{t_o+T} f_{ac}^2(t)\, dt$$

The first term in the above expression

$$\frac{1}{T} \int_{t_o}^{t_o+T} F_{dc}^2\, dt = F_{dc}^2$$

is the square of the RMS value of the DC component.

The second term is equal to zero because it is equal to the average value of $f_{ac}(t)$, which is zero by its definition. That is,

$$\frac{1}{T} \int_{t_o}^{t_o+T} 2F_{dc}f_{ac}(t)\, dt = \frac{2F_{dc}}{T} \int_{t_o}^{t_o+T} f_{ac}(t)\, dt = \frac{2F_{dc}}{T} \cdot 0 = 0$$

The last term

$$F_{acrms}^2 = \frac{1}{T} \int_{t_o}^{t_o+T} f_{ac}^2(t)\, dt$$

is by the definition of root-mean-square, equal to the square of the RMS value of the AC component $f_{ac}(t)$.

Combining these individual results shows that the square of the RMS value of $f(t)$ is simply

$$F_{rms}^2 = F_{dc}^2 + F_{acrms}^2$$

The squares of the RMS values of the two components F_{dc} and $f_{ac}(t)$ add. Therefore, the RMS value of $f(t)$ is given by the square root expression

$$F_{rms} = \sqrt{F_{dc}^2 + F_{acrms}^2}$$

where F_{acrms} is the RMS value of $f_{ac}(t)$.

This fundamental relationship is useful when a DC component is added to an AC waveform that has zero average or DC value.

Even and Odd Symmetry

Depending on where the vertical $t = 0$ axis appears in a periodic waveform, the waveform may have even or odd symmetry. **A waveform has even symmetry if**

$$f(t) = f(-t)$$

In this case, there is symmetry about the $t = 0$ axis.

And a waveform has odd symmetry if

$$f(t) = -f(-t)$$

In this case there is anti-symmetry about the $t = 0$ axis.

These two symmetries are most easily recognized using sinusoids as shown in the following figure.

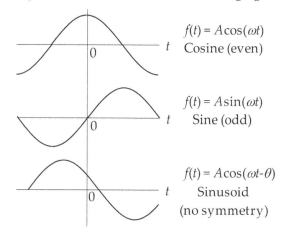

$f(t) = A\cos(\omega t)$
Cosine (even)

$f(t) = A\sin(\omega t)$
Sine (odd)

$f(t) = A\cos(\omega t - \theta)$
Sinusoid
(no symmetry)

Using these definitions, the square wave, pulse train, rectified sinusoid, unipolar PWM, and bipolar PWM waveforms illustrated earlier have even symmetry. The triangle wave has odd symmetry, as does the revised sawtooth waveform shown below.

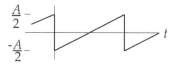

If the square wave and triangle wave are shifted one quarter of a period, $\pm T/4$, they have the opposite symmetry as shown in the following figures.

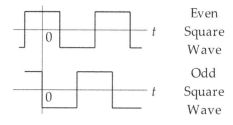

Even Square Wave

Odd Square Wave

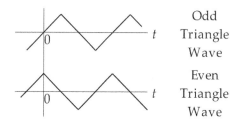

Odd Triangle Wave

Even Triangle Wave

Even and odd symmetries are simple to identify and useful to note about a waveform.

It is also important to identify waveforms that have odd symmetry if they are redrawn to have zero average value as the revised sawtooth demonstrates in the following figure. In this case, the original sawtooth has odd symmetry except for the presence of its average or DC value.

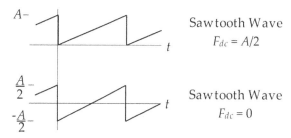

Sawtooth Wave
$F_{dc} = A/2$

Sawtooth Wave
$F_{dc} = 0$

To state this fact mathematically, if F_{dc} is the average value of a waveform $f(t)$, and $f_{odd}(t)$ is the waveform having zero average value and odd symmetry, then the original waveform $f(t)$ can be written as

$$f(t) = F_{dc} + f_{odd}(t)$$

The waveform $f(t)$ is composed of two parts, a DC value and a waveform having odd symmetry.

As will be shown later, the presence of even or odd symmetry is often helpful in determining more detailed characteristics of a periodic waveform.

Half Wave Symmetry

Another form of symmetry identifies symmetry along the time axis without regard to the vertical $t = 0$ axis. Half wave symmetry exists when the value of the waveform simply changes sign every half period, $T/2$. **That is, a waveform has half wave symmetry if**

$$f(t) = -f\left(t \pm \frac{T}{2}\right)$$

The square wave, triangle wave, and all sinusoids have this property. Waveforms that have this property have zero average value, $F_{dc} = 0$. **Half wave symmetry is independent of even and odd properties.**

For example, all square waves have half wave symmetry including those having even or odd symmetry.

Half wave symmetry is simple to identify and useful to note about a waveform. It is also important to identify waveforms that have half wave symmetry if they are redrawn to have zero average value $F_{dc} = 0$. For example, the pulse train waveform has half wave symmetry if it is centered about the horizontal $f(t) = 0$ axis as shown in the following figure.

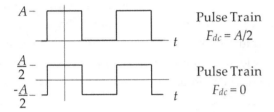

$A-$ Pulse Train $F_{dc} = A/2$

$\frac{A}{2}-$ $-\frac{A}{2}-$ Pulse Train $F_{dc} = 0$

In this case, the zero average waveform becomes a square wave that has half wave symmetry. So, the pulse train has half wave symmetry except for the presence of its average or DC value.

If F_{dc} is the average value of a waveform $f(t)$, and $f_{hw}(t)$ is the waveform having half wave symmetry, then the original waveform $f(t)$ can be written as the sum

$$f(t) = F_{dc} + f_{hw}(t)$$

The waveform $f(t)$ is composed of two parts, a DC value and a waveform having half wave symmetry.

As a counterexample, neither the original sawtooth nor the revised sawtooth having zero average value exhibit half wave symmetry as shown in the earlier figure illustrating both waveforms.

As will be shown later, the presence of half wave symmetry is often helpful in determining more detailed characteristics of a periodic waveform.

8.3 Building Periodic Sources

Think about the piano keyboard. It has 88 keys. The "C" note key closest to the center of the keyboard is called "middle C." It is the fourth "C" note key on the keyboard starting from the left. The fundamental frequency of this note is $f_o = 261.625565$ Hz. If you go to the right, up to the next "C" note key, the frequency is $2f_o$. On the other hand, if you go to the left from middle "C", down to the previous "C" note key,

Periodic Waveform Properties	
	$f(t) = f(t+T)$
Definition:	T = period $f_o = 1/T$, Hz $\omega_o = \dfrac{2\pi}{T}$, rad/s
DC Value:	$F_{dc} = \dfrac{1}{T} \displaystyle\int_{t_o}^{t_o+T} f(t)dt$ F_{dc} is not a function of time, and not a function of the period or frequency.
RMS Value:	$F_{rms} = \sqrt{\dfrac{1}{T} \displaystyle\int_{t_o}^{t_o+T} f(t)^2 dt}$ F_{rms} is not a function of time, and not a function of the period or frequency.
Separating AC from DC:	$f(t) = F_{dc} + f_{ac}(t)$ $F_{rms} = \sqrt{F_{dc}^2 + F_{acrms}^2}$
Odd Symmetry:	$f(t) = -f(-t)$ $\sin(\omega t)$ is odd.
Even Symmetry:	$f(t) = f(-t)$ $\cos(\omega t)$ is even.
Half Wave Symmetry:	$f(t) = -f\left(t \pm \dfrac{T}{2}\right)$ Half wave symmetry is independent of odd and even symmetries. It does not depend on where $t = 0$ appears.

the frequency is $f_o/2$. This factor of two relationship applies to all "C" notes on the keyboard. The frequency of each "C" note is a factor of two different from its neighboring "C" notes. When this holds, the frequencies are said to be harmonically related. If the lowest "C" note key on the keyboard is a fundamental frequency f_o, then the next "C" note is at $2f_o$, which is the second harmonic.

That musical note frequencies are harmonically related is not chosen arbitrarily. This harmonic frequency relationship was chosen because it matches what occurs in nature.

If two musical instruments play the same note, the fundamental frequency f_o of the tones emanating from the two instruments are the same. The two instruments sound different even though they are playing the same note. They sound different because the periodic music waveforms emanating from the instruments are different, even though they share the same fundamental frequency f_o. The two periodic music waveforms have different content at the harmonic frequencies, $2f_o$, $3f_o$, $4f_o$, and so on. These differences in harmonic content are what make the same music note played on different instruments sound different.

To illustrate this idea, consider the even periodic triangle waveform shown in the following figure.

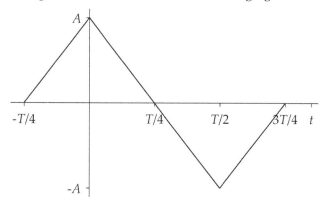

The fundamental frequency of this waveform is

$$\omega_o = \frac{2\pi}{T}$$

A sinusoid at this frequency, as shown in the following figure, is given by

$$f_1(t) = \cos(\omega_o t)$$

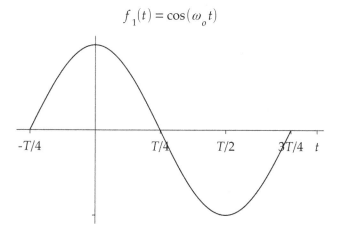

This sinusoid captures the basic shape of the triangle because it is an even function that matches the period of the triangle.

If the sinusoid

$$f_3(t) = \frac{1}{9}\cos(3\omega_o t)$$

at the third harmonic $3\omega_o$ is added to the sinusoid $f_1(t)$, the net waveform becomes

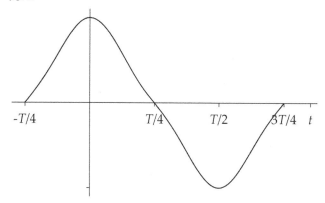

This shape more closely resembles the triangle wave because in addition to being even and having the same period, it is beginning to exhibit the peaks of the triangle.

Continuing in this fashion, adding the sinusoids

$$f_5(t) = \frac{1}{25}\cos(5\omega_o t)$$

$$f_7(t) = \frac{1}{49}\cos(7\omega_o t)$$

$$f_9(t) = \frac{1}{81}\cos(9\omega_o t)$$

$$f_{11}(t) = \frac{1}{121}\cos(11\omega_o t)$$

one at a time, the resulting waveforms are as shown in the following figure.

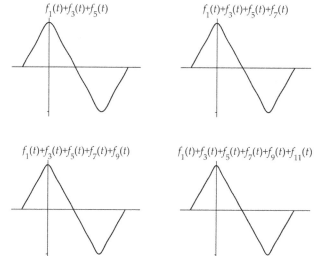

Adding yet further sinusoids of the form

$$f_n(t) = \frac{1}{n^2}\cos(n\omega_o t) \quad n = 13, 15, \cdots$$

for odd values of n makes the result resemble the triangle waveform more and more. Therefore, the even triangle wave can be written in the form of a sum of sinusoids as

$$f(t) = a_1 \cos(\omega_o t) + a_3 \cos(3\omega_o t) + a_5 \cos(5\omega_o t) + \cdots$$

$$f(t) = \sum_{1,3,5,\cdots}^{\infty} a_n \cos(n\omega_o t)$$

where the coefficients a_n are proportional to $1/n^2$. The exact value of the coefficients depends on the triangle waveform amplitude. As will be shown later, the coefficients are given by

$$a_n = \frac{8A}{\pi^2 n^2} \quad \text{for } n = 1,3,5,\cdots$$

where A is the triangle wave amplitude.

It should not be surprising that cosines were used here rather than sines. The triangle waveform exhibits even symmetry, so it is composed of sinusoids having even symmetry, i.e., cosines. **Simply put, the sum of even waveforms is an even waveform.** So cosines add to form the even triangle waveform.

If the triangle wave is drawn to have odd symmetry, sine functions would be used rather than cosines, because the sine function has odd symmetry. **You cannot add even waveforms together to create an odd waveform result.**

It should also not be surprising that the amplitude of the added sinusoids decrease with increasing harmonic frequency. Each added sinusoid simply "tweaks" the previous result. So as the partial result gets closer to the final result, the amount of tweaking needed decreases.

Based on this simple example, it makes sense that a musical tone at the fundamental frequency f_o, when played on different musical instruments, produces a different sound. The shapes of the musical waveforms differ, but the period $T = 1/f_o$ is the same for both instruments. The two musical waveforms are composed of sinusoids having different amplitudes at the harmonic frequencies, nf_o, for $n = 1, 2, 3,\ldots$. In general, all harmonics exist. The triangle waveform is a special case where only odd harmonics exist.

8.4 Fourier Series

The fact that practical periodic waveforms are composed of sinusoids at harmonic frequencies was first

noted by Jean Baptiste Joseph Fourier in 1822 (yes, ~200 years ago!). To take into account the possibility that a waveform may have even symmetry or odd symmetry or neither symmetry, Fourier wrote the sum of sinusoids at harmonic frequencies as

$$f(t) = a_{dc} + \sum_{n=1}^{\infty} \left(a_n \cos(n\omega_o t) + b_n \sin(n\omega_o t) \right)$$

This expression defines what is called the Fourier series expansion of the periodic waveform $f(t)$. The leading term a_{dc} takes into account the fact that $f(t)$ may have an average or DC value. Because the average value of a sinusoid is zero, all the sinusoidal terms have zero average value. **So a_{dc} identifies the DC value of $f(t)$.**

Each term in the summation, e.g.,

$$f_n(t) = a_n \cos(n\omega_o t) + b_n \sin(n\omega_o t)$$

is called a harmonic component. The general term above is called the nth **harmonic component** and $n\omega_o$ **is called the nth harmonic frequency.** When a specific value for n is given, the component is named based on the value of n. For example,

$$f_3(t) = a_3 \cos(3\omega_o t) + b_3 \sin(3\omega_o t)$$

is called the third harmonic component, and

$$f_{15}(t) = a_{15} \cos(15\omega_o t) + b_{15} \sin(15\omega_o t)$$

is the fifteenth harmonic component.

The harmonic component

$$f_1(t) = a_1 \cos(\omega_o t) + b_1 \sin(\omega_o t)$$

is not called the first harmonic component. Rather, it is called **the fundamental component** or simply the fundamental, because it is at the fundamental frequency ω_o and all other sinusoidal components are at frequencies that are multiples of ω_o.

Fourier showed that the Fourier series coefficients can be computed using the relationships

$$a_{dc} = \frac{1}{T} \int_{t_o}^{t_o+T} f(t)\,dt$$

$$a_n = \frac{2}{T} \int_{t_o}^{t_o+T} f(t)\cos(n\omega_o t)\,dt$$

$$b_n = \frac{2}{T} \int_{t_o}^{t_o+T} f(t)\sin(n\omega_o t)\,dt$$

For the most part, no one chooses to compute the a_n and b_n coefficients using the above integral relationships. For many common waveforms, analytic expressions for the coefficients can be found in textbooks and online. For less common and more complex waveforms, the coefficients are easily computed using a numerical algorithm that approximates the above integrals with more than sufficient accuracy. As a result, **being able to use Fourier series productively does not require the ability to solve these integral relationships for a_n and b_n.**

Many textbooks dwell on the computation of Fourier series coefficients and give simplified expressions for special cases. These expressions simply distract one from the more important practical aspects of Fourier series. **The fundamental importance of the Fourier series is that periodic waveforms have content spread across many harmonic frequencies.**

Symmetry Properties

The Fourier series expression

$$f(t) = a_{dc} + \sum_{n=1}^{\infty} \left(a_n \cos(n\omega_o t) + b_n \sin(n\omega_o t) \right)$$

is composed of both cosines and sines. If $f(t)$ has even symmetry, then the sine term coefficients b_n are all zero since sine is an odd function. If $f(t)$ has odd symmetry, then the cosine term coefficients a_n are all zero since cosine is an even function.

As noted in the preceding section, odd functions cannot add together to form an even waveform, and even functions cannot add together to form an odd waveform. **Therefore, the coefficients a_n appear when the waveform $f(t)$ is even and the coefficients b_n appear when the waveform $f(t)$ is odd.**

When $f(t)$ has neither even or odd symmetry, both sets of coefficients a_n and b_n will appear.

In the preceding section demonstrating the Fourier series expansion of a triangle wave, the waveform has both even and half wave symmetry. Since it has even symmetry, all the sine term coefficients b_n are zero.

Interestingly, all the harmonic components at even harmonic frequencies are zero as well. That is, the triangle waveform has no second harmonic, fourth harmonic, sixth harmonic, etc. It has only odd harmonic components, *e.g.*, a fundamental, third harmonic, fifth harmonic, seventh harmonic, etc. It is possible to show that this holds whenever a waveform has half wave symmetry. That is the reason why half wave symmetry was defined earlier in this chapter. **When a waveform has half wave symmetry, it has no even harmonic components.** When a waveform has half wave symmetry, the harmonics are separated by $2\omega_o$, e.g., ω_o, $3\omega_o$, $5\omega_o$, etc. When a waveform does not have half wave symmetry, the harmonics are separated by ω_o, e.g., ω_o, $2\omega_o$, $3\omega_o$, etc.

Alternate Form

The preceding form of the Fourier series is convenient for computing coefficients. However, the fact that it includes both cosine and sine terms makes it cumbersome to use when they both exist. It is usually more convenient to write each harmonic term in the sinusoidal form used for phasor analysis, *i.e.*, a cosine waveform with a phase angle.

It is possible to combine the cosine and sine terms in each harmonic component by using the following identity that was derived in Chapter 1.

$$D\cos(\theta - \phi) = B_1 \cos(\theta) + B_2 \sin(\theta)$$

$$D = \left| B_1 + jB_2 \right| = \sqrt{B_1^2 + B_2^2}$$

$$\phi = \angle(B_1 + jB_2) = \operatorname{atan2}(B_2, B_1)$$

In this situation, applying this identity to the nth harmonic component gives

$$c_n \cos(n\omega_o t - \phi_n) = a_n \cos(n\omega_o t) + b_n \sin(n\omega_o t)$$

where

$$c_n = \left| a_n + jb_n \right| = \sqrt{a_n^2 + b_n^2}$$

$$\phi_n = \angle(a_n + jb_n) = \operatorname{atan2}(b_n, a_n)$$

Using this identity, the Fourier series expression becomes

$$f(t) = a_{dc} + \sum_{n=1}^{\infty} c_n \cos(n\omega_o t - \phi_n)$$

where each harmonic term is now in the form of a cosine with a phase angle.

In addition to the above forms of the Fourier series, there is yet another form that utilizes the Euler identity to write the expansion in terms of complex exponential functions. Analysis using this form is best left for a later course on signals and linear systems.

The following table identifies some Fourier series.

Common Fourier Series	

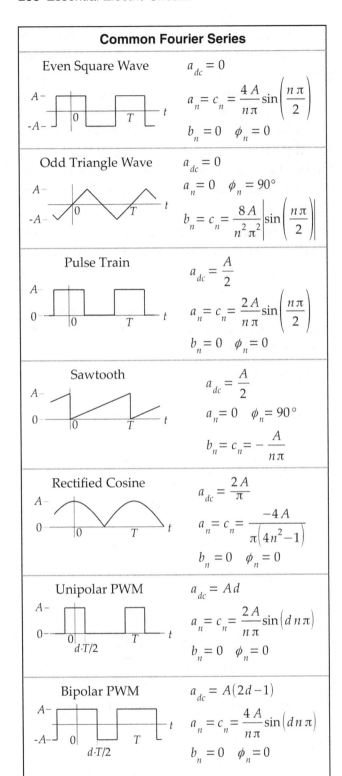

Even Square Wave

$a_{dc} = 0$

$a_n = c_n = \dfrac{4A}{n\pi}\sin\left(\dfrac{n\pi}{2}\right)$

$b_n = 0 \quad \phi_n = 0$

Odd Triangle Wave

$a_{dc} = 0$

$a_n = 0 \quad \phi_n = 90°$

$b_n = c_n = \dfrac{8A}{n^2\pi^2}\left|\sin\left(\dfrac{n\pi}{2}\right)\right|$

Pulse Train

$a_{dc} = \dfrac{A}{2}$

$a_n = c_n = \dfrac{2A}{n\pi}\sin\left(\dfrac{n\pi}{2}\right)$

$b_n = 0 \quad \phi_n = 0$

Sawtooth

$a_{dc} = \dfrac{A}{2}$

$a_n = 0 \quad \phi_n = 90°$

$b_n = c_n = -\dfrac{A}{n\pi}$

Rectified Cosine

$a_{dc} = \dfrac{2A}{\pi}$

$a_n = c_n = \dfrac{-4A}{\pi(4n^2 - 1)}$

$b_n = 0 \quad \phi_n = 0$

Unipolar PWM

$a_{dc} = Ad$

$a_n = c_n = \dfrac{2A}{n\pi}\sin(dn\pi)$

$b_n = 0 \quad \phi_n = 0$

Bipolar PWM

$a_{dc} = A(2d - 1)$

$a_n = c_n = \dfrac{4A}{n\pi}\sin(dn\pi)$

$b_n = 0 \quad \phi_n = 0$

n	1	2	3	4	5	6	7	8	9
$\sin\left(\dfrac{n\pi}{2}\right)$	1	0	−1	0	1	0	−1	0	1
$\left|\sin\left(\dfrac{n\pi}{2}\right)\right|$	1	0	1	0	1	0	1	0	1

Fourier Series Summary

$$f(t) = a_{dc} + \sum_{n=1}^{\infty}\left(a_n\cos(n\omega_o t) + b_n\sin(n\omega_o t)\right)$$

$$f(t) = a_{dc} + \sum_{n=1}^{\infty} c_n\cos(n\omega_o t - \phi_n)$$

$$a_{dc} = \frac{1}{T}\int_{t_o}^{t_o+T} f(t)\,dt = \text{DC value}$$

$$a_n = \frac{2}{T}\int_{t_o}^{t_o+T} f(t)\cos(n\omega_o t)\,dt$$

$$b_n = \frac{2}{T}\int_{t_o}^{t_o+T} f(t)\sin(n\omega_o t)\,dt$$

$$c_n = \left|a_n + jb_n\right| = \sqrt{a_n^2 + b_n^2}$$

$$\phi_n = \angle(a_n + jb_n) = \text{atan2}(b_n, a_n)$$

$b_n = 0$ if $f(t)$ has even symmetry

$a_n = 0$ if $f(t)$ has odd symmetry

$a_n = b_n = 0$ for even n if $f(t)$ has half wave symmetry

Fourier Series and RMS Values

Earlier in the general discussion of periodic waveforms, it was shown that a waveform can be split into two components, one being the DC value and the other being the AC component,

$$f(t) = F_{dc} + f_{ac}(t)$$

It was shown that the RMS value of $f(t)$ was related to the RMS values of the two components by

$$F_{rms} = \sqrt{F_{dc}^2 + F_{acrms}^2}$$

This same phenomenon occurs when $f(t)$ is written as a Fourier series. In this case, after some tedious algebra, it is possible to show that the RMS value of a periodic waveform can be written as

$$F_{rms} = \sqrt{F_{dc}^2 + \sum_{n=1}^{\infty} F_{nrms}^2}$$

The first three waveforms in the table above have half wave symmetry and their coefficients contain the term $\sin(n\pi/2)$ or $|\sin(n\pi/2)|$. Evaluating these terms gives the following progression showing that the even harmonic values are equal to zero as required by half wave symmetry.

where F_{nrms} is the RMS value of the nth harmonic component

$$F_{nrms} = \frac{c_n}{\sqrt{2}} = \sqrt{\frac{a_n^2 + b_n^2}{2}}$$

This relationship is called Parseval's theorem for the Fourier series. Because the summation includes an infinite number of terms, the RMS value of a waveform is almost never computed in this way. It is almost always easier to compute the RMS value using the equation defining the RMS value. Parseval's theorem is useful if the Fourier series coefficients are numerically computed in a computer program.

Waveforms with Discontinuities

Waveforms with discontinuities are common in engineering. For example in the earlier waveform table, the square wave, pulse train, sawtooth, unipolar PWM, and bipolar PWM all have discontinuities.

Consider the discontinuity at $t = 0$ in the sawtooth waveform as shown in the following figure.

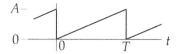

If the sawtooth waveform is given by $f(t)$, then $f(0)$ is undefined because the waveform jumps from $f(0^-) = A$ to $f(0^+) = 0$ at this discontinuity. In strict mathematical terms, the derivative or slope is undefined at discontinuities. In engineering, the slope is said to be infinite at discontinuities. Some would say that the slope is negative infinity for the sawtooth discontinuities because the value jumps downward at the discontinuities.

Sinusoidal functions cannot accurately capture discontinuities because the slope of a sinusoid is never infinite; it is simply another sinusoid having finite slope. Because of this, computing values of a waveform using a finite number of harmonic components

$$f(t) \approx a_{dc} + \sum_{n=1}^{N} \left(a_n \cos(n\omega_o t) + b_n \sin(n\omega_o t) \right)$$

$$f(t) \approx a_{dc} + \sum_{n=1}^{N} c_n \cos(n\omega_o t - \phi_n)$$

where $N < \infty$ does not lead to a visually appealing approximation of the actual function.

To illustrate this phenomenon, consider the sawtooth waveform and its approximation shown in the following figure for $N = 11$ harmonic components and $N = 51$ harmonic components. **The ripples in the approximations around the discontinuities are known as Gibbs phenomenon.** In a later signal processing course you may study the properties of these ripples. Here they are just a visual annoyance that is otherwise not important in circuits.

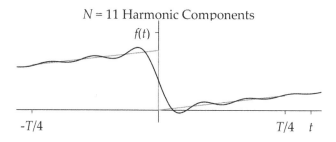

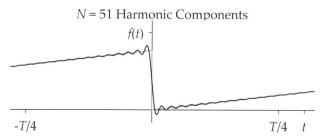

The ripples that appear around discontinuities can be visually reduced by tweaking the Fourier series coefficients, a_n, b_n, and c_n. As you will likely learn in a digital signal processing course, this tweaking is done with a window function. Since there is no ideal window function, many window funcitons have been defined.

A simple and effective window function for this application is the Hamming window that is given by

$$w_n = 0.54 + 0.46 \cos\left(\frac{\pi n}{N}\right)$$

This window function starts at one for $n = 0$, the DC term, and decreases to $0.54 - 0.46 = 0.08$ at the highest harmonic component computed, $n = N$.

Using this function the revised or windowed Fourier series coefficients become

$$\tilde{a}_n = a_n \cdot w_n \qquad \tilde{b}_n = b_n \cdot w_n \qquad \tilde{c}_n = c_n \cdot w_n$$

The following figure repeats the above plot using the revised or windowed Fourier series coefficients.

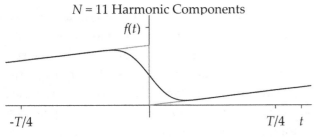

N = 11 Harmonic Components

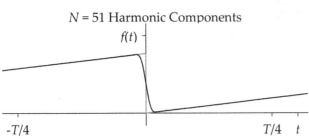

N = 51 Harmonic Components

Visually, the approximations look better, especially as the number of harmonic components N increases. The ripples are gone, but the transition at the discontinuity is not as sharp as it was without windowing.

Waveform Smoothness

According to Wikipedia, *"In mathematical analysis, smoothness has to do with how many derivatives of a function exist and are continuous."*

If you compare the square wave to the triangle wave as shown in the following figure, the square wave has discontinuities, therefore it cannot be differentiated to produce a continuous function. So a square wave has zero smoothness. In other words, it is sharp because it can be differentiated $k = 0$ times.

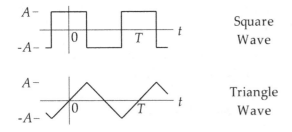

Square Wave

Triangle Wave

However, the triangle wave is continuous. If it is differentiated, the resulting waveform becomes a square wave because, as shown in the above figure, the triangle wave slope alternates between positive and negative values. The triangle wave has degree one smoothness. It can be differentiated $k = 1$ times, at which point the result is not continuous.

The degree of smoothness a waveform has plays a fundamental role in the amplitudes of the Fourier series coefficients. The smoother a function is, the **faster the amplitudes of the Fourier series coefficients decrease or fall to zero.**

To demonstrate this fact, consider the Fourier series coefficients for the square wave

$$a_n = \frac{4A}{n\pi}\sin\left(\frac{n\pi}{2}\right)$$

The magnitude of the ratio of a_n to a_1 is

$$\left|\frac{a_n}{a_1}\right| = \left|\frac{\frac{4A}{n\pi}\sin\left(\frac{n\pi}{2}\right)}{\frac{4A}{\pi}\sin\left(\frac{\pi}{2}\right)}\right| = \frac{1}{n} \quad \text{for } n = 1, 3, 5, \cdots$$

The Fourier series coefficients of the square wave fall off at a $1/n$ rate. For example, the amplitude of the 11th harmonic component of the square wave is $(1/11)$th the amplitude of the component at ω_o.

The Fourier series coefficients of triangle waveform are

$$b_n = \frac{8A}{n^2\pi^2}\left|\sin\left(\frac{n\pi}{2}\right)\right|$$

and the magnitude of the ratio of b_n to b_1 is

$$\left|\frac{b_n}{b_1}\right| = \left|\frac{\frac{8A}{n^2\pi^2}\left|\sin\left(\frac{n\pi}{2}\right)\right|}{\frac{8A}{\pi^2}\left|\sin\left(\frac{\pi}{2}\right)\right|}\right| = \frac{1}{n^2} \quad \text{for } n = 1, 3, 5, \cdots$$

The Fourier series coefficients of the triangle waveform fall off at a $1/n^2$ rate. For example, the amplitude of the 11th harmonic component of the triangle waveform is $(1/11^2) = (1/121)$th the amplitude of the fundamental component at ω_o.

Comparing these two results, the relative amplitude 11th harmonic component of the triangle wave 1/121 is much smaller than that of the square wave, 1/11. The amplitude of the 121st harmonic component of the square wave has a relative amplitude of 1/121. **Therefore, the square wave has much greater content, *e.g.*, power, at higher frequencies than the triangle wave.**

This relationship between function smoothness and how fast the amplitude of the Fourier series coefficients fall off applies to all periodic waveforms. While this relationship can be proven, doing so is well beyond the scope of this material.

Stated simply, the rate at which the relative amplitude of the Fourier series coefficients for a waveform falls off is

$$\frac{1}{n^{k+1}}$$

where k is the number of times the waveform can be differentiated to produce a discontinuous waveform. As shown earlier, the value for k is zero for the square wave and one for the triangle wave.

> The more times a waveform can be differentiated before producing a waveform with discontinuities, the smoother the waveform is, and the less high frequency content the waveform has because the Fourier series coefficients go to zero faster. **Sharper waveforms have greater high frequency content.**

8.5 Periodic Sources in Electric Circuits

Since all realistic periodic sources have a Fourier series description, the response of a circuit to any number of harmonic components can be found by using **superposition and phasor analysis**.

Let the input voltage $v_i(t)$ to the following circuit, having frequency response $H(\omega)$, be a periodic waveform having the Fourier series expansion

$$v_i(t) = v_{idc} + \sum_{n=1}^{\infty} v_n(t)$$

where

$$v_{idc} = a_{dc}$$

is the DC component of the input voltage and

$$v_n(t) = c_n \cos(n\omega_o t - \phi_n)$$

is the nth harmonic component of the input voltage.

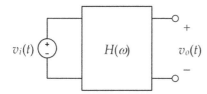

The output voltage $v_o(t)$ response of the circuit to this periodic input can be found by applying superposition. That is, the input can be split up into multiple sources as shown in the following circuit.

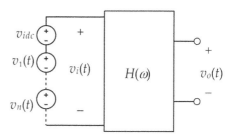

In applying superposition, each source is considered individually with all the other sources shut OFF, *i.e.*, set to zero volts. For example, with just the DC component turned ON and all the harmonic components shut OFF, the circuit can be simplified as shown below.

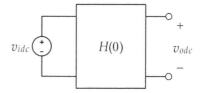

The output in this case is simply

$$v_{odc} = H(0)\, v_{idc}$$

The circuit frequency response $H(\omega)$ is evaluated at the frequency of the input, which is zero because a constant or DC value is at zero frequency,

$$v_{idc} = v_{idc} \cos(0t) = v_{idc} \cdot 1$$

In this case, **$H(0)$ is called the DC gain of the circuit.**

The output due to each of the harmonic components of the input voltage follows accordingly. If the nth harmonic component is turned ON and all the others sources are shut OFF, the circuit becomes as shown next.

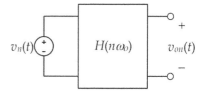

In this case, writing the input as a phasor gives

$$v_n(t) = c_n \cos(n\omega_o t - \phi_n) \quad \Leftrightarrow \quad \underline{V}_n = c_n \angle -\phi_n$$

Then the resulting output voltage component can be written in phasor form using the frequency response relationship as

$$\underline{V}_{on} = H(n\omega_o)\, \underline{V}_n$$

where the circuit frequency response $H(\omega)$ is evaluated at the frequency of the input harmonic component, $n\omega_0$.

Given the frequency response in polar form

$$H(\omega) = |H(\omega)|\angle\theta(\omega)$$

the resulting output voltage amplitude is

$$d_n = |V_{on}| = |H(n\omega_0)| \cdot c_n$$

and the resulting output voltage phase is

$$\alpha_n = \theta(n\omega_0) - \phi_n$$

In the time domain, this output is

$$v_{on}(t) = \left(|H(n\omega_0)| c_n\right)\cos\left(n\omega_0 t + \theta(n\omega_0) - \phi_n\right)$$

or more simply as

$$v_{on}(t) = d_n\cos(n\omega_0 t + \alpha_n)$$

where

$$d_n = |H(n\omega_0)| c_n$$

and

$$\alpha_n = \theta(n\omega_0) - \phi_n$$

The sinusoidal input at $\omega = n\omega_0$ produces a sinusoidal output at $\omega = n\omega_0$ modified by the gain $|H(n\omega_0)|$ and phase $\theta(n\omega_0)$ of the frequency response evaluated at $\omega = n\omega_0$.

After computing all of these intermediate solutions and adding them together to complete the superposition process, the final output voltage $v_0(t)$ can be written as

$$v_0(t) = v_{odc} + \sum_{n=1}^{\infty} v_{on}(t)$$

$$v_0(t) = v_{odc} + \sum_{n=1}^{\infty} d_n\cos(n\omega_0 t + \alpha_n)$$

As a result, when the input is described in terms of a Fourier series, the output is a Fourier series as well.

While superposition provides a straightforward way of describing the response of a circuit to a periodic input waveform, the output is seldom computed by hand in this way. There are simply too many harmonic components to compute. Mathematically, there are an infinite number of them. Trying to do this by hand is clearly a waste of time. However, computing the response of a circuit by hand for one

or at most a few important harmonic components can be accomplished without undue effort.

In practice, the output can be found using superposition using a computer or online tool to evaluate the response to all harmonic components that have significant amplitude. Since the amplitude of the Fourier series harmonic components decrease or fall off with increasing frequency $n\omega_0$, fewer than 50 harmonics are generally sufficient for most engineering work. From a practical point of view, using a reasonable number of harmonic components provides a good way to numerically compute the response of a circuit to a periodic input.

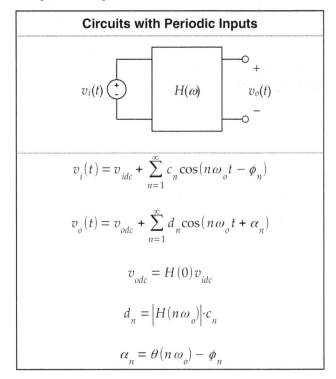

Circuits with Periodic Inputs

$$v_i(t) = v_{idc} + \sum_{n=1}^{\infty} c_n\cos(n\omega_0 t - \phi_n)$$

$$v_0(t) = v_{odc} + \sum_{n=1}^{\infty} d_n\cos(n\omega_0 t + \alpha_n)$$

$$v_{odc} = H(0)v_{idc}$$

$$d_n = |H(n\omega_0)| c_n$$

$$\alpha_n = \theta(n\omega_0) - \phi_n$$

Example 1

Consider the following circuit having the first order low pass filter response

$$H(\omega) = \frac{1}{1 + j\frac{\omega}{\omega_c}}$$

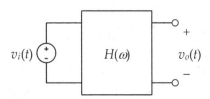

Let the input to the circuit be the square wave

$$v_i(t) = \sum_{n=1}^{\infty} c_n\cos(n\omega_0 t)$$

where

$$c_n = \frac{4A}{n\pi} \sin\left(\frac{n\pi}{2}\right)$$

For this example, let the amplitude be $A = 1$. Let the lowpass filter cutoff frequency be $\omega_c = 2\omega_o$.

Using a computer so that all significant harmonics can be considered, the resulting filter input and output waveforms are shown in the figure below.

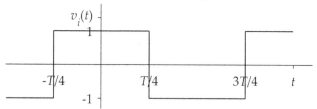

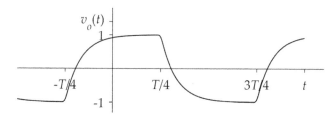

All harmonic components of the input beyond the fundamental at ω_o are attenuated because they are in the stopband of the filter past $\omega_c = 2\omega_o$. As a result, the output waveform differs from the input square wave. If the filter was constructed using an RC circuit, the output clearly shows the capacitor charging and discharging in response to the input squarewave.

In addition to the time solution above, it is useful to consider the solution versus frequency. One can plot the amplitudes of the input Fourier series coefficients $|c_n|$ versus the frequency at which they appear as shown in the **line spectra plot** below where the circles visually mark the amplitudes of each coefficient.

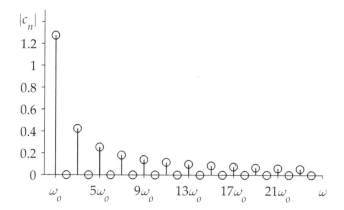

The frequency response gain $|H(\omega)|$, can be plotted as shown below where the values $|H(n\omega_o)|$ at the harmonic frequencies $n\omega_o$ for $n = 1, 2, \ldots$ are specifically marked by circles.

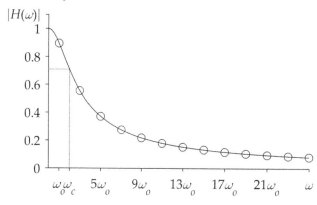

Finally, the amplitudes of the output Fourier series coefficients $|d_n| = |H(n\omega_o)| \cdot |c_n|$ versus the frequency at which they appear are shown in the following line spectra plot.

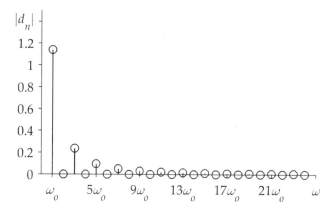

The output is the product of the corresponding points $|c_n|$ from the input line spectra plot and those from $|H(n\omega_o)|$ shown above.

Comparing the line spectra plots for the input $|c_n|$ to that of the output $|d_n|$, clearly shows that the harmonics components beyond the fundamental at ω_o are significantly attenuated. In particular, the output harmonic components at $11\omega_o$ and greater are at or near zero, whereas they are not in the input waveform.

Example 2

Reconsider the previous example, but let the cutoff frequency of the low pass filter be $\omega_c = 20\omega_o$.

Once again, using a computer so that all significant harmonics can be considered, the resulting filter input and output waveforms are shown in the following figure.

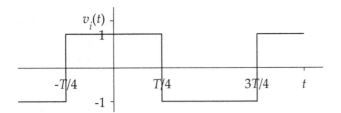

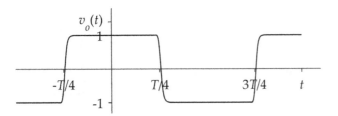

The output waveform now closely resembles that of the input square wave. This is true because the bandwidth of the filter is large compared to the fundamental frequency ω_0 of the input square wave as shown in the following figure. In this case, all the harmonics up to $n = 19$ make it through the filter passband to the output.

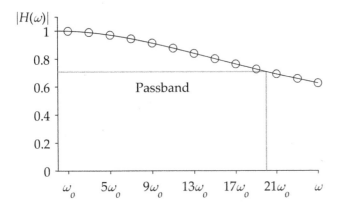

Example 3

Consider the bandpass filter described by the frequency response

$$H(\omega) = \frac{j\omega \dfrac{\omega_c}{Q}}{\omega_c^2 - \omega^2 + j\omega \dfrac{\omega_c}{Q}}$$

where the resonant or center frequency is denoted ω_c rather than ω_0 to avoid confusing the center frequency with the fundamental frequency, both of which customarily use the notation ω_0.

When the quality factor Q is ten, the frequency response gain is as shown in the following figure.

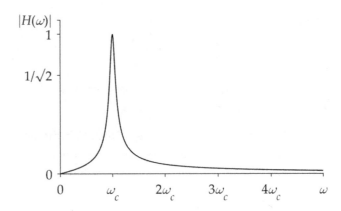

If the center frequency of this filter is set equal to one of the harmonic frequencies in a periodic input waveform, the output will be nearly sinusoidal at the center frequency of the filter because, the frequency response gain $|H(\omega)|$ is close to zero outside the narrow bandwidth $\beta = \omega_c/Q$ of the filter.

Once again let the input to the filter be a square wave having an amplitude equal to one

$$v_i(t) = \sum_{n=1}^{\infty} c_n \cos(n\omega_0 t)$$

$$c_n = \frac{4}{n\pi} \sin\left(\frac{n\pi}{2}\right)$$

Let the center frequency of the filter be equal to the third harmonic of the input square wave

$$\omega_c = 3\omega_0$$

Using a computer so that all significant harmonics can be considered, the filter input $v_i(t)$ and resulting filter output $v_o(t)$ are shown in the figures below.

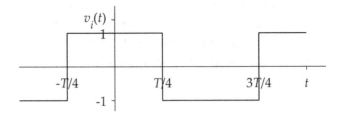

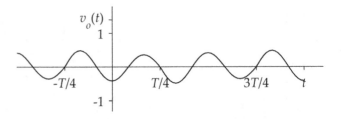

In addition, line spectra plots for the input waveform coefficients c_n and output waveform coefficients d_n are shown below.

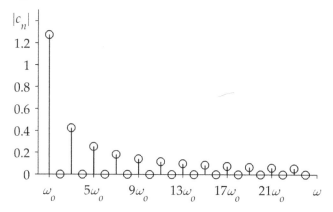

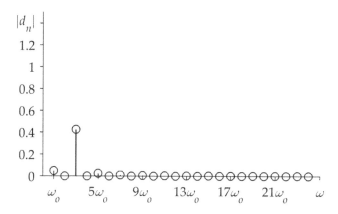

The line spectra plot for the output waveform clearly shows that the output is dominated by the component at $3\omega_o$, with very small components at ω_o and $5\omega_o$. The other components appearing in the input waveform are attenuated significantly by the bandpass filter. The resulting output waveform is very nearly a pure sinusoidal waveform at $3\omega_o$, which is visually confirmed by looking at the output waveform on the preceding page. This filter essentially rejects all harmonic components of the input square wave except for the third harmonic. As a result, the output is a sinusoid at the third harmonic.

8.5 Summary

Periodic Waveform Properties	
Definition:	$f(t) = f(t+T)$ $T = \text{period}$ $f_o = 1/T$, Hz $\omega_o = \dfrac{2\pi}{T}$, rad/s
DC Value:	$F_{dc} = \dfrac{1}{T} \displaystyle\int_{t_o}^{t_o+T} f(t)dt$ F_{dc} is not a function of time, and not a function of the period or frequency.
RMS Value:	$F_{rms} = \sqrt{\dfrac{1}{T} \displaystyle\int_{t_o}^{t_o+T} f(t)^2 dt}$ F_{rms} is not a function of time, and not a function of the period or frequency.
Separating AC from DC:	$f(t) = F_{dc} + f_{ac}(t)$ $F_{rms} = \sqrt{F_{dc}^2 + F_{acrms}^2}$
Odd Symmetry:	$f(t) = -f(-t)$ $\sin(\omega t)$ is odd.
Even Symmetry:	$f(t) = f(-t)$ $\cos(\omega t)$ is even.
Half Wave Symmetry:	$f(t) = -f\left(t \pm \dfrac{T}{2}\right)$ Half wave symmetry is independent of odd and even symmetries. It does not depend on where $t = 0$ appears.

Fourier Series Summary

$$f(t) = a_{dc} + \sum_{n=1}^{\infty}\left(a_n \cos(n\omega_o t) + b_n \sin(n\omega_o t)\right)$$

$$f(t) = a_{dc} + \sum_{n=1}^{\infty} c_n \cos(n\omega_o t - \phi_n)$$

$$a_{dc} = \frac{1}{T}\int_{t_o}^{t_o+T} f(t)\,dt = \text{DC or average value}$$

$$a_n = \frac{2}{T}\int_{t_o}^{t_o+T} f(t)\cos(n\omega_o t)\,dt$$

$$b_n = \frac{2}{T}\int_{t_o}^{t_o+T} f(t)\sin(n\omega_o t)\,dt$$

$$c_n = \left|a_n + jb_n\right| = \sqrt{a_n^2 + b_n^2}$$

$$\phi_n = \angle(a_n + jb_n) = \text{atan2}(b_n, a_n)$$

$b_n = 0$ if $f(t)$ has even symmetry

$a_n = 0$ if $f(t)$ has odd symmetry

$a_n = b_n = 0$ for even n if $f(t)$ has half wave symmetry

Circuits with Periodic Inputs

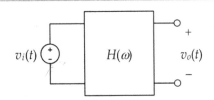

$$v_i(t) = v_{idc} + \sum_{n=1}^{\infty} c_n \cos(n\omega_o t - \phi_n)$$

$$v_o(t) = v_{odc} + \sum_{n=1}^{\infty} d_n \cos(n\omega_o t + \alpha_n)$$

$$v_{odc} = H(0)\,v_{idc}$$

$$d_n = \left|H(n\omega_o)\right|\cdot c_n$$

$$\alpha_n = \theta(n\omega_o) - \phi_n$$

Common Fourier Series

Even Square Wave

$a_{dc} = 0$

$a_n = c_n = \dfrac{4A}{n\pi}\sin\left(\dfrac{n\pi}{2}\right)$

$b_n = 0 \quad \phi_n = 0$

Odd Triangle Wave

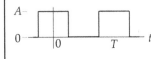

$a_{dc} = 0$

$a_n = 0 \quad \phi_n = 90°$

$b_n = c_n = \dfrac{8A}{n^2\pi^2}\left|\sin\left(\dfrac{n\pi}{2}\right)\right|$

Pulse Train

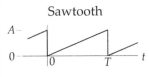

$a_{dc} = \dfrac{A}{2}$

$a_n = c_n = \dfrac{2A}{n\pi}\sin\left(\dfrac{n\pi}{2}\right)$

$b_n = 0 \quad \phi_n = 0$

Sawtooth

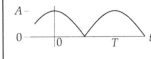

$a_{dc} = \dfrac{A}{2}$

$a_n = 0 \quad \phi_n = 90°$

$b_n = c_n = -\dfrac{A}{n\pi}$

Rectified Cosine

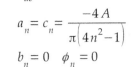

$a_{dc} = \dfrac{2A}{\pi}$

$a_n = c_n = \dfrac{-4A}{\pi(4n^2-1)}$

$b_n = 0 \quad \phi_n = 0$

Unipolar PWM

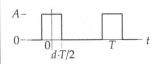

$a_{dc} = Ad$

$a_n = c_n = \dfrac{2A}{n\pi}\sin(dn\pi)$

$b_n = 0 \quad \phi_n = 0$

Bipolar PWM

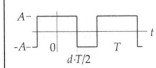

$a_{dc} = A(2d-1)$

$a_n = c_n = \dfrac{4A}{n\pi}\sin(dn\pi)$

$b_n = 0 \quad \phi_n = 0$

Waveform Smoothness

If k is the number of times a waveform can be differentiated **before** discontinuities appear, the amplitude of the Fourier series coefficients fall off as $1/n^{k+1}$. **Sharper waveforms have greater high frequency content.**

8.6 Problems

8.1 The periodic waveforms shown below are described respectively by the following expressions.

$$f_a(t) = \begin{cases} A\cos(\omega_o t) & -T/4 \le t \le T/4 \\ 0 & T/4 \le t \le 3T/4 \end{cases}$$

$$f_b(t) = \begin{cases} A\cdot\left(\dfrac{t}{d\cdot T}\right) & 0 \le t \le d\cdot T \\ A\cdot\left(1-\dfrac{t-d\cdot T}{(1-d)\cdot T}\right) & d\cdot T \le t \le T \end{cases}$$

$$f_c(t) = \begin{cases} A & -T/6 \le t \le T/6 \\ A\cdot\left(1-\dfrac{12}{T}\cdot(t-T/6)\right) & T/6 \le t \le T/3 \\ -A & T/3 \le t \le 2T/3 \\ A\cdot\left(\dfrac{12}{T}\cdot(t-2T/3)-1\right) & 2T/3 \le t \le 5T/6 \end{cases}$$

(a)

(b)

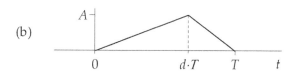

(c)

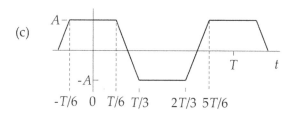

Waveform $f_a(t)$ is called a half wave rectified sinusoid. Waveform $f_b(t)$ is a generalized sawtooth waveform where the variable d is a parameter $0 \le d \le 1$. For example, when $d = 1$, it is the sawtooth waveform. When $d = 0$, it is a reverse sawtooth. When $d = 1/2$, it is a raised triangle waveform. Waveform $f_c(t)$ is the trapezoidal waveform.

(a) For $f_a(t)$ find F_{dc} and F_{rms}, (b) For $f_b(t)$ show that F_{dc} and F_{rms} are not a function of the variable d? (c) For $f_c(t)$ find F_{dc} and F_{rms}.

8.2 What symmetry properties do the waveforms in problem **8.1** have? If the time origin, $t = 0$, is moved to other points in the waveforms, do the symmetry properties disappear or change? Sketch examples that demonstrate these modified symmetries.

8.3 Derive the Fourier series coefficients for the waveforms in problem **8.1**, (a) $f_a(t)$, (b) $f_b(t)$, and (c) $f_c(t)$.

8.4 How many times can each of the waveforms in problem **8.1** be differentiated until discontinuities appear? Using this information, how fast do the Fourier series coefficients fall off with respect to n, i.e., what is the ratio $|c_n/c_1|$ for each waveform?

8.5 Derive the DC and rms values of common periodic waveforms illustrated in this chapter: (a) Square Wave, (b) Triangle Wave, (c) Pulse Train, (d) Sawtooth Wave, (e) Rectified Cosine, (f) Unipolar PWM, and (g) Bipolar PWM.

8.6 Derive the Fourier series coefficients of common periodic waveforms illustrated in this chapter: (a) Square Wave, (b) Triangle Wave, (c) Pulse Train, (d) Sawtooth Wave, (e) Rectified Cosine, (f) Unipolar PWM, and (g) Bipolar PWM.

8.7 The Fourier series of a differentiable even waveform can be written as

$$f(t) = \sum_{n=1}^{\infty} a_n \cos(n\omega_o t)$$

From this expression, find the Fourier series coefficients of the derivative of $f(t)$,

$$\dot{f}(t) = \frac{df}{dt} = \sum_{n=1}^{\infty} \left(\hat{a}_n \cos(n\omega_o t) + \hat{b}_n \sin(n\omega_o t)\right)$$

What symmetry properties does the derivative df/dt have? Relative to $|a_n/a_1| = 1/n^k$ for $f(t)$, how fast do the coefficients of the derivative df/dt fall off as the harmonic frequency $n\omega_o$ increases?

8.8 Repeat Problem **8.7** for a differentiable odd waveform having Fourier series

$$f(t) = \sum_{n=1}^{\infty} b_n \sin(n\omega_o t)$$

What symmetry properties does the derivative df/dt have? Relative to $|b_n/b_1| = 1/n^k$ for $f(t)$, how fast do the coefficients of the derivative df/dt fall off as the harmonic frequency $n\omega_o$ increases?

8.9 The waveform below is generated using a TRIAC semiconductor device to control the power in a load from a sinusoidal source.

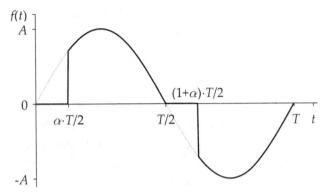

Two common applications of this waveform are in household light dimmers for incandescent lamps and in the burner heating elements on an electric range. Changing the variable α electrically using a potentiometer, changes the RMS value of the waveform from the standard sinusoidal value of $A_{rms} = A/\sqrt{2}$ when $\alpha = 0$ to zero when $\alpha = 1$. Show that the RMS value of this waveform $F_{rms}(\alpha)$ can be written as

$$F_{rms}(\alpha) = A_{rms}\sqrt{1 - \alpha + \frac{\sin(2\pi\alpha)}{2\pi}}$$

The plot of $F_{rms}(\alpha)/A_{rms}$ shown below illustrates how the RMS value varies as a function of α.

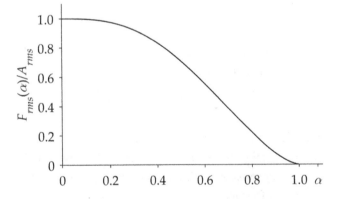

8.10 The input $v_i(t)$ to the RC filter below is an odd triangle waveform having amplitude $A = 5$ V and fundamental frequency $\omega_o = 10$ krad/s. Choose practical component values for the RC filter below so that the amplitude of the third harmonic at $3\omega_o$ is attenuated by 3 dB (3 dB attenuation is equal to $|H(\omega)|_{dB} = -3$ dB gain). Then compute the output $v_o(t)$ of the filter at the fundamental ω_o and fifth harmonic $5\omega_o$ frequencies.

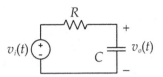

8.11 The frequency response of a bandpass filter is

$$H(\omega) = \frac{V_o}{V_i} = \frac{j\omega\beta}{\omega_c^2 - \omega^2 + j\omega\beta}$$

where the center frequency of the filter is denoted ω_c rather than ω_o to avoid confusing it with the fundamental frequency ω_o of the input waveform. Let the input $v_i(t)$ to this filter be a **pulse train** waveform having an amplitude of $A = 5$ V and a fundamental frequency of $\omega_o = 24$ krad/s. If the center frequency of the bandpass filter is $\omega_c = 5\omega_o$ and its quality factor is $Q = 5$, find the output $v_o(t)$ of the filter at the frequencies, $\omega = 0$, $3\omega_o$, $5\omega_o$, and $7\omega_o$.

8.12 Let the input $v_i(t)$ to the filter shown below be a **unipolar PWM** waveform having a fundamental frequency of $\omega_o = 100$ krad/s and an amplitude of $A = 20$ V. Choose practical component values for the resonant second order lowpass filter so that the DC component of the input passes through the filter with no attenuation and the fundamental component a_1 is attenuated by at least 40 dB (40 dB attenuation is equal to $|H(\omega)|_{dB} = -40$ dB gain). Compute the output $v_o(t)$ of the filter at DC and at the fundamental, to confirm your design. Given these results, sketch the filter output versus time.

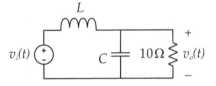

If the duty cycle d of the input unipolar PWM waveform changes very slowly over time compared to its period $T = 2\pi/\omega_o$, sketch what you expect the output to look like? For example, sketch the output if the duty cycle is $d(t) = 0.5 + 0.45\cos((\omega_o/100)\cdot t)$?

8.13 Repeat problem **8.12**, but let the input $v_i(t)$ to the filter be a **bipolar PWM** waveform having a fundamental frequency of $\omega_o = 100$ krad/s and an amplitude of $A = 20$ V.

9 The Real World

Using concepts from preceding chapters, this chapter covers real world topics and applications. The material contained in this chapter cannot be found in other textbooks on electric circuits, but yet the material found here is fundamental to real world circuit design. Most engineers learn this material informally on the job. Often times this material is learned in response to failure.

9.1 Real Components

In previous chapters, ideal resistors, capacitors, and inductors were introduced and studied. Saying the word "ideal" should automatically cause some concern. The world we live in is not "ideal." Rather, it is real. The real world is not neat and tidy. Murphy's law, *"anything that can go wrong will,"* resides in the real world. As a result, designing and building circuits with "real" components often require greater insight, thought, and care than one would expect based on knowledge of "ideal" components.

Parasitic Elements

Resistors, capacitors, and inductors used to create actual electric circuits contain extraneous or parasitic elements beyond the chosen values for the resistance, capacitance, and inductance.

Resistance exists whenever current flows through a path. The inherent resistance of the path forms a parasitic resistor R_x. The most common parasitic resistance is formed by the resistance of the wire and circuit board traces that connect components together.

When a parasitic resistance R_x is in series with a chosen resistor R as shown in the following figure, it is important that it be as small as possible. For example, the parasitic resistance is generally insignificant if it is less than one percent of the chosen resistance.

When a parasitic resistance R_x is in parallel with a chosen resistor R, as shown in the following figure, it is important that it be as large as possible. For example, the parasitic resistance is generally insignificant if it is 100 times larger than the chosen resistance. When these criteria are met, one can generally ignore parasitic resistances.

A capacitor is formed whenever two conductors are separated by an insulator. The ideal capacitor was described in this way in Chapter 5. Therefore, a parasitic capacitor is formed any time two conductors are separated by an insulator. Wires separated from each other and distinct circuit board traces all form parasitic capacitances. Because the area involved is typically very small, and the distance between the conductors is relatively large, parasitic capacitor values are typically very small. They are often in the picofarad or smaller range.

Inductance exists whenever a magnetic field is created by the presence of current. Therefore, all conductors form parasitic inductors. Furthermore, mutual inductance is formed whenever the magnetic fields from different currents interact with each other.

All of these parasitic elements inherently exist. They are properties of nature. Real resistors, capacitors, and inductors simply create known, desired values of resistance, capacitance, and inductance respectively.

Real Components

Resistors: A model for a real resistor is shown in the following figure. The resistor R includes the chosen resistance value plus whatever parasitic resistance exists in the leads. The parasitic inductance L_x is primarily due to the leads, and the parasitic capacitance C_x is due to the separation between the leads on each end of the resistor. Depending on the physical size of the resistor and whether it has leads or not, the parasitic capacitance and inductance values may or may not be significant.

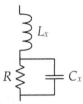

One way to assess the relative importance of the parasitic capacitance and inductance is to compute their reactances and compare those reactances to the chosen resistance. For example, inductance has a reactance of

$$X_L = \omega L = 2\pi f L$$

Solving this for the frequency f gives

$$f = \frac{X_L}{2\pi L}$$

Now, if the inductance is 1 nH and the reactance is 1 Ω, the frequency becomes

$$f = \frac{X_L}{2\pi L} = \frac{1}{2\pi 10^{-9}} = 159 \text{ MHz}$$

One nanohenry (1 nH) of inductance is a reactance of one ohm at 159 MHz. At frequencies under 159 MHz, the reactance is even smaller. If the inductance were 10 nH instead of 1 nH, it would have a reactance of 1 Ω at 15.9 MHz.

Using the above information as a guide, when the chosen resistance is in the kiloohm range, the parasitic inductance or frequency would have to be very large for the parasitic inductance to have any significant effect on circuit behavior.

This same process can be applied to parasitic capacitance. A capacitance has a reactance that can be described by

$$X_c = \frac{1}{\omega C} = \frac{1}{2\pi f C}$$

Solving this for the frequency f gives

$$f = \frac{1}{2\pi C X_c}$$

Now, if the capacitance is 1 pF and the reactance is 1 MΩ, the frequency becomes

$$f = \frac{1}{2\pi C X_c} = \frac{1}{2\pi 10^{-12} \cdot 10^6} = 159 \text{ kHz}$$

One picofarad (1 pF) of capacitance is a reactance of one megaohm at 159 kHz. At frequencies under 159 kHz the reactance is even greater. Since the parasitic capacitance is in parallel with the resistor, its reactance must be at least 100 times greater than the chosen resistor value for it to have a negligible effect on circuit behavior.

Capacitors: A model for a real capacitor is shown in the figure below. The capacitor C is the chosen capacitance value. The parasitic inductance L_x is formed by the capacitor leads as well as by the plates making up the capacitor. **The parasitic resistance R_{esr} is called the equivalent series resistance, ESR.** This value takes into account the resistance of the leads and the resistance incurred by charge moving over the plates. It also takes into account the fact that the insulating material between the two plates is not a perfect insulator. The equivalent series resistance takes into account all of the losses in the capacitor. Because those losses are a function of frequency, the ESR is also a function of frequency. In general ESR increases with increasing frequency. In addition, ESR is a function of the physical size of the capacitor and the materials used in its construction.

Given this model, a real capacitor is a series RLC circuit. At low frequencies, the reactance of the parasitic inductance is negligible compared to that of the capacitor, so the capacitor acts as the capacitor one expects. However, as frequency increases, the reactance of the parasitic inductance becomes significant. Eventually, resonance is reached where the inductive reactance is equal in magnitude to the capacitive reactance. At resonance, only the parasitic resistance remains. **At frequencies above resonance, the capacitor acts as an inductor because the inductive reactance dominates the impedance!** This phenomenon was illustrated in Chapter 7.

The series impedance of this series RLC circuit can be written as

$$Z_s = R_{esr} + j X_L - j X_c = R_{esr} + j\omega L_x - j\frac{1}{\omega C}$$

Resonance occurs at the resonant frequency ω_o where $X_L = -X_c$, which was derived in Chapter 7 as

$$\omega = \omega_o = \frac{1}{\sqrt{L_x C}}$$

Therefore, at resonance the series impedance is equal to the equivalent series resistance

$$Z = R_{esr} + j\omega_o L_x - j\frac{1}{\omega_o C} = R_{esr} + j0$$

As a general rule, the resonant frequency of a real capacitor is inversely proportional to its capacitance. Using the resonant frequency in units of Hz,

$$\omega_o = 2\pi f_o = \frac{1}{\sqrt{L_x C}}$$

$$f_o = \frac{1}{2\pi\sqrt{L_x C}}$$

if a 100 µF capacitor has a parasitic inductance of 10 nH, the resonant frequency is

$$f_o = \frac{1}{2\pi\sqrt{10^{-8}10^{-4}}} = \frac{1}{2\pi\sqrt{10^{-12}}} = \frac{10^6}{2\pi} = 159 \text{ kHz}$$

so this capacitor is generally useful up to 159 kHz. However, if the capacitance is 1 µF and the inductance is unchanged, the resonant frequency becomes

$$f_o = \frac{1}{2\pi\sqrt{10^{-8}10^{-6}}} = \frac{1}{2\pi\sqrt{10^{-14}}} = \frac{10^7}{2\pi} = 1.59 \text{ MHz}$$

This capacitor is useful up to 1.59 MHz. When the capacitance value drops by a factor of 100, the resonant frequency increases by a factor of 10.

When the impedance of a real capacitor passes through resonance at relatively low frequencies, it is very common to see two capacitors in parallel as shown in the following circuit. One capacitor is often 100 to 1000 times smaller than the other, *e.g.*, 10 µF and 0.01 µF.

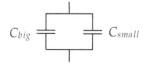

If the parasitic elements of the two capacitors are ignored, placing these capacitors in parallel seems silly since the resulting equivalent capacitance is the sum of the two, $C_{eq} = C_{big} + C_{small}$. The smaller capacitance makes an insignificant change in the total capacitance. This is especially true when it is common for capacitors to have ±10% tolerance and the added smaller capacitor adds just 0.1% to 1% to the total capacitance.

However, when the inherent parasitic elements in the two capacitors are considered, placing a much smaller capacitor in parallel with a desired larger capacitor makes a great deal of sense as shown in the following figure.

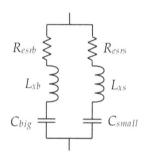

Once the larger capacitor passes through its resonance and effectively becomes an inductor, the smaller capacitor takes over and provides capacitance because its resonant frequency occurs at a much higher frequency. The table on the following page illustrates this phenomenon.

nanofarads (nF) and millifarads (mF): For a variety of reasons, it is uncommon in the real world for capacitors to be specified in nanofarads (nF) or millifarads (mF). Rather, the scale factors micro (µ) and pico (p) are stretched to accommodate values that would normally be given with nano- and milli- scalings. For example, a 100 nF capacitor is often given as 0.1 µF and a 1 nF capacitor is often given as 0.001 µF etc. Similarly, a 1 mF capacitor is often given as 1,000 µF and a 100 mF capacitor is often given as 100,000 µF, etc. Given the use of micro- and pico-scalings, these terms are sometimes informally spoken as "mike" and "puff" respectively, *e.g.*, 1 µF is "One mike" and 100 pF is "100 puff."

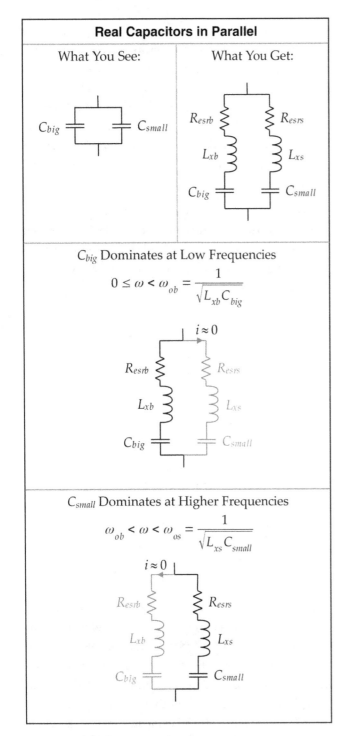

Real Capacitors in Parallel

What You See: | What You Get:

C_{big} C_{small}

R_{esrb} R_{esrs} L_{xb} L_{xs} C_{big} C_{small}

C_{big} Dominates at Low Frequencies

$$0 \leq \omega < \omega_{ob} = \frac{1}{\sqrt{L_{xb}C_{big}}}$$

$i \approx 0$

R_{esrb} R_{esrs} L_{xb} L_{xs} C_{big} C_{small}

C_{small} Dominates at Higher Frequencies

$$\omega_{ob} < \omega < \omega_{os} = \frac{1}{\sqrt{L_{xs}C_{small}}}$$

$i \approx 0$

R_{esrb} R_{esrs} L_{xb} L_{xs} C_{big} C_{small}

Polarized Capacitors: The volume of a capacitor grows with its value. So, for example, a 1 μF capacitor generally requires much more volume or space than a 1 nF capacitor requires. To minimize the volume required for capacitances greater than about 1 μF, capacitors are commonly constructed where the insulating layer is a very thin oxide layer formed on one capacitor plate and the other plate is formed by a solid or non-solid electrolyte. Capacitors formed in this way are called **electrolytic capacitors**. Such capacitors provide much greater capacitance per unit

volume than is possible in capacitors formed by two metallic plates separated by an insulating layer. As a result, electrolytic capacitors are used whenever possible when capacitances greater than about 1 μF are needed.

The inherent down side of electrolytic capacitor construction is that the capacitor is **polarized. That is, the capacitor acts as a capacitor only if the polarity of the applied voltage across it remains in a specific polarity or direction. If the polarity of the applied voltage becomes reversed, *i.e.*, reverse biased, the capacitor no longer acts as a capacitor—it acts like a resistor!**

Unintended results can be expected if a polarized electrolytic capacitor becomes reverse biased at any time during circuit operation. For example, sinusoidal voltages cannot be applied across a polarized capacitor. When a sinusoidal voltage has one polarity, the capacitor has a capacitance and acts like a capacitor, whereas, when the voltage has the opposite polarity, the capacitor acts as a resistor.

Because electrolytic capacitors are polarized, they are commonly drawn using the schematic symbol shown on the left below where the curved plate is the negative terminal. The figure below also shows the two operating states of a polarized capacitor. The voltage must have the polarity as shown on the upper symbol for the capacitor to act as a capacitor.

$+$ $-$ $\Rightarrow$ capacitor, farads, F

$-$ $+$ $\Rightarrow$ resistor, ohms, Ω

Inductors: A model for a real inductor is shown in the following figure. The inductor L has the chosen inductance value. The parasitic resistance models the finite resistance of the wire used to construct the inductor. The parasitic capacitance models the capacitance that exists between the individual turns of the wire used to construct the inductor.

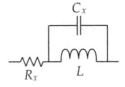

C_x

R_x L

Given this model, a real inductor exhibits parallel resonance at

$$f_o = \frac{1}{2\pi\sqrt{LC_x}}$$

At this frequency, the inductive reactance and capacitive reactance cancel each other out, making the impedance infinite as illustrated earlier in Chapter 7. At frequencies above resonance, the inductor behaves like a capacitor, so an inductor is generally not useful above resonance.

9.2 Bypass Capacitors

Bypass or decoupling capacitors commonly appear across the DC power supply terminals of integrated circuits, *i.e.*, ICs. They also commonly appear across the power supply input and across the regulated output of voltage regulator ICs. These capacitors decouple the dynamic power needs of an IC from its DC power supply. Because capacitors store charge, they provide transient currents required by an IC, thereby letting these currents bypass the DC power supply.

Bypass capacitors can be analyzed using transient analysis. In this case, the analysis mimics digital circuits where changing logic states can make abrupt changes in the current required from the power supply. Bypass capacitors can also be analyzed by considering sinusoidal currents. In this case, the analysis uses phasors and applies to analog circuits.

Before studying the digital and analog circuit cases, consider the following general circuit where the DC power supply on the left is providing power to the circuit on the right. The wires or printed circuit board traces between the power supply and the circuit on the right inherently have parasitic inductance that is lumped into a single inductor as shown.

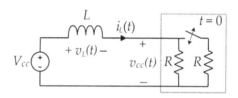

The DC power supply creates a constant DC voltage labeled V_{cc}. However, the supply voltage $v_{cc}(t)$ at the electric circuit is a function of time since KVL dictates that

$$v_{cc}(t) = V_{cc} - v_L(t) = V_{cc} - L\frac{di_L}{dt}$$

The presence of the parasitic inductance introduces a voltage disturbance or noise onto the power supply connections to the electric circuit whenever the current through the parasitic inductance varies with time. Because the electric circuit was designed and intended to work from a pure DC voltage, this added disturbance or noise can cause the electric circuit to produce noisy responses, function erratically, or at worst break into oscillation where voltages within the circuit become uncontrolled periodic functions of time. Needless to say, when any of these undesirable behaviors are exhibited, something must be done to eliminate or at least minimize the problem.

Transient Analysis

The Problem: It is common for the power supply current to abruptly change in an electronic circuit. To analyze this situation, consider the following circuit that captures the essential aspects of this phenomenon. Whenever the switch changes state, the current required from the power supply changes abruptly.

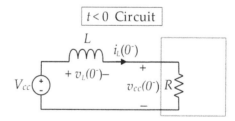

First consider the case where the switch closes at $t = 0$. The $t < 0$ circuit is shown below.

$t < 0$ Circuit

Since the circuit is at rest, the voltage across the inductor is zero, and Ohm's law gives the initial inductor current as

$$i_L(0^-) = i_L(0^+) = \frac{V_{cc}}{R}$$

The $t > 0$ circuit is shown in the following figure.

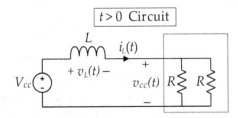

$t > 0$ Circuit

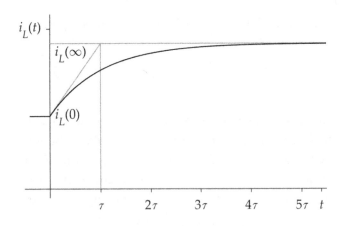

The equivalent resistance is $R\|R = R/2$. So the time constant is

$$\tau = \frac{L}{R/2} = \frac{2L}{R}$$

When time goes to infinity, the circuit is at rest, the voltage across the inductor is zero again, and Ohm's law gives the final inductor current as

$$i_L(\infty) = \frac{V_{cc}}{R/2} = \frac{2V_{cc}}{R}$$

The current doubles because the resistance dropped by a factor of two when the switch closes.

Using these results, the inductor current can be written as

$$i_L(t) = i_L(\infty) + \left(i_L(0^-) - i_L(\infty)\right)e^{-t/\tau}, \quad t \geq 0$$

$$i_L(t) = \frac{2V_{cc}}{R} + \left(\frac{V_{cc}}{R} - \frac{2V_{cc}}{R}\right)e^{-t/\tau}, \quad t \geq 0$$

$$i_L(t) = \frac{2V_{cc}}{R} - \frac{V_{cc}}{R}e^{-t/\tau}, \quad t \geq 0$$

$$i_L(t) = \frac{V_{cc}}{R}\left(2 - e^{-t/\tau}\right), \quad t \geq 0$$

This result agrees with the initial and final values found earlier,

$$i_L(0^-) = i_L(0^+) = \frac{V_{cc}}{R}\left(2 - e^{-0/\tau}\right) = \frac{V_{cc}}{R}\left(2 - 1\right) = \frac{V_{cc}}{R}$$

$$i_L(\infty) = \frac{V_{cc}}{R}\left(2 - e^{-\infty/\tau}\right) = \frac{V_{cc}}{R}\left(2 - 0\right) = \frac{2V_{cc}}{R}$$

The following plot illustrates this result.

Knowing the inductor current allows the supply voltage to the resistors $v_{cc}(t)$ to be found by applying Ohm's law. At $t = 0^-$ the voltage is

$$v_{cc}(0^-) = i_L(0^-)R = \frac{V_{cc}}{R}R = V_{cc}$$

Because the current through the inductor cannot jump at $t = 0$, the instant the switch changes state the voltage is

$$v_{cc}(0^+) = i_L(0^+)\frac{R}{2} = i_L(0^-)\frac{R}{2} = \frac{V_{cc}}{R}\frac{R}{2} = \frac{V_{cc}}{2}$$

Therefore, the supply voltage to the resistors is discontinuous and drops by a factor of two instantaneously when the switch changes state.

The final value of the supply voltage is

$$v_{cc}(\infty) = i_L(\infty)\left(\frac{R}{2}\right) = \frac{2V_{cc}}{R}\frac{R}{2} = V_{cc}$$

And for positive time, the voltage can be written as

$$v_{cc}(t) = i_L(t)\left(\frac{R}{2}\right), \quad t > 0$$

or

$$v_{cc}(t) = \frac{V_{cc}}{R}\left(2 - e^{-t/\tau}\right)\left(\frac{R}{2}\right), \quad t > 0$$

$$v_{cc}(t) = \frac{V_{cc}}{2}\left(2 - e^{-t/\tau}\right), \quad t > 0$$

$$v_{cc}(t) = V_{cc}\left(1 - 0.5e^{-t/\tau}\right), \quad t > 0$$

This results agrees with the initial and final values found earlier,

$$v_{cc}(0^+) = V_{cc}\left(1 - 0.5e^{-0/\tau}\right) = V_{cc}\left(1 - 0.5\right) = \frac{V_{cc}}{2}$$

$$v_{cc}(\infty) = V_{cc}\left(1 - 0.5e^{-\infty/\tau}\right) = V_{cc}\left(1 - 0\right) = V_{cc}$$

The following plot illustrates the discontinuity and transient aspects of the supply voltage $v_{cc}(t)$.

The voltage starts at V_{cc} and ends at V_{cc}, but suffers from a voltage spike when the resistance changes abruptly. Since the inductance L is usually quite small, *e.g.*, in the nanohenry (nH) range, the voltage spike does not last long, *e.g.*, microseconds. If this happens repeatedly, the power supply will contain many noise spikes. This is particularly trouble-

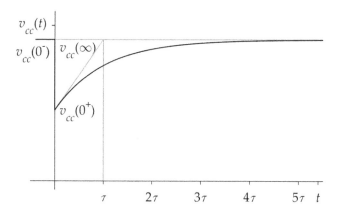

placing a capacitor across the power supply connections at the circuit as shown below, the voltage cannot jump when there is a discontinuity in the load, thereby eliminating the voltage spikes.

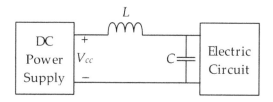

This bypass capacitor should have very short leads and be placed as close as possible to the circuit's power supply connections. This closeness minimizes the lead inductance of the capacitor and minimizes the remaining lead inductance in the power supply connection between the capacitor's placement and the circuitry using the power supply. These remaining stray inductances keep the capacitor from behaving ideally since the current through these inductances cannot jump instantaneously.

The value of the bypass capacitor is determined by the amount of current the circuit uses and the frequency at which the noise spikes occur. If the spikes occur at sufficiently high frequency, two bypass capacitors may be needed, one much smaller than the other. In this case, the smaller one provides capacitance at frequencies beyond the series resonant frequency of the larger capacitor.

To illustrate the impact of the bypass capacitor, reconsider the original circuit where the switch closes at $t = 0$, with the bypass capacitor in place. The $t = 0^+$ circuit is shown below.

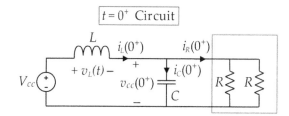

Earlier, the initial inductor current was found to be

$$i_L(0^-) = i_L(0^+) = \frac{V_{cc}}{R}$$

and the initial value of supply voltage was

$$v_{cc}(0^-) = i_L(0^-)R = \frac{V_{cc}}{R}R = V_{cc}$$

some if the power supply leads go on to yet other circuits as illustrated in the following figure. In this case, all the succeeding circuits experience the noise spikes from all previous circuits on their power supply leads. The further circuits are away from the DC power supply, the worse this problem becomes.

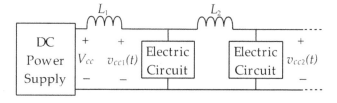

It is possible to show that if the switch in the circuit goes the opposite direction at $t = 0$, the circuit resistance goes from $R\|R = R/2$ to R, and the supply voltage $v_{cc}(t)$ jumps from $v_{cc}(0^-) = V_{cc}$ to $v_{cc}(0^+) = 2V_{cc}$. In this case the voltage spike is equal to twice the DC power supply value. The resulting supply voltage can be written as

$$v_{cc}(t) = V_{cc}, \quad t < 0$$
$$v_{cc}(t) = V_{cc}\left(1 + e^{-t/\tau}\right), \quad t > 0$$

and is illustrated in the following figure.

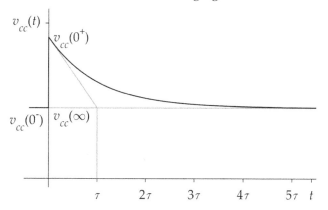

The Solution: The solution to this problem is to use a capacitor because the voltage across a capacitor cannot jump, i.e., it must be continuous. Therefore, by

The presence of the bypass capacitor makes the supply voltage continuous from $t = 0^-$ to $t = 0^+$, namely

$$v_{cc}(0^+) = v_{cc}(0^-) = V_{cc}$$

So the supply voltage does not jump at $t = 0$.

Applying KCL at the top right node in the circuit at $t = 0^+$ gives

$$i_L(0^+) = i_C(0^+) + i_R(0^+)$$

Solving this for the bypass capacitor current and simplifying leads to

$$i_C(0^+) = i_L(0^+) - i_R(0^+)$$

$$i_C(0^+) = i_L(0^+) - \frac{v_{cc}(0^+)}{R/2}$$

$$i_C(0^+) = \frac{v_{cc}(0^+)}{R} - \frac{2v_{cc}(0^+)}{R}$$

$$i_C(0^+) = -\frac{v_{cc}(0^+)}{R}$$

$$i_C(0^+) = -\frac{V_{cc}}{R}$$

This is the current leaving the capacitor and entering the equivalent load resistance $R/2$. This current is needed to keep the supply voltage from jumping when the switch changes state.

Given the initial bypass capacitor current the associated rate of change in the capacitor voltage is

$$\frac{dv_{cc}}{dt} = \frac{i_C(t)}{C}$$

$$\frac{dv_{cc}(0^+)}{dt} = \frac{i_C(0^+)}{C}$$

$$\frac{dv_{cc}(0^+)}{dt} = -\frac{v_{cc}(0^+)}{RC}$$

The voltage on the bypass capacitor decreases because it is discharging into the equivalent load. From this expression it is clear that the larger the bypass capacitance, the less quickly the capacitor discharges. Because of this, larger capacitances are generally better. However, as described earlier, the larger the capacitance C, the lower its series resonant frequency is. Therefore, if a large capacitance is needed, a second much smaller one in parallel with the larger one will be required as well. In practice, the choice of capacitor value or values is based on experimental testing.

Sinusoidal Analysis

The Problem: The inherent existence of parasitic inductance in the DC power supply leads connected to analog circuits is also a potential source of problems.

Consider the basic scenario as shown in the following figure where the electric circuit is an amplifier that provides current to the load resistor R_L. This load current comes from the DC power supply connected to the amplifier. As a result, the inductor current $i_L(t)$ includes the load current $i_o(t)$ and all other currents required within the amplifier.

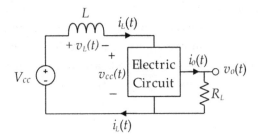

Applying KVL as was done earlier, the power supply voltage at the amplifier can be written as

$$v_{cc}(t) = V_{cc} - v_L(t) = V_{cc} - L\frac{di_L}{dt}$$

Given this relationship, any time the current from the DC power supply $i_L(t)$ varies, the power supply voltage at the amplifier will vary about the DC voltage V_{cc}. For example, if the inductor current is sinusoidal

$$i_L(t) = I_m\cos(\omega t)$$

then the voltage across the inductor is

$$v_L(t) = L\frac{di_L}{dt} = -\omega L\sin(\omega t)$$

and the power supply voltage at the amplifier becomes

$$v_{cc}(t) = V_{cc} - v_L(t) = V_{cc} + \omega L\sin(\omega t)$$

Depending on the frequency ω and inductance L, this added sinusoidal component can create significant ripple or noise on the power supply to the amplifier.

If the inductor current is some other periodic waveform, it can be described by a Fourier series. Then, the ripple or noise would itself be a Fourier series.

As stated earlier, this added ripple or noise can cause the electric circuit to produce noisy responses, function erratically, or at worst break into oscillation where voltages within the circuit become uncontrolled periodic functions of time.

The Solution: The solution here is the same as it was earlier. Place a capacitor across the power supply connections to the amplifier. This bypass capacitor should have very short leads and be placed as close as possible to the amplifier's power supply connections. This closeness minimizes the lead inductance of the capacitor and minimizes the remaining lead inductance in the power supply connection between the capacitor's placement and the circuitry using the power supply. In addition, depending on the frequency content of the ripple or noise, two bypass capacitors may be needed, with one being much smaller than the other.

The goal in this case is to minimize the Thévenin impedance seen looking back to the DC power supply. As shown in figure below, if the parasitic inductance did not exist, and the source is shut OFF, the Thévenin impedance is zero and there would be no noise on the amplifier's power supply terminals.

$$jwL = j0$$

$V_{cc} = 0$ $\Leftarrow Z_{TH} = 0$

Since the parasitic inductance is not zero, the added bypass capacitor makes the Thévenin impedance appear as a parallel LC circuit as shown in the following circuit.

Z_L

$V_{cc} = 0$ Z_c $\Leftarrow Z_{TH} = Z_L \| Z_c$

So, in this case, the capacitor value should be chosen so that the parallel LC is operating beyond its resonant frequency at all frequencies that appear in the power supply current of the amplifier. Beyond resonance, the capacitor's reactance is much less than that of the parasitic inductance. Because the bypass capacitor has its own parasitic components, it is common

to use two capacitors in parallel, one much smaller than the other.

9.3 10X Oscilloscope Probe

An oscilloscope, or more simply, a "scope," is a common piece of test equipment that allows one to measure and display voltages as a function of time. When a set of measurement leads, called a scope probe, is connected to the scope, the scope input impedance measured at the end of the leads appears as shown in the figure below.

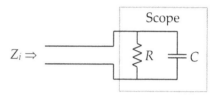

The resistance R is that of the oscilloscope's input circuitry and C is the combined capacitance of the input amplifier and the scope probe cable. The resistance R is typically equal to 1 MΩ and the parasitic capacitance C is often in the range of 10 pF to 100 pF.

When this probe is connected to a circuit, its input impedance Z_i can load the circuit it is connected to and draw sufficient current to alter the measurement being made. This loading issue is particularly true when the measured voltage contains high frequencies where the capacitor's impedance is small relative to the resistance R.

The simplest way to increase the input impedance of the scope and probe to minimize the amount it loads or disturbs measurements is to add a series resistor as shown in the following figure.

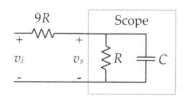

This added resistance makes the input impedance much larger. However, the added $9R$ resistor decreases the voltage measured by the scope by a factor of ten at DC when the capacitor is an open circuit. That is, at zero frequency, $\omega = 0$,

$$v_s = \frac{R}{9R + R} v_i = \frac{R}{10R} v_i = \frac{v_i}{10}$$

Therefore, the amplitude scale on the scope must be increased by a factor of ten. For example, a reading of 0.5 V is equal to a measured voltage of 5.0 V.

The Problem

While this fix does increase the input impedance of the scope, it also creates a lowpass filter. The frequency response is found using voltage division as

$$\frac{V_s}{V_i} = H(\omega) = \frac{Z_{RC}}{Z_{RC} + 9R}$$

where Z_{RC} is the impedance of the parallel combination of R and the impedance of the capacitor C,

$$\frac{1}{Z_{RC}} = Y_{RC} = \frac{1}{R} + j\omega C$$

The frequency response simplifies to

$$H(\omega) = \frac{Z_{RC}}{Z_{RC} + 9R} \cdot \left(\frac{Y_{RC}}{Y_{RC}}\right)$$

$$H(\omega) = \frac{1}{1 + 9RY_{RC}}$$

$$H(\omega) = \frac{1}{1 + 9R(1/R + j\omega C)}$$

$$H(\omega) = \frac{1}{10 + j\omega 9RC}$$

$$H(\omega) = \left(\frac{1}{10}\right)\frac{1}{1 + j\omega(9/10)RC}$$

$$H(\omega) = \left(\frac{1}{10}\right)\frac{1}{1 + j\dfrac{\omega}{\omega_c}}$$

The DC gain of 1/10 appears first in the above expression. This is followed by a low pass filter response having a critical or cutoff frequency of

$$\omega_c = \frac{1}{(9/10)RC}$$

Using typical values for R and C, the critical frequency becomes

$$\omega_c = \frac{10}{9RC} = \frac{10}{9(10^6)(10^{-10})} = \frac{10}{9(10^{-4})} = 11.1 \text{ krad/s}$$

Written in terms of hertz, this is

$$f_c = \frac{\omega_c}{2\pi} = 1.77 \text{ kHz}$$

Wow! The input impedance of the scope probe is much improved, but the frequency response of the modified probe is very poor. All frequency components of measured voltages that exist above 1.77 kHz are reduced in amplitude, i.e., attenuated, by at least 3 dB. As a result, voltages displayed on the scope will not at all look like the actual measured circuit voltages. This fix to increase the input impedance of the scope probe failed.

The Solution

The solution to this problem is to create capacitive voltage division in addition to the resistive voltage division. Since the impedance of a capacitor is inversely proportional to capacitance, $Z_c = -j1/(\omega C)$, the added capacitor is $C/9$ as shown in the following circuit. Because this capacitance is nine times smaller, its impedance is nine time greater than the other capacitor.

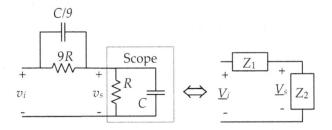

The frequency response of this circuit is once again found by voltage division,

$$\frac{V_s}{V_i} = H(\omega) = \frac{Z_2}{Z_2 + Z_1}$$

where

$$\frac{1}{Z_2} = Y_2 = \frac{1}{R} + j\omega C$$

and

$$\frac{1}{Z_1} = \frac{1}{9R} + j\omega\frac{C}{9} = \frac{1}{9}\left(\frac{1}{R} + j\omega C\right) = \frac{1}{9}(Y_2) = Y_1$$

Therefore

$$Y_2 = 9Y_1$$

The frequency response can be written in terms of admittances, $Y = 1/Z$, as

$$H(\omega) = \frac{Z_2}{Z_2 + Z_1}$$

$$H(\omega) = \frac{Z_2}{Z_2 + Z_1} \cdot \left(\frac{Y_1 Y_2}{Y_1 Y_2}\right) = \frac{Y_1}{Y_1 + Y_2}$$

Then substituting the admittance relationship $Y_2 = 9Y_1$ gives

$$H(\omega) = \frac{Y_1}{Y_1 + 9Y_1} = \frac{Y_1}{10Y_1} = \frac{1}{10}$$

That is it! The frequency response is simply the desired gain of one-tenth at all frequencies. **This is an all pass filter since content at all frequencies gets through the circuit equally well.** Measured voltages and those at the input amplifier inside the scope are identical.

In practice, the $9R$ resistor and $C/9$ capacitance reside in the scope probe. In addition, the value of the $C/9$ capacitance is commonly made adjustable with a screwdriver or other tool so that $Y_2 = 9Y_1$ can be assured.

9.4 Power Dissipation in Logic Circuits

A typical digital IC contains thousands to billions of transistors. These transistors form logic gates that switch from logic True to logic False and back as part of the IC's operation. Each of these transitions creates loss due to the current required to change logic states. This loss appears in the form of heat that must be dissipated.

To investigate the fundamental aspects of this phenomenon, consider the following simple circuit model for MOS transistor logic. The output of the logic gate on the left is driving the input of the logic gate on the right.

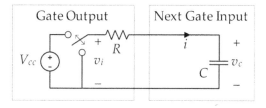

The logic gate on the left is shown as a Thévenin equivalent with a switch to denote the two logic states. The voltage v_i is either equal to the supply voltage V_{cc} or equal to zero volts, where V_{cc} typically denotes logic True and zero volts denotes logic False.

As shown in the figure, when the switch is in the logic-True upper position, the Thévenin equivalent is a voltage source in series with a resistor. And when the switch is in the logic-False lower position, the

Thévenin equivalent is simply a resistor. This Thévenin equivalent drives the input to the next logic gate, which is modeled simply by a capacitance, the MOS gate capacitance.

Transition to Logic True

This circuit is a simple RC circuit. When the switch moves from logic False to logic True, the switch moves from the lower position to the upper position. In this case, the capacitor charges from zero volts to the supply voltage V_{cc}, following the standard step response

$$v_c(t) = V_{cc}\left(1 - e^{-t/\tau}\right), \quad t \ge 0$$

where the time constant is

$$\tau = RC$$

Because it takes five time constants, 5τ, for the capacitor to fully charge, the transition time T_d to logic True cannot be shorter than five time constants. That is

$$T_d \ge 5\tau = 5RC$$

If this does not hold, there is no assurance that the next logic gate registers the logic True state. If it does not, the intended logic operation fails.

The current flowing through the resistor before $t = 0$ is zero because it is assumed that the MOS gate capacitor is discharged,

$$i(t) = 0, \quad t < 0$$

And after $t = 0$, the resistor current is given by KCL as

$$i(t) = \frac{V_{cc} - v_c(t)}{R}$$

$$i(t) = \frac{V_{cc} - V_{cc}\left(1 - e^{-t/\tau}\right)}{R}$$

$$i(t) = \frac{V_{cc}}{R} e^{-t/\tau}, \quad t > 0$$

The following plots illustrate the voltage v_c and current i associated with the transition to logic True.

Transition to Logic False

When the switch moves from logic True to logic False, the switch moves from the upper position to the lower position. In this case, the capacitor discharges from the supply voltage V_{cc} to zero volts following the standard natural response

$$v_c(t) = V_{cc} e^{-t/\tau}, \quad t \ge 0$$

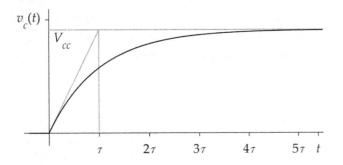

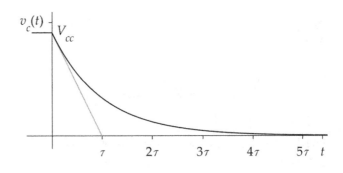

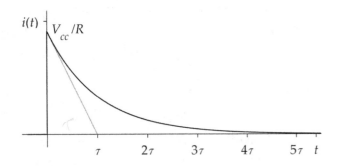

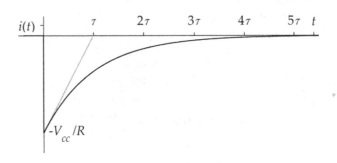

where, once again, the transition time to logic False must be at least five time constants, $T_d \geq 5\tau = 5RC$, to assure that the circuitry registers the logic False state.

The associated resistor current is zero for $t < 0$ and for $t > 0$ it is given by Ohm's law as

$$i(t) = \frac{-v_c(t)}{R}$$

which simplifies to

$$i(t) = \frac{-V_{cc}\, e^{-t/\tau}}{R}$$

$$i(t) = -\frac{V_{cc}}{R}\, e^{-t/\tau}, \quad t > 0$$

The discharge current is identical to the charging current except for its direction. During discharge, the current flows out of the capacitor; when charging the current flows into it.

The following plots illustrate the voltage v_c and current i associated with the transition to logic False.

Peak Current

For either transition, the peak current is

$$I_{peak} = \max\left(\left|i(t)\right|\right) = \frac{V_{cc}}{R}$$

So, the peak current required to change logic states is directly proportional to the supply voltage V_{cc} and inversely proportional to the resistance R. If the resis-

tance is decreased to make the transition occur in shorter time, the current required to do so increases.

Instantaneous and Average Power

Given the current for either transition, the instantaneous power dissipated by the resistor is given by

$$p(t) = i(t)^2 R$$

$$p(t) = \left(\pm \frac{V_{cc}}{R}\, e^{-t/\tau}\right)^2 \cdot R$$

$$p(t) = \frac{V_{cc}^2}{R^2}\left(e^{-2t/\tau}\right) \cdot R$$

$$p(t) = \frac{V_{cc}^2}{R}\, e^{-2t/\tau}, \quad 0 < t < T_d$$

As discovered in the study of AC power, the instantaneous power generally does not provide useful information. On the other hand, the average power better describes the power dissipated by the resistor. If T_d is the time duration of either logic transition, the average power dissipated by the resistor is

$$P = \frac{1}{T_d} \int_0^{T_d} p(t)\, dt$$

$$P = \frac{1}{T_d} \int_0^{T_d} \frac{V_{cc}^2}{R}\, e^{-2t/\tau}\, dt$$

$$P = \frac{V_{cc}^2}{R T_d} \int_0^{T_d} e^{-2t/\tau}\, dt$$

$$P = \frac{V_{cc}^2}{RT_d}\left(\frac{-\tau}{2}\right)e^{-2t/\tau}\Big|_0^{T_d}$$

$$P = \frac{V_{cc}^2}{RT_d}\left(\frac{-RC}{2}\right)\left[e^{-2T_d/\tau} - e^{-2\cdot0/\tau}\right]$$

$$P = \frac{-V_{cc}^2 C}{2T_d}\left[e^{-2T_d/\tau} - 1\right]$$

$$P = \frac{V_{cc}^2 C}{2T_d}\left[1 - e^{-2T_d/\tau}\right]$$

Since the transition time duration T_d must be at least five time constants, i.e., $T_d \geq 5\tau$, the exponential in the above expression is at best $e^{-2\cdot(5)} = e^{-10} = 4.54\cdot10^{-5} \approx 0$ so the average power dissipated becomes

$$P = \frac{V_{cc}^2 C}{2T_d}[1-0] = \frac{V_{cc}^2 C}{2T_d}$$

Maximum Operating Frequency

The following plots illustrate the input voltage $v_i(t)$, the capacitor voltage $v_c(t)$, and the instantaneous power $p(t)$ dissipated for the scenario where the switch changes position periodically every T_d seconds. This scenario mimics a clock signal propagating through logic gates.

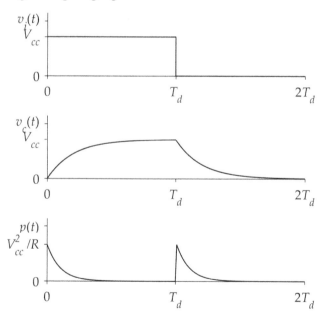

If the transitions between logic True and logic False occur periodically every five time constants, i.e., $T_d = 5\tau = 5RC$, the minimum period of the clock signal is $T_{min} = 2T_d$. The associated maximum clock frequency is

$$f_{max} = \frac{1}{T_{min}} = \frac{1}{2T_d} = \frac{1}{10RC}$$

Substituting this into the average power expression gives

$$P_{max} = \frac{V_{cc}^2 C}{2T_d} = \frac{V_{cc}^2 C}{T_{min}} = V_{cc}^2 C f_{max}$$

This result demonstrates the basic fact that power dissipation rises with increasing clock frequency. The faster a digital circuit operates, the more heat it generates. While the capacitance C of a single logic gate may be in the femptofarad range, i.e., $\sim10^{-15}$ F, the fact that there may be millions to billions, i.e., 10^6 to 10^9, of such switching events occurring at any one time makes the net power dissipated and heat generated significant.

This result also makes it clear why common power supply voltage values have dropped over the years. Because power is proportional to supply voltage squared, when the supply voltage drops by a factor two, from V_{cc} to $V_{cc}/2$, the power dissipated drops by a factor of four. As a result, it is not uncommon for a modern cpu core to use a supply voltage of 2 volts or less.

Summary

The current required to charge and discharge the gate capacitance C of a MOS logic device inherently creates a loss in the associated resistance R carrying the current. This power loss creates heat that the IC must dissipate.

The peak current per logic gate is

$$I_{peak} = \frac{V_{cc}}{R}$$

and the average power dissipated by the resistance is

$$P = \frac{V_{cc}^2 C}{2T_d}$$

where T_d is the time duration allocated for the transition from one logic state to the next.

Since it takes five time constants to charge or discharge a capacitor, the maximum clock frequency is given by

$$f_{max} = \frac{1}{10RC}$$

and the associated maximum average power dissipated is

$$P_{max} = V_{cc}^2 C f_{max}$$

These expressions illustrate inherent tradeoffs. For example, decreasing the resistance R increases the maximum clock frequency f_{max}, but it also increases the peak current I_{peak}. So the faster logic is driven, the greater the current required from the power supply. Decreasing the resistance R is achieved by making MOS devices larger. This generally makes the capacitance C larger, which increases the power dissipated and counteracts the effect of the changing resistance on the maximum clock frequency. For example, if R decreases by a factor of two, but C increases by a factor of two as well, the maximum clock frequency does not change. The easiest way to reduce power consumption is to reduce the power supply voltage.

9.5 Single Supply Op Amp Operation

In many cases, the input and output voltages of an op amp circuit are bipolar, meaning that the voltages take on positive and negative values over time. The simplest example would be when the input is sinusoidal.

To accommodate positive and negative output voltages, an op amp must be supplied with bipolar power supply voltages, *e.g.*, ±15 V. In this case, to function as expected, the op amp output voltage $v_o(t)$ must stay within the limits dictated by the positive power supply voltage V^+ and the negative power supply voltage V^- as shown in the figure below.

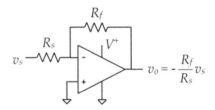

As shown, the output voltage cannot reach either power supply limit. Rather there is an upper limit V_{OH} that is somewhat less than V^+, and a lower limit V_{OL} that is somewhat greater than V^-.

The term "**headroom**" describes the differences between the upper and lower output voltage limits and their respective power supply values. In addition, it

is common to refer to the power supply values as the supply "**rails.**" Using this terminology, many modern op amps are called "**rail to rail**" op amps because their headroom is often as small as 0.1 V = 100 mV, meaning that the op amp output voltage can essentially reach both power supply values or "rails." This is different from more traditional op amps where the op amp output voltage cannot get any closer than 1 to 1.5 volts of either power supply value.

The need to supply both positive and negative voltages to an op amp circuit often means creating a negative power supply specifically for the op amps, since the other devices in the circuit commonly require just a positive power supply. This is especially true for battery operated circuits. The alternative is to find ways to make an op amp work from a single power supply.

The Problem

Consider the following "rail to rail" inverting op amp circuit that is connected to a single supply voltage. If $R_f/R_s = 2$, $V^+ = 5$ V, and the input is $v_s(t) = \cos(\omega t)$, the plots on the top of the next page shows the input and output voltages.

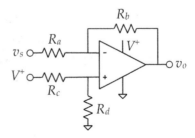

The output voltage v_o is highly distorted because the op amp output simply cannot generate the negative portions of the output $v_o(t) = -2v_s(t) = -4\cos(\omega t)$. When the V^- supply is zero volts, the output simply cannot go negative.

A Solution

A simple solution is to add a DC term to the output that is equal to one half the power supply voltage, $V^+/2$. For the inverting amplifier, this becomes the difference amplifier shown in the following op amp circuit.

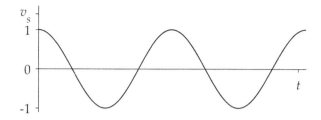

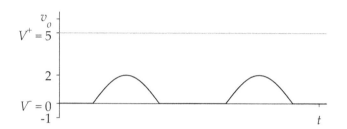

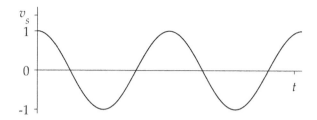

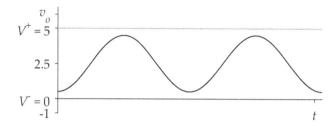

The output of this op amp circuit is given by the difference amplifier gain expression

$$v_o = -\frac{R_b}{R_a} v_s + \left(1 + \frac{R_b}{R_a}\right)\left(\frac{R_d}{R_c + R_d}\right) V^+$$

The first term in the preceding expression provides the desired gain of the input signal, and the gain of the second term is set equal to one half so that the output due to this term is $V^+/2$,

$$\frac{1}{2} = \left(1 + \frac{R_b}{R_a}\right)\left(\frac{R_d}{R_c + R_d}\right)$$

This expression can be solved for the ratio R_c/R_d, leading the final expression

$$\frac{R_c}{R_d} = 2\left(1 + \frac{R_b}{R_a}\right) - 1$$

Using the same values as used in the earlier example, if $R_f/R_s = R_b/R_a = 2$, $V^+ = 5$ V, and $v_s(t) = \cos(\omega t)$, then $R_c/R_d = 2 \cdot (1+2) - 1 = 5$. The following plots show the input and output voltages.

The output has the desired gain of two and is not distorted, but it is shifted upward by $V^+/2 = 2.5$ volts so that the output remains within the limits set by the power supply rails.

The above solution works, but has several weaknesses. One weakness is that the supply voltage V^+ typically contains a noise component. That is, the supply voltage is better described as

$$V^+ = V_{dc} + v_{ac}(t)$$

where V_{dc} is the desired DC supply voltage and $v_{ac}(t)$ is the AC noise on the power supply.

Since the op amp gain for the V^+ input is equal to one half, the op amp gain for $v_{ac}(t)$ is also one half. Therefore, noise on the power supply gets added to the desired op amp output.

Because the noise is an AC signal, often concentrated at high frequencies, and V_{dc} is at DC or zero frequency, the impact of the noise $v_{ac}(t)$ is easily minimized by low pass filtering the V^+ input to the op amp as shown in the circuit below. The added noise bypass capacitor C_n does not change the DC voltage $V^+/2$ at the positive terminal (+) of the op amp, but it does reduce or attenuate the noise $v_{ac}(t)$.

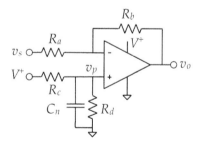

This filter is easily analyzed by considering just the noise $v_{ac}(t)$ and finding the frequency response between it and the voltage $v_p(t)$ at the positive terminal (+) of the op amp as shown in the following time domain and phasor circuits.

The frequency response of this circuit is

$$H(\omega) = \frac{V_p}{V_{ac}} = \frac{Z_{RC}}{Z_{RC} + R_c}$$

where Z_{RC} is the parallel combination of R_d and C_n,

$$Y_{RC} = \frac{1}{Z_{RC}} = \frac{1}{R_d} + j\omega C_n$$

Substituting this expression into the frequency response and simplifying gives

$$H(\omega) = \frac{Z_{RC}}{Z_{RC} + R_c} \cdot \left(\frac{Y_{RC}}{Y_{RC}}\right) = \frac{1}{1 + R_c Y_{RC}}$$

Further simplification leads to

$$H(\omega) = H(0)\frac{1}{1 + j\frac{\omega}{\omega_c}}$$

where

$$H(0) = \frac{R_d}{R_c + R_d}$$

is the DC gain, and

$$\omega_c = \frac{1}{(R_c \| R_d)C_n}$$

is the cutoff frequency ω_c of the low pass filter.

This expression for the bandwidth provides guidance for the selection of the capacitor value. **The cutoff frequency ω_c should be chosen so that the lowest frequency component in the noise $v_{ac}(t)$ is ten or more times greater than ω_c.** At the frequency $\omega = 10\omega_c$, the relative gain of the lowpass filter is approximately

$$\frac{|H(10\omega_c)|}{|H(0)|} \approx -20 \text{ dB} = 1/10$$

So, at this frequency, the impact of noise is reduced by a factor of ten. Of course, since this is a low pass filter, higher frequency components are attenuated even more.

Another Solution

When the input signal to the op amp $v_s(t)$ does not contain a DC component, it is possible to decouple or separate the gain for $v_s(t)$ from that for V^+. That is, if the input $v_s(t)$ is an AC signal, consider the following circuit where a capacitor C_a is in series with R_a, and

where the V^+ input has been dropped for now, but will be added back in later.

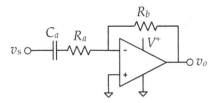

The frequency response of this op amp circuit is

$$H(\omega) = \frac{V_o}{V_s} = -\frac{R_b}{R_a + Z_c}$$

where

$$Y_c = \frac{1}{Z_c} = j\omega C_a$$

This simplifies as

$$H(\omega) = -\frac{R_b}{R_a + Z_c} \cdot \left(\frac{Y_c}{Y_c}\right)$$

$$H(\omega) = -\frac{j\omega C_a R_b}{1 + j\omega R_a C_a}$$

$$H(\omega) = -\frac{j\omega R_a C_a (R_b/R_a)}{1 + j\omega R_a C_a}$$

$$H(\omega) = -\frac{R_b}{R_a}\frac{j\omega R_a C_a}{1 + j\omega R_a C_a}$$

$$H(\omega) = -\frac{R_b}{R_a}\left(\frac{j\frac{\omega}{\omega_a}}{1 + j\frac{\omega}{\omega_a}}\right)$$

The term in parentheses in this expression is a high pass filer and ω_a is the cutoff frequency given by

$$\omega_a = \frac{1}{R_a C_a}$$

The DC gain of this op amp circuit is zero,

$$H(0) = -\frac{R_b}{R_a}\left(\frac{j\frac{0}{\omega_a}}{1 + j\frac{0}{\omega_a}}\right) = -\frac{R_b}{R_a}\cdot(0) = 0$$

so if $v_s(t)$ has a DC component, it will not appear in the output $v_o(t)$.

If the lowest frequency component of the input $v_s(t)$ is ten times greater than the cutoff frequency, i.e., $\omega = 10\omega_a$, the gain becomes

$$H(10\omega_a) = -\frac{R_b}{R_a}\left(\frac{j\frac{10\omega_a}{\omega_a}}{1+j\frac{10\omega_a}{\omega_a}} \right)$$

$$H(10\omega_a) = -\frac{R_b}{R_a}\left(\frac{j10}{1+j10} \right)$$

$$H(10\omega_a) \approx -\frac{R_b}{R_a}\left(\frac{j10}{j10} \right)$$

$$H(10\omega_a) \approx -\frac{R_b}{R_a}$$

The circuit gain at this frequency is essentially equal to that for the earlier circuit without the capacitor C_a. At higher frequencies, the gain is even closer to the ideal value. **Therefore, the capacitor C_a must be chosen so that the cutoff frequency ω_a is at least a decade below the lowest frequency component in $v_s(t)$.**

Next consider the op amp circuit below with a V^+ input, but with the $v_s(t)$ input set to zero for now.

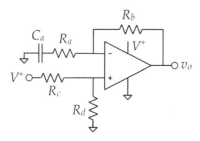

The frequency response of this op amp is

$$H(\omega) = \frac{V_o}{V^+} = \left(1+\frac{R_b}{R_a+Z_c}\right)\frac{R_d}{R_c+R_d}$$

The second term in parentheses in the above expression was found earlier. Using that result, the gain of this op amp circuit is

$$H(\omega) = \left[1 + \frac{R_b}{R_a}\left(\frac{j\frac{\omega}{\omega_a}}{1+j\frac{\omega}{\omega_a}} \right)\right]\frac{R_d}{R_c+R_d}$$

At DC, the gain becomes

$$H(0) = \left[1 + \frac{R_b}{R_a}\left(\frac{j\frac{0}{\omega_a}}{1+j\frac{0}{\omega_a}} \right)\right]\frac{R_d}{R_c+R_d} = \frac{R_d}{R_c+R_d}$$

Since the V^+ input is a DC value, setting the op amp output to $V^+/2$ simply means making $R_c = R_d$.

Combined Solution

The following circuit combines the preceding two op amp circuits to include both inputs $v_s(t)$ and V^+.

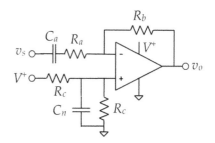

Given appropriate choices for C_n and C_a as identified earlier, the output of the op amp circuit is

$$v_o(t) = -\frac{R_b}{R_a}v_s(t) + \frac{V_{dc}}{2}$$

The bypass capacitor C_n is chosen so that the cutoff frequency

$$\omega_c = \frac{1}{(R_c \| R_c)C_n} = \frac{2}{R_c C_n}$$

of the low pass filter formed from C_n and the two resistors having value R_c is at least ten times lower than the lowest frequency component contained in the power supply noise $v_{ac}(t)$. Because this lowest frequency depends on the characteristics of the power supply, the number and type of ICs used, and the printed circuit board layout, the choice of C_n is often based on experimental testing.

If ω_n is the lowest frequency component contained in the power supply noise $v_{ac}(t)$, then C_n is given by

$$\omega_c = \frac{2}{R_c C_n} \le 10\omega_n$$

$$\frac{2}{10R_c\omega_n} \le C_n$$

In terms of the frequency ω_n specified in hertz, i.e., $\omega_n = 2\pi f_n$, this expression becomes

$$C_n \ge \frac{1}{10\pi R_c f_n}$$

The capacitor C_a is chosen so that the cutoff frequency

$$\omega_a = \frac{1}{R_a C_a}$$

of the high pass filter formed by R_a and C_a is at least ten times lower than the lowest frequency component contained in the input signal $v_s(t)$. If ω_s is the lowest frequency in $v_s(t)$, then C_a is given by

$$\omega_a = \frac{1}{R_a C_a} \le 10\omega_s$$

$$\frac{1}{10 R_a \omega_s} \le C_a$$

In terms of the frequency ω_s specified in hertz, *i.e.*, $\omega_s = 2\pi f_s$, this expression becomes

$$C_a \ge \frac{1}{20\pi R_a f_s}$$

Example: Consider the case where the input signal $v_s(t)$ is to be amplified by a factor of two, $v_s(t)$ contains content above $f_s = 10$ Hz, noise on the power supply exists at $f_n = 100$ Hz and above, and a 5 volt power supply is available.

Using these specifications, let the resistor values be

$$R_a = 100 \text{ k}\Omega$$

$$R_b = 200 \text{ k}\Omega$$

$$R_c = 100 \text{ k}\Omega$$

The noise bypass capacitor C_n is chosen so that

$$C_n \ge \frac{1}{10\pi R_c f_n} = \frac{1}{10\pi\cdot 100\text{k}\cdot 100} = 3.18 \text{ nF}$$

This is quite small, so be conservative and choose a larger standard value; let $C_n = 10$ nF $= 0.01$ μF.

The capacitor C_a is chosen so that

$$C_a \ge \frac{1}{20\pi R_a f_s} = \frac{1}{20\pi\cdot 100\text{k}\cdot 10} = 15.9 \text{ nF}$$

To be conservative, choose a larger standard value of $C_a = 22$ nF $= 0.022$ μF.

The following circuit illustrates this solution.

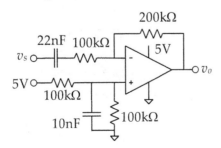

The gain relationship for this design is

$$v_o(t) = -\frac{R_b}{R_a} v_s(t) + \frac{V_{dc}}{2}$$

$$v_o(t) = -\frac{200\text{k}}{100\text{k}} v_s(t) + \frac{5}{2}$$

$$v_o(t) = -2v_s(t) + 2.5 \text{ V}$$

A Noninverting Solution

The above solutions inverted the input signal $v_s(t)$. By using the inverting op amp configuration, the input signal and the DC offset input V^+ are separated. One is applied to the positive op amp input terminal (+) and the other is applied to the negative input terminal (–). Because of this, the analysis and design are simplified.

When positive gain is desired, both the input signal and the DC offset are applied to the positive input terminal (+) as shown in the circuit below.

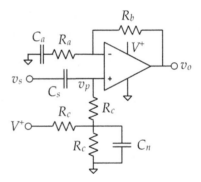

In this circuit, the capacitor C_a plays the same role it did in the earlier circuit. It makes the DC gain of the circuit equal to one. This is easily shown by finding the frequency response between the voltage $v_p(t)$ at the positive input terminal (+) and the output,

$$H_p(\omega) = \frac{V_o}{V_p} = 1 + \frac{R_b}{R_a + Z_c}$$

$$H_p(\omega) = 1 + \frac{R_b}{R_a + Z_c}\cdot\left(\frac{Y_c}{Y_c}\right)$$

$$H_p(\omega) = 1 + \frac{j\omega R_b C_a}{1 + j\omega R_a C_a}$$

$$H_p(\omega) = 1 + \frac{j\omega R_a C_a(R_b/R_a)}{1 + j\omega R_a C_a}$$

$$H_p(\omega) = 1 + \frac{R_b}{R_a}\left(\frac{j\omega R_a C_a}{1 + j\omega R_a C_a}\right)$$

$$H_p(\omega) = 1 + \frac{R_b}{R_a}\left(\frac{j\frac{\omega}{\omega_a}}{1 + j\frac{\omega}{\omega_a}}\right)$$

where the cutoff frequency is

$$\omega_a = \frac{1}{R_a C_a}$$

At DC, this gain is equal to

$$H_p(0) = 1 + \frac{R_b}{R_a}\left|\frac{j\frac{0}{\omega_a}}{1 + j\frac{0}{\omega_a}}\right| = 1\cdot(0) = 1$$

At frequencies ten or more larger than ω_a, i.e., $\omega > \omega_a$, this gain simplifies to the desired ideal value

$$H_p(\omega) \approx 1 + \frac{R_b}{R_a} \quad \text{for } \omega \gg \omega_a$$

The value of capacitor C_a is chosen using the same guidelines as presented earlier for the inverting configuration.

The relationship between the input $v_s(t)$ and the voltage $v_p(t)$ is described by the following circuits where V^+ has been set to zero.

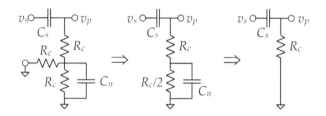

The original circuit on the left simplifies to the circuit in the middle by combing the two resistors R_c in parallel. The circuit on the right holds at sufficiently high frequencies where the impedance of the noise bypass capacitor C_n is much less than $R_c/2$ and can be approximated as a short circuit.

The original circuit on the left and its equivalent in the center can be analyzed. However, the resulting frequency response $H(\omega) = \underline{V}_p/\underline{V}_s$ lacks useful simplicity. If the noise bypass capacitance C_n is chosen sufficiently large, so that it is effectively a short circuit at the frequency components in the input $v_s(t)$, then the simplified circuit on the right above applies with sufficient accuracy.

The simplified circuit on the right provides guidance for the selection of C_s. The frequency response of this circuit is a simple high pass filter,

$$H_s(\omega) = \frac{\underline{V}_p}{\underline{V}_s} = \frac{R_c}{R_c + Z_c}$$

$$H_s(\omega) = \frac{R_c}{R_c + Z_c}\cdot\left(\frac{Y_c}{Y_c}\right)$$

$$H_s(\omega) = \frac{j\omega R_c C_s}{1 + j\omega R_c C_s}$$

$$H_s(\omega) = \frac{j\frac{\omega}{\omega_c}}{1 + j\frac{\omega}{\omega_c}}$$

where the cutoff frequency of the high pass filter is

$$\omega_c = \frac{1}{R_c C_s}$$

The value of the capacitor C_s follows from that of C_a in the previous inverting op amp circuit. The cutoff frequency of this filter should be at least ten times lower than the lowest frequency component contained in the input signal $v_s(t)$. If ω_s is the lowest frequency content in $v_s(t)$, then C_s is given by

$$\omega_c = \frac{1}{R_c C_s} \le 10\,\omega_s$$

$$\frac{1}{10 R_c \omega_s} \le C_s$$

In terms of the frequency ω_s specified in hertz, i.e., $\omega_s = 2\pi f_s$, this expression becomes

$$C_s \ge \frac{1}{20\pi R_c f_s}$$

Next, setting the input $v_s(t)$ to zero and considering the relationship between the power supply input V^+ and the voltage $v_p(t)$ lead to the following equivalent circuits.

As before, the frequency response $H(\omega) = \underline{V}_p/\underline{V}^+$ can be found, but it too lacks useful simplicity. The circuit on the right can be simplified further by replacing the elements to the left of C_n by their Thévenin equivalent as shown in the following circuit.

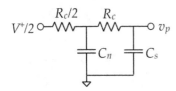

The circuit is now two cascaded RC lowpass filters.

The power supply voltage consists of two components

$$V^+ = V_{dc} + v_{ac}(t)$$

where V_{dc} is the desired DC voltage and $v_{ac}(t)$ is the unwanted AC noise on the power supply.

At DC, $\omega = 0$, the capacitors are open circuits, so the circuit becomes a series resistance of $R_{eq} = R_c/2 + R_c$. Therefore, at DC, the output is equal to the desired offset voltage $v_p(t) = V_{dc}/2$ since the voltage across R_{eq} is zero and the current through R_{eq} and into the op amp is zero.

The unwanted AC noise component $v_{ac}(t)$ of the supply voltage V^+ is filtered by the two RC low pass filters. As a result, this component does not get amplified by the op amp and does not appear in the output $v_o(t)$.

The value of the capacitor C_s was determined earlier based on the assumption that the capacitor C_n was a short circuit for all frequencies in the input $v_s(t)$. For this to be true, the cutoff frequency of the first RC filter,

$$\omega_1 = \frac{1}{(R_c/2)C_n} = \frac{2}{R_c C_n}$$

should be at least ten times lower than that of the second RC filter,

$$\omega_2 = \frac{1}{R_c C_a}$$

which means that

$$\omega_1 \leq \frac{\omega_2}{10}$$

Substituting the two cutoff frequencies into this expression gives

$$\frac{2}{R_c C_n} \leq \frac{1}{10 R_c C_a}$$

$$\frac{2}{C_n} \leq \frac{1}{10 C_a}$$

$$\frac{C_n}{2} \geq 10 C_a$$

$$C_n \geq 20 C_a$$

If these guidelines are followed, the gain relationship for this noninverting, single supply op amp circuit becomes

$$v_o(t) = \left(1 + \frac{R_b}{R_a}\right) v_s(t) + \frac{V_{dc}}{2}$$

Example: Consider the case where the input signal $v_s(t)$ is to be amplified by two, $v_s(t)$ contains content above $f_s = 10$ Hz, noise on the power supply exists at $f_n = 100$ Hz and above, and a 5 volt power supply is available.

Using these specifications, let the resistor values be

$$R_a = R_b = R_c = 100 \text{ k}\Omega$$

The capacitor C_a is chosen so that

$$C_a \geq \frac{1}{20\pi R_a f_s} = \frac{1}{20\pi \cdot 100\text{k} \cdot 10} = 15.9 \text{ nF}$$

To be conservative, choose a larger standard value of $C_a = 22$ nF $= 0.022$ µF.

The capacitor C_s is chosen so that

$$C_s \geq \frac{1}{20\pi R_c f_s} = \frac{1}{20\pi \cdot 100\text{k} \cdot 10} = 15.9 \text{ nF}$$

To be conservative, choose a larger standard value of $C_s = 22$ nF $= 0.022$ µF.

The noise bypass capacitance is given simply as

$$C_n \geq 20 C_a = 20 \cdot 15.9\text{nF} = 318 \text{ nF}$$

To be conservative, choose a larger standard value of $C_n = 330$ nF $= 0.33$ µF.

The following circuit illustrates this solution.

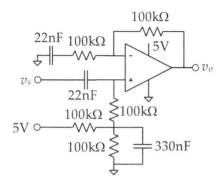

The gain relationship for this design is

$$v_o(t) = \left(1 + \frac{R_b}{R_a}\right) v_s(t) + \frac{V_{dc}}{2}$$

$$v_o(t) = \left(1 + \frac{100\,\text{k}}{100\,\text{k}}\right) v_s(t) + \frac{5}{2}$$

$$v_o(t) = 2\,v_s(t) + 2.5\ \text{V}$$

Summary

This section introduced the basic operation of single supply op amps. Much more in depth information can be found in other texts and online.

9.6 Crosstalk

Historically, the term crosstalk described hearing another phone conversation in the background while conversing with someone on an analog land line telephone. Because many phones lines are bundled together inside phone cables, the talk on phone lines could cross over to other phone lines, leading to crosstalk.

More generally, **crosstalk is any disturbance or noise created in one circuit caused by voltages and currents in adjacent circuits or wires. These voltages and currents create electric and magnetic fields that are commonly called electromagnetic interference, or EMI.**

The simplest description of EMI is that every conductor is an antenna that both radiates signals and receives signals.

In terms of electric circuit principles, crosstalk is created by naturally occurring parasitic capacitance and mutual inductance between parts of an electric circuit, between printed circuit board traces, or along the length of cables carrying digital or analog signals.

Capacitance and mutual inductance increase with decreasing separation between components. There-

fore, the possibility of creating crosstalk generally increases as circuits, traces, and cables become more compact.

Because the impedance of a capacitor is inversely proportional to frequency, i.e., $|Z_c| = 1/(\omega C)$, crosstalk due to parasitic capacitance generally increases with frequency. Because the voltage induced due to mutual inductance increases with increasing frequency, i.e., $\underline{V}_2 = j\omega M \underline{I}_1$, crosstalk due to mutual inductance generally increases with increasing frequency as well.

There are a number of well established techniques for minimizing crosstalk. They include the use of twisted pairs in cables, differential signaling, and common mode chokes.

Twisted Pairs

The following figure illustrates twisted pairs where there are four sets of wire pairs twisted along the length of the cable.

To understand how the use of twisted pairs reduces crosstalk, consider the following figure where current is flowing out of the page in the conductor in the center of the figure. This current creates a magnetic field that circulates around the wire in counter-clockwise direction as shown by the concentric circles and corresponding arrows surrounding the conductor. The strength or amplitude of the magnetic field decreases with increasing radius from the conductor. If the current flow changes direction, the magnetic field simply flows in the opposite direction as well. The presence of this magnetic field creates an inductance, which creates a voltage along the conductor's length given by the inductor relationship $v = L\,di/dt$.

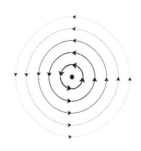

If a second conductor is placed within the magnetic field of first conductor as shown on the right in the following figure, a voltage $v_2(t)$ is induced along the length of the second conductor given by the mutual inductance relationship $v_2 = M di_1/dt$, where $i_1(t)$ is the current in the first conductor and M is the mutual inductance between the two conductors.

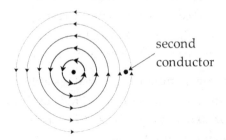

second conductor

Based on this description, consider the following figure where the output of the circuit on the left is connected to the input of the circuit on the right by the two conductors shown. In an ideal setting, the input voltage $v_i(t)$ is equal to the output voltage $v_o(t)$.

However, when this connection is in the presence of another conductor (not shown) that carries current, the magnetic field from this other conductor passes through the loop formed by the conductors between the two circuits. This magnetic field is denoted by the x symbols in the following figure.

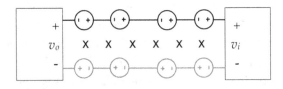

When the current in the other conductor varies with time, the created magnetic field varies with time as well. This varying magnetic field induces voltages along the length of the two conductors, where the polarity on the bottom conductor is the opposite of that on the top conductor. In this case, the input voltage $v_i(t)$ is NOT equal to the output voltage $v_o(t)$. Rather, by KVL

$$v_i(t) = v_o(t) + v_n(t)$$

where $v_n(t)$ is the sum of all the incrementally induced voltages around the loop formed by the conductors and the two circuits. All the individual sources have the same polarity, so they accumulate to form $v_n(t)$. The voltage $v_n(t)$ is crosstalk noise that can interfere with the intended operation of the circuit.

Twisting the conductors along their length as shown below minimizes $v_n(t)$ because the sum of all incrementally induced voltages around the loop formed by the conductors and the two circuits alternate in sign from one twist to the next depending on their relative placement.

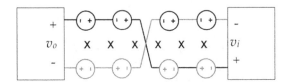

In this case, under ideal conditions, one half of all the induced voltages have the opposite polarity as the other half when one sums the incrementally induced voltages around the loop formed between the two circuits. Therefore, in this ideal case

$$v_i(t) = v_o(t) + 0$$

In reality, this cancellation is not perfect, but is optimized if the twists are closely spaced and exist along the entire length of the conductors as illustrated in the following figure.

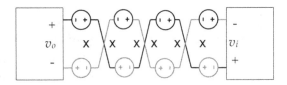

Examples of common cables that utilize twisted pairs include: (a) USB version 2 cables have one twisted pair for data transmission in both directions. (b) USB version 3 cables have three twisted pairs for data transmission. Because USB version 3 is backward compatible, one pair is the USB version 2 pair and the other two twisted pairs are the separate transmit and receive signals for USB version 3. (c) HDMI cables have four twisted pairs. Three twisted pairs are for data and the fourth is for a clock signal. Given the closeness of all the wires in a cable, the use of twisted pairs dramatically reduces the crosstalk among all the signals in the cable.

Differential Signaling

There are many cases where the connections between two circuits share a common ground conductor or ground plane as illustrated in the figure below. In this case, the mutual inductance created by magnetic fields emanating from other parts of a circuit also induces voltages on all the connections as illustrated by the sources and the magnetic field X symbols below.

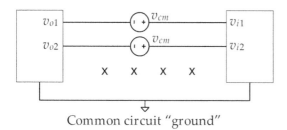

Common circuit "ground"

In this case, all the conductors between the circuit on the left and those on the right share a noise voltage component $v_{cm}(t)$ that is common to all the conductors. As a result, this is called **common mode noise**.

This phenomenon occurs with twisted pairs as well, whenever an additional conducting path between the two circuits exists as shown in the above figure. So, the two conductors shown in the figure could be separate signals using the common ground, or they could be the two conductors of a twisted pair. **The use of twisted pairs only cancels the induced voltage due to magnetic fields passing between the two twisted conductors themselves. Voltages induced by other magnetic fields are common mode noise.**

Using the circuit ground as the reference, and the associated node voltages identified in the figure, the input voltages to the circuit on the right are given by

$$v_{i1}(t) = v_{o1}(t) + v_{cm}(t)$$
$$v_{i2}(t) = v_{o2}(t) + v_{cm}(t)$$

Both inputs are polluted with common mode noise having the same polarity.

The common mode voltage $v_{cm}(t)$ can be eliminated if it somehow can be subtracted. For example, if the circuit on the right computes the difference between its inputs

$$v_i(t) = v_{i1}(t) - v_{i2}(t)$$
$$v_i(t) = v_{o1}(t) + v_{cm}(t) - \left(v_{o2}(t) + v_{cm}(t)\right)$$
$$v_i(t) = v_{o1}(t) - v_{o2}(t)$$

the common mode noise voltage disappears. The resulting voltage $v_i(t)$ has a great deal of value if the output voltages $v_{o1}(t)$ and $v_{o2}(t)$ differ by a factor of negative one. That is, if

$$v_{o1}(t) = v_o(t)$$
$$v_{o2}(t) = -v_o(t)$$

then computing the difference between the inputs of the circuit on the right gives

$$v_i(t) = v_{i1}(t) - v_{i2}(t)$$
$$v_i(t) = v_{o1}(t) - v_{o2}(t)$$
$$v_i(t) = v_o(t) - \left(-v_o(t)\right)$$
$$v_i(t) = 2v_o(t)$$

The common mode noise disappears and the desired signal $v_o(t)$ has a gain of two.

Putting this into practice is called differential signaling. **Differential signaling is used in both analog and digital circuits.**

For example, the twisted pairs in USB and HDMI cabling carry information composed of two digital signals that are binary complements of each other. That is, if one conductor in the twisted pair carries the logic signal

$$V^+$$

the other carries its complement

$$V^- = \overline{V^+}$$

Whenever V^+ is logic True, V^- is logic False, and vice versa. The two signals are always binary complements of each other.

The reference or ground for these two signals appears as a separate conductor or as a shield surrounding its associated twisted pair. When implemented in this way, common mode noise induced in the cable is canceled by processing the difference between the two signals.

Professional audio cabling is a common analog example. If you have ever attended a concert, you may have noticed that all audio from the stage is routed through cables to a mixing station that faces the stage, but resides many meters back from the center of the stage. There are usually dozens of audio cables going to the mixing station and back.

At the mixing station, a mixing engineer adjusts the volume and mixture of all the microphone and instrument audio signals coming from the stage. These signals are then sent back to the stage where they are amplified and sent to their associated loud-speakers.

XLR cable and connectors are commonly used for this application. The connectors for these cables are shown in the following figure.

There are three conductors in the most common XLR cables. One conductor carries v^+, the other carries its negative $v^- = -v^+$, and the third is the reference or ground for these two signals. The v^+ and v^- conductors form a twisted pair and are encased by the reference conductor as a shield.

By using differential signaling and shielded twisted pairs (STP), professional audio customarily experiences no discernible crosstalk.

There are a number of ways to create analog differential signals. In addition to commercially available op amps having differential outputs, it is possible to construct differential analog signals with two op amps. Once such example was demonstrated in the Op Amp chapter.

The processing of analog differential signals is most often performed by a difference amplifier. Several such examples were demonstrated in the Op Amp chapter. The inherent tolerances on the resistors used in these circuits keep a difference amplifier from performing perfect subtraction, which is required if the common mode noise is to be canceled. As a result, high precision resistors are often required. Alternatively, difference amplifier ICs are available that provide high precision by incorporating high precision resistors inside the IC.

The only problem with op amp solutions for creating and processing analog differential signals is the need for a power supply. In many cases, a simple transformer having two secondary windings can be used as shown in the following figure.

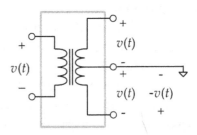

Here all three transformer windings have the same number of turns. When an AC voltage $v(t)$ is applied to the primary on the left, both secondary windings have the same voltage $v(t)$ across their respective terminals because both turns ratio are equal to one. When the circuit reference is chosen as the center node in the secondary as shown in the figure, the output produces the two differential signals. In practice, this is called converting an unbalanced signal $v(t)$ into a balanced signal composed of $v(t)$ and $-v(t)$.

This transformer also works in the reverse direction. If a balanced signal composed of $v(t)$ and $-v(t)$ is applied on the right, the associated unbalanced signal $v(t)$ appears on the left. This should not be surprising since the transformer is a passive circuit element. It simply does not matter which side is used as the primary or the secondary.

Because of the utility of this transformer to go back and forth between balanced and unbalanced signals, it is commonly called a **balun**, which is composed of the first letters from the words "**bal**anced" and "**un**balanced."

A balun does not require a power supply. It works very well as long as it is designed and constructed to operate over the range of frequencies contained in the signal $v(t)$. Since it is a transformer, it does not work at DC.

Common Mode Choke

The term "common mode choke" refers to a transformer designed to impede or choke off common mode currents, while letting differential mode currents pass unimpeded.

A typical common mode choke on a USB cable is shown in the following figure, where the common mode choke is in the cylindrical bulge surrounding the cable on the left in the figure.

The bulge is composed of a ferrite core that surrounds the cable, which in turn is surrounded by a protective cover. Since ferrite conducts magnetic field very well compared to air, it acts to increase inductance in the same way that a steel or other ferrous core would. Secondarily, the ferrite is usually designed to be increasingly lossy as frequency increases. In this way, the common mode choke absorbs power from high frequency common mode currents and therefore reduces their amplitude even more.

The easiest way to understand a common mode choke is to consider the simple transformer model shown in the following figure. The transformer is composed of two windings having multiple turns wound around a ferrite or ferrous rod.

The following figure illustrates the magnetic field polarities created by current flow into the two windings.

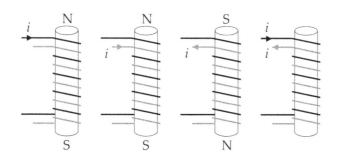

The **two examples on the left** show that if current flows into the top of either winding, the top becomes a North pole and the bottom becomes a South pole.

The **second example from the right** shows that if the current changes direction, the magnetic poles

change as well. **Finally, in the example all the way to the right, if equal currents are applied to both coils, but in the opposite direction, no magnetic field is created.** The net current is zero, so the net magnetic field is zero. The magnetic fields created by the two windings cancel each other out.

The fact that currents flowing in the same direction create a magnetic field, but equal and opposing currents creates none is what makes a common mode choke work. Currents flowing in the same direction create a magnetic field and therefore the windings have inductance and induced voltages when currents vary with time. However, **equal opposing currents do not create a magnetic field, so the windings have no inductance and therefore there is no induced voltage across the windings. In this case, the windings appear to be short circuits.**

The following electric circuit and its phasor equivalent model this phenomenon.

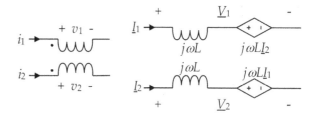

The windings have the same number of turns and they are tightly coupled, so the individual self inductances are equal $L_1 = L_2 = L$, and the mutual inductance is equal to the self inductance, $M = L$.

The voltages across the windings are found by applying KVL,

$$\underline{V}_1 = j\omega L \underline{I}_1 + j\omega L \underline{I}_2 = j\omega L \left(\underline{I}_1 + \underline{I}_2 \right)$$
$$\underline{V}_2 = j\omega L \underline{I}_2 + j\omega L \underline{I}_1 = j\omega L \left(\underline{I}_1 + \underline{I}_2 \right)$$

Given these equations, consider the situation where the currents $\underline{I}_1$ and $\underline{I}_2$ are each composed of two components

$$\underline{I}_1 = \underline{I}_{dm} + \underline{I}_{cm}$$
$$\underline{I}_2 = -\underline{I}_{dm} + \underline{I}_{cm}$$

where $\underline{I}_{cm}$ is a common mode current flowing in the same direction inside the transformer, and $\underline{I}_{dm}$ is a differential mode current flowing in opposite directions inside the transformer. The differential mode current carries a desired signal, such as the data signals in a

USB cable. Currents I_{dm} and $-I_{dm}$ generated by data transmission flow with equal amplitude in opposite direction in the cable. The undesired common mode current I_{cm} created by electromagnetic interference, EMI, directs current in the same direction in both conductors.

Therefore, differential mode currents I_{dm} should pass through the common mode choke as if it wasn't there, and common mode currents I_{cm} should be impeded by the common mode choke.

Substituting these currents into the expressions for the voltages across the windings gives

$$V_1 = j\omega L\left(I_1 + I_2\right)$$
$$V_1 = j\omega L\left(I_{dm} + I_{cm} - I_{dm} + I_{cm}\right)$$
$$V_1 = j\omega L\left(2 I_{cm}\right)$$
$$V_1 = j\omega (2L) I_{cm}$$

and, because the expression for V_2 is the same as that for V_1,

$$V_2 = j\omega (2L) I_{cm}$$

As desired, the differential mode current I_{dm} does not contribute to the winding voltages. This current does not appear in either voltage expression. The common mode choke does not impede the flow of differential currents. For these currents, it appears as a short circuit as shown in the following circuit.

On the other hand, to common mode currents, the impedance of each winding appears as the inductive impedance

$$\frac{V_1}{I_{cm}} = \frac{V_2}{I_{cm}} = j\omega (2L)$$

Therefore, to common mode currents, the common mode choke windings each appears as an inductor having value $2L$ as shown in the following circuit.

The process of impeding the flow of common mode currents diminishes their amplitude and potential for causing problems.

The utility of a common mode choke, such as that on the USB cable shown earlier, is now apparent. The data signals passing through the cable produce only differential mode currents. So they are not impeded by the common mode choke. However, if there are any common mode currents, they are impeded by the impedance $j\omega(2L)$. Since common mode currents often contain energy at high frequencies, this impedance substantially reduces their potential negative impact on desired circuit operation.

9.7 Summary

This chapter introduced real world topics and applications that could be understood based on the material found in the preceding chapters. This material cannot be found in other introductory electric circuits books. In fact, this material is largely absent from all academic texts. But yet the material covered here is fundamental to real world circuit design. Because of the nature of this text, the material in this chapter is introductory and not exhaustive. Much greater detail can be found in other resources.